THE BONE RANGER

Louisa Bennet

Clan Destine
P R E S S

Published by Clan Destine Press in 2021

Clan Destine Press
PO Box 121, Bittern
Victoria, 3918 Australia

National Library of Australia Cataloguing-In-Publication data:

Bennet, Louisa

The Bone Ranger
 (Monty Dog Detective series)

ISBNs: 978-0-6452899-8-5 (hardback)
          978-0-6452899-9-2 (paperback)
          978-0-6453167-0-4 (eBook)

Cover & Internal illustrations by Judith Rossell
Cover typography by Willsin Rowe
Design & Typesetting by Clan Destine Press

To Pickles and Lilly, my inspiration.

1

Mud flies. With my front paws deep in the hole, I claw at the damp earth, soft and squishy after two days of rain. My furry bottom points skywards, my tail swishing side to side as if it is waving at the birds flying past. Momentarily I pause and, nose pressed into the rich soil, inhale deeply. Ahh. Rotting leaves, earthworms and, oh yes, duck poo. What better smell is there? Distracted, I almost forget why I am digging up the flowerbed, then I spot my deliciously manky, doggishly-smelly, yellow toy duck. I glance back at the wonky cottage where I live with my owner, Detective Constable Rose Sidebottom, hoping that she hasn't yet noticed my excavations.

'Monty!' Rose calls from the back door, her hands on her hips.

Oops!

Normally I'm a good dog. A smiley, loyal, obedient Golden Retriever. But when it comes to washing my duck, I have to make a stand. Rose, like other hoomans, simply doesn't appreciate that my duck pongs to perfection. I'm going to bury my furry friend so she can't find it. Then she can't put him in the washing machine. I've chosen a perfect digging spot behind a camellia bush, but I guess the clumps of mud flying through the air is a bit of a giveaway. I drop my duck into the hole and paw loose soil over it as fast as I can. I hear the stamp of boots on paving stones then the soft thud of Rose walking across the grass. I can smell her aroma of vanilla and peppermint and the sea.

'Stop that!' Rose says, almost upon me.

Caught in the middle of my crime, I lie across my half-filled cavity and pretend there is nothing to see here.

'It's no use pretending. Look at the state of you.'

Rose bends down. She is the youngest trainee detective in England and I'm so proud of her. I look up at her heart-shaped face and ponytail which reminds me of a fox's tail. She's smiling, which is a relief. But her eyes are sad. Since her near-death experience at the hands of a killer, Rose hasn't been herself. Her boss insisted that she take sick leave, but it isn't helping. Rose is not very confident at the best of times but now she is like a dog that's been scolded too often. She hangs her head and hides away. She only goes out to walk me or buy food. She sleeps fitfully and has terrible nightmares. I do my best to comfort her, but my efforts have so far been in vain. I had hoped that a bit of hide-and-seek might cheer her up.

The dirt on my muzzle tickles and I sneeze.

'You're covered in mud.' She sighs. 'I'm going to have to clean you too!'

What? No!

She wraps her delicate fingers around my collar and gives it a gentle tug. 'Out of there.'

I reluctantly leave the hole and the camellia bush. Rose tells me to sit, then stay. She plunges her hand into the earth and brings up my muddy duck. 'Got to be washed now.'

I bark twice.

We've practised this, over and over again. Two barks is no. One bark is yes. When she asks me if I want to be fed, I respond with one bark. Do I want to go for a walk? One bark. Do I love her? One big bark.

'You know, it's almost as if you understand me,' she says.

Rose usually enjoys this game we play. Today, her voice is heavy and her smile is gone in an instant.

She strokes my head. 'Why don't you like me washing your bed and your duck? I don't understand.'

That is my point exactly. I have tried to demonstrate as best I can that my duck and my bed are not for washing. Earlier this morning, when Rose picked up said duck and headed for the kitchen where the front-loading washing machine lives, I swiped my fluffy friend from her loose grip and ran out of the door. She gave chase and I had great fun running around the duck pond, even if the little quackers did kick up a stink about what they called 'the disturbance.'

Rose resorted to treats to lure me close, knowing full well that food is my weakness. I didn't see the trap until it was too late. I dropped the duck. Rose snatched it and headed back into the house. So I ran ahead and then sat, head held high, in front of the washing machine, so Rose couldn't load it. I mean, what more can I do to communicate that I like my bed and duck exactly as they are, thank you very much.

While Rose gets the washing machine going, I slink off and plonk myself down on the saturated lawn, my back to the ivy-covered shed. It's early December and the garden is a quagmire of puddles. I resist the temptation to roll in one. Instead, I rest my head between my paws, enjoying the feel of the winter sun on my back, and ponder why it is that I understand Rose, and yet Rose doesn't understand me.

The problem, of course, is that I can't show Rose that I do understand her. Not beyond the yes and no game we play. I'm meant to be a dumb dog who obeys commands – although I'm not very good at the obedience thing. The big secret is that dogs pretend to be dumb so that hoomans don't feel threatened. I probably shouldn't try to communicate with Rose, but there is so much I want to tell her and it's frustrating that she doesn't understand. *Hurrumph!*

I hear her mobile phone's chiming ringtone. I lift my head and prick my ears. Will Rose answer it? She's been ignoring calls. Except from Big Man Joe, otherwise known as PC Salisbury, who is her best buddy. Except for me, of course. She always asks Joe the same question: has the DCI mentioned anything about her returning to work? I wander inside the cottage to find Rose chewing her lower lip as she eyeballs the phone. She leans closer, sees the caller's ID, and rears up like she's just been bitten.

'No, I can't,' she mutters.

The phone stops chiming. Rose exhales loudly as if she has been holding her breath. Her tense body relaxes a fraction. I wonder why phone calls are such a big deal for her. She used to like chatting to her friends.

The phone chimes again. Rose wrings her hands. 'I suppose I have to.'

She takes the call. 'Dr Doom, lovely to hear from you.' Her voice quivers.

Ah, now I know why she doesn't want to take *that* call. Dr Doris Doom is the psychiatrist who is supposed to be helping Rose with her PTSD thing. I wish I knew what PTSD is because then I could try to help her get better.

I listen into their conversation, hoping to learn more. It's not hard to overhear Dr Doom on the other end of the line; she has a loud nasal voice as if she has a peg on her nose.

'Rose, glad I caught you. When can you come in and see me?'

Rose's mouth opens and closes but no sound comes out. She stares around the kitchen as if seeking inspiration. 'Sorry, I've been madly busy. You know how it is. I don't have my diary to hand so may I phone you back?'

'I'd rather we agreed a time now. You've cancelled our last four appointments and I can't help you if we don't meet.'

'I don't need help, Doris. Really. I'm absolutely fine. I just need to get back to work.'

'Of course you do. You love your job. I understand. However, as you know, you can only return to work if I give you a clean bill of health. How about this afternoon at four? I've had a cancellation.'

Rose looks at me, her eyes pleading. It's clear she doesn't want to see Dr Doom and she's looking for an excuse. So I roll onto my back and close my eyes, my paws hanging limply, playing dead. 'Yes, that's it,' Rose says. 'Monty.'

'Monty?' asks Dr Doom.

'Yes. He's ill. I…err…have to take him to the vet. At that time. At four.' I open my eyes and roll over onto my stomach, my role playing over. Rose gives me a thumbs-up. I wag my tail. Yeah! What a team!

'Okay, then,' says Dr Doom. 'When *can* you come in?'

'I…aah…maybe in a month? I'll have to get back to you.'

'Rose, I'm here to help you. I can only do that if you see me regularly.' Dr Doom suggests a day next week and Rose reluctantly agrees, then ends the call.

For a moment Rose stares into space. She looks down at me still lying on the floor at her feet. 'Oh. The vet!' she suddenly exclaims. 'I think I forgot your jabs.'

Is this for real or are we still pretending?

She makes a phone call and books me in for this afternoon with Malcolm Kerr. I can't believe it. This *is* for real.

I hate going to the vet's. They think they can get away with sticking a thermometer where it really shouldn't go, just because they give you a measly liver treat or two. The first time I went there I ended up with stitches and a plastic cone of shame around my neck. I can't tell you how maddening it is to have an itchy ear and be unable to scratch it. Scratching, after all, is one of the things we dogs live for.

I lower my head between my two front paws, giving Rose my best sad-eyes look and sigh a loud *hurrumph*. She kneels down and runs her fingers through the fur along my back.

'I haven't been much fun recently, have I?' she says. I lift my head and give the back of her hand a lick. 'I love being a police officer. It's all I ever wanted to be. Now I feel so…lost. I have no purpose.' She gives me a chest rub. Bliss! 'You understand, don't you?'

I bark, just the once. Yes, I do. I miss our crime-busting adventures too, but not as much as Rose. She's like a fish without water. A bird without the sky. A dog without a hooman.

2

I lie at Rose's feet at the Geldeford Vet Hospital waiting to see Malcom Kerr. I sniff the air and ignore the astringent disinfectant and the corn chip smell of cat coming from consulting room two. I home in on the intoxicating aroma of cheese, tomato and ham on, let me see – I inhale deeply – ah yes, sourdough bread, coming from the small kitchen at the back of the surgery. Somebody has left the door open and I catch a glimpse of their cling-wrapped sandwich on the countertop. Big mistake. Before I know it, I'm stalking towards the kitchen, belly to the floor, hoping no-one will notice me.

'Monty, stay!' Rose says, which snaps me out of my hypnotic state.

But I can't stop drooling. Two long strands of slobber hang either side of my jowls.

Malcolm bursts through the back door like he's got the scent of a rabbit and nothing will stop him chasing it. Quite impressive, actually. Rose flinches as if she's heard gunshot, then when she sees it's just the vet, she exhales a jagged breath and her shoulders relax. I watch as Malcolm removes his wax jacket and struggles into the white coat he wears when he's working. He then hurtles down the corridor towards us, eyes locked on Rose. He has dark, unruly hair that sticks out at odd angles, which he desperately tries to flatten as he approaches us.

'Sorry to keep you waiting, Rose. Had an emergency,' Malcolm says. 'The Beagle's first, then Monty.' He gives me a pat.

'Okay,' Rose says. 'We can wait.'

We can? I think we should go. I feel fine. I don't need an injection.

'Mrs Holt?' Malcolm calls out.

A few feet away, a Beagle has his nose to the ground and is hoovering up smells as if his life depends on it. A vet nurse with a mop wipes up a blood trail around the dog. His ear is badly torn. At the other end of the Beagle's lead is a woman in Barbour jacket and sensible, lace-up shoes. She glares at Malcolm, her mouth a tightly closed slit.

'Please follow me,' he says.

Beagle lady strides up to Malcolm, dragging the dog with her across the slippery floor.

'At last!' Mrs Holt says at full volume. 'I do hate it when *you people* are late.'

'Ah,' says Malcolm looking down, 'your bloody Beagle.'

Mrs Holt stiffens, her wiry eyebrows so furrowed they almost touch, and is clearly about to abuse the young vet for his rudeness when she realises that she does, indeed, have a bloody Beagle.

'Quite right,' she mutters as she strides ahead of Malcolm into his consulting room, blood still dripping from the dog's torn ear. 'Barbed wire is a bastard.'

Malcom shuts the door.

A white-haired woman who smells like Victoria sponge cake stares pointedly at Rose from across the waiting room. Curled up on her lap is a Pug.

'You're that detective, aren't you?' the old lady asks Rose.

Rose looks up. 'Um…'

'I knew it! I saw your photo in the papers a few months back. You arrested that killer. The one that murdered a professor?'

I whimper. I can't help it. The murdered professor was my previous owner.

Rose strokes my head, no doubt sensing my anguish. 'It's okay Monty. You know I love you.'

I do know. I also know that Rose's pulse is pounding. I can feel it.

She doesn't like to talk about the night she faced the killer. It makes her very agitated.

'Yes, I remember the photo of you and the dog.' The old lady peers at me. 'He doesn't look like the kind of dog that could tackle a killer.' But I did. I would have defended Rose until my dying breath. 'Is he a police dog?'

'Not really. But he's a very special boy nonetheless.' Rose gives my head another stroke.

I sit up straight, my chest puffed out, feeling very proud.

Rose rummages in her pocket for her phone and stares at the screen, which is blank. She pretends to read. But Pug Woman won't stop.

'That Malcolm keeps saying I feed Mr Squishy too much. Utter rubbish!'

Her Pug is so round he looks as if he's about to burst. Mr Squishy doesn't appear to have a neck, just one circular body with eyes at one end and a curly tail at the other.

The old lady continues, 'And what's wrong with giving him Bourbon Cream biscuits? He likes them.'

Biscuits? Did someone say biscuits?

Rose gives Pug Woman a weak smile, then resumes her focus on the blank screen, making *mmm* noises as if she's reading something very interesting.

From Malcolm's consulting room there's a sudden *crash* as something metal hits the floor, then a fast flapping like sheets in a strong wind. The Beagle must be shaking his head.

We hear Mrs Holt's booming voice. 'Look at all that blood. Like one of those TV crime scenes.' Her laugh is surprisingly masculine.

'It would really help if you could hold Bertie still while I bandage his ear.' Malcolm says.

'Don't be ridiculous. That's your job,' Mrs Holt snaps.

Claws scrape across a solid surface. There's a low growl that builds to a sharp bark.

Rose and the old lady exchange glances.

'Right,' says Malcolm from the consulting room. 'That's done. Now for the antibiotic. It won't hurt a bit.'

Mr Squishy's ears prick up. He struggles to stand in his owner's lap. Clearly he doesn't like syringes either. He jumps to the floor and heads for the exit, but he only gets as far as the length of his lead.

'These young vets,' says the old lady, using her stick to help her up, 'are too rough. I'm not having him touch Mr Squishy.' She waddles towards the exit.

Her Pug looks back at me. 'Have you read this morning's wee-mails?' he wheezes.

I give Mr Squishy a quick bark. 'Not yet.'

'You should. Something strange is going on.'

 3

Malcolm invites us into consulting room one. Uh-oh! Malcolm's heart-rate is through the roof. Maybe he's having one of those things hoomans talk about. A heart attack? I lean into him and whimper an, 'Are you okay?'

He pats my head. He doesn't keel over so it must be something else.

The room is flooded with the metallic scent of blood on the walls and floor even though Malcolm has cleaned it up. He's also changed his coat; the one with red spots lies in a crumpled heap in the corner. He continues to pat me, but his eyes are fixed on Rose.

'Um, you've got…' Rose wiggles a finger at his face. '…blood on your face.'

Rose is right. He looks as if he's got what hoomans call measles.

'Oh. Right.' Malcolm uses a damp paper towel to clean the blood away then he starts to feel under my chin, listens to my chest through two tubes with a silver disc at the end, then runs his hands over my abdomen. So far so good. No syringe. Maybe he'll forget. I wag my tail hopefully.

'How are you?' Malcolm asks Rose, giving her a concerned glance.

'I'm well, thank you,' she says cheerily, but she avoids eye-contact and flushes red like a stop light. 'And you?'

I peer up at Rose, mystified. She's not well at all. Even a dog like me knows that.

Malcolm's thick black brows dip. He blinks rapidly. He looks as confused as I am.

'I'm fine. Busy, you know,' Malcolm replies, still feeling my abdomen. It's like he's kneading dough. How long is he going to do this? 'How… how are you finding your, you know, new-found freedom? Must be nice, you know, not having to go to work.'

I may only be a dog but I'm pretty sure that going to work every day is exactly what Rose wants to do.

'Oh, you know,' Rose says, staring at the floor. 'Taking time out. I needed a holiday.'

If Rose is having a holiday, then I'm a Chihuahua.

'Is there anything I can do to help? You went through a terrifying ordeal.'

'I don't need help,' Rose snaps, then blushes at her sharp response. 'Sorry, I'd rather not talk about it.'

'Right. Um, Rose, would, um, you…I mean, Joe and I, we're going to the pub Friday night.'

I didn't know that Rose's friend, Joe, is also friends with Malcolm. As a result, Malcolm goes up in my estimation quite a lot.

'Yes, Joe mentioned it,' Rose says. 'Boys' night, he said.'

'It's not!' Malcolm says, almost tripping over me as he shoots upright. What's the matter with him?

Rose jolts, startled. Her mobile phone rings. She checks the screen. Her eyes brighten. Must be someone she wants to talk to.

'I should take this.' She leaves the consulting room.

Malcolm grimaces then mumbles to himself, 'Idiot!'

Our eyes meet.

'I know,' Malcolm says to me, shaking his head. 'I'm making a complete pig's ear of this.'

I look around for said pig's ear – one of my favourite snacks – but can't detect their oily yumminess anywhere. The only things remotely edible in here are some liver treats in a jar near the basin.

Through the door I hear Rose say, 'Hello, sir. This is a nice surprise.'

That must be The Leach. DCI Craig Leach.

While I'm not looking, Malcolm gives me the vaccination in the loose skin at the back of my neck and I hardly feel it. Sneaky devil. Maybe injections aren't that bad after all.

'Yes, tomorrow morning's fine,' I hear Rose say. 'See you then.'

When she comes back into the room her eyes glisten and she has a broad smile on her face.

'All done,' Malcolm says. He stares at Rose, lips parted, but no words come out for a second or two. 'I wanted to ask–'

'Sorry Malcom, I have to go. Got to prepare for a meeting.' She opens the door.

'Why don't you, um, join us?' he blurts.

'I'll leave a boys' night to the boys.'

'It's not a…'

Malcolm drops his head like the dog in the kennel that isn't getting a walk today. Rose races to the reception desk and produces a piece of rectangular plastic that she calls her "flexible friend" from her purse. She taps some buttons on a handheld machine then dives for the exit. I manage to sniff a corner wall outside the door where several dogs have urinated – or more correctly, have left wee-mails. Wee-mailing is how us dogs communicate. It's very similar to an email: it conveys a message. The difference is that the messages we leave are available for any passing dog to sniff. We can then reply with our own wee-mail. In addition, wee-mails convey our mood. Happy, sad, jealous, excited.

I sniff two warning wee-mails.

Dogs are disappearing. Stay home, stay safe.

He who must not be named is back! Be vigilant.

Both messages convey the same mood – fear. The fur all down my spine sticks up. My ears are pricked. I'm on high alert. A memory flashes into my head like lightning in the sky. I see a Golden Retriever yelping as a man drags her away. I see the terror in her eyes. I whimper. Rose must have heard me because she bends down to look into my eyes.

'What's the matter, Monty?'

The memory evaporates like snowflakes in the morning sun. But an uneasy feeling settles upon me, heavy as a blanket. I have to find out what's going on. I cock my leg on the wall and add my own message.

Who is taking the dogs? And where from?

I don't have to sign my name. We all have a unique scent and super snozzles that can sift smells like nothing else.

'Cheer up, Monty,' Rose says, as we walk to the car. 'I think I'm about to get my job back.' She grins at me.

I haven't seen her this excited for a long time. I wag my tail.

'That's right,' she continues. 'We get to solve cases again. You and me, the super-sleuths, huh?'

Wooferoo! I have a bounce in my step like a pony at a gymkhana.

4

Rose was late for her 10am Tuesday meeting with DCI Leach. A bad start, given that her boss was a stickler for punctuality. Why, oh why, had her car decided not to start, today of all days? A neighbour had come to her rescue and jump-started the engine, but it had delayed her departure.

Rose pulled into the Geldeford Police car park at five past ten agitated and sweaty. The Valium she had taken clearly wasn't working. She left Monty in the car with the windows down and strict instructions not to bark. Leach's office overlooked the car park where she had parked her battered old Honda Jazz. The last thing she wanted to do was irritate a man who was easily irritated.

Rose nodded at a police officer she knew who was having a smoke near the building's rear door, then hurried through the narrow corridor, past the locker room, and raced up two flights of stairs, before pausing to catch her breath outside the double doors leading to Major Crime.

There were sweaty patches under her arms and strands of hair had fallen free from the band she'd used to tie a ponytail. Her skin tingled with agitation and she knew her face was flushed. And how on earth had she managed to spill cereal down her best suit this morning? Rose held up a hand and stared at its tremor. Not exactly the cool, calm and collected image she was hoping to present to Leach.

'Fake it till you make it,' she mumbled to herself.

Through the little rectangles of glass in each door, she saw familiar faces. She searched for Joe Salisbury, but she couldn't see him. She spotted the dapper DS Kamlesh Varma, the gentleman of the Major Crime unit who was well known for his politeness, even to the criminals he arrested. Rose felt better for seeing him. Then her heart sank. Varma shifted in his seat and a fair-haired man in a brown leather jacket came into view – DI Dave Pearl.

Before her career went pear-shaped, she had been tipped for great things. Top of her class at the College of Policing, she'd excelled as a beat officer and earned a coveted position as a trainee Detective Constable in one of the most sought-after units – Major Crime. Pearl was appointed her mentor but he'd disliked Rose from the start, accusing her of nepotism. Her aunt Kay had been a Detective Inspector in the very same unit, until she died of cancer. Pearl assumed Rose was only in the squad because of her connection to Kay.

But at just twenty-one years of age her arrest rate was phenomenal. Her success was down to hard work and an uncanny ability to know when someone was lying. It was more than instinct. Rose had a physical reaction to people lying: a tingling feeling in her hands and feet, like pins and needles. The problem, as she had learned though bitter experience, was that Rose couldn't detect lies by omission.

Behind her, she heard heavy boots on the stairs.

'Hey Rose, what are you doing here?'

It was Joe, all six feet three of him. He had baby spew on one shoulder of his black uniform, no doubt from baby Daniel.

'You've got…' She pointed at the smudge on his shoulder.

'So have you.' Joe pointed at her lapel. 'Here to see the boss?'

'Yes. Looks like I'm back in.'

'Really? Leach said that, did he?'

Why did Joe look so shocked?

'Well not exactly. But he asked to see me, so…' She checked her watch. 'I'm late. See you later.'

Joe threw open the doors and strode in. Rose followed.

'Look who it is!' Joe announced.

Every head turned in her direction. She thought she was going to pee her pants. She suddenly felt totally overwhelmed.

'Hi.' She gave them a little wave, then wanted to slap her hand down. She was meant to be a tough detective. She was behaving like a little girl.

Varma smiled broadly and came over to her. 'Good to see you, Rose. We miss you, you know?'

'And I miss you guys. Hopefully I'll be back with you very soon.'

Somebody muttered something that sounded like, 'Over my dead body.'

Rose glanced at Pearl who gave her a curt nod. 'Managed to stay out of the loony bin?' He laughed. One of Pearl's mates chuckled.

Leach's office door opened. 'There you bloody are. Get in here now,' Leach called across the room.

'Good luck,' Joe whispered.

Rose scurried into Leach's office and closed the door behind her. His melamine desk was as messy as ever, littered with files. The force was supposed to be moving to paperless policing, but Leach was old school. His shirt sleeves were rolled up to reveal muscular forearms covered in tattoos, one of which was the Manchester United logo.

'You're late,' Leach growled, rubbing the top of his shaved, snooker ball head that appeared to sit directly on muscular shoulders without a neck. 'We'll have to keep this short.' His Mancunian accent was still as strong as the day he'd moved south to head up Geldeford's Major Crime unit.

'I'm sorry, sir. It won't happen again.' She knew that Leach found her quietly-spoken voice irritating, so she deliberately upped the volume.

'Okay, no need to shout. I'm not deaf.'

Maybe she upped it a little too much.

Leach placed his large hands on his desk and interlocked his fingers. His expression softened. 'How are you doing?'

'Much better, sir. Perfectly fine, actually. Ready and raring to get back in the field.'

Leach nodded, as if weighing her statement like it was testimony. 'You've been through the ringer, that's for sure. Not many officers look death in the face the way you did. There's no shame in taking time to get over it.'

'And I have got over it, sir.' Rose deliberately kept her hands clenched together in her lap so he couldn't see them shaking. 'I'm looking forward to making a valuable contribution to the next case.'

Leach pursed his lips. 'Still having nightmares?'

'Well, not exactly.'

'Panic attacks?'

'I don't think so, no.' She had always been a bad liar and from the frown on Leach's face she was pretty certain Leach saw straight through hers.

'Your psychiatrist tells me you haven't been going to your sessions.'

'Been busy, that's all.'

'Says she's concerned you're in denial. That you've shown little progress.'

Rose gawped. 'I thought those sessions were meant to be confidential, sir.'

'Not when they're coming out of my budget and the decision about whether you're fit for duty rests on her report.'

Her head was throbbing. What was happening? Wasn't this supposed to be about her returning to work?

'I'm not in denial, sir. I recognise my near-death experience impacted my self-confidence for a while.' Leach's frown deepened. 'I also recognise that I've had a few panic attacks since. But I'm over that. Haven't had one for weeks.' She pressed her fingernails into her palms hoping he wouldn't notice her lie.

'Nobody blames you, Rose. You could have died. But I need to know I can rely on you. That my team can rely on you.'

'I've been resting and recovering for almost three months now, sir. I want to come back to work.'

Leach leaned back in his wheelie chair which creaked in protest. She swore she saw sympathy in his eyes. 'You can't return to work until Dr Doom says you're ready.' He shook his large head. 'What a bloody awful name for a doctor,' he muttered, then continued. 'You have to attend your sessions with her, Rose. If you don't, you won't get reinstated.'

She gasped. She couldn't stop herself. Her job was everything. She couldn't begin to imagine life without being a police officer.

'I'll do paperwork. Stay at my desk. I'll prove to you I'm a valuable team member.'

'I can't do that Rose. I'm sorry.'

A hot flush rose up her neck like a flood tide. Her throat felt constricted. She couldn't let Leach see that she was panicking. 'I'm bored senseless at home.' She was short of breath. She tried to calm herself. 'I need a project, something worthwhile. I love my job, sir. Solving crimes means everything to me.' She sounded as if she had run a race. 'Don't you see, sir? Keeping busy is what I need. Staying at home just isn't working.'

'This job is mentally gruelling. The stress levels are high. I can't have a loose cannon on the team.'

Rose knew she had hit a wall with Leach. She was close to tears but determined not to let it show. She blinked rapidly. 'Thank you for your advice, sir. I'll see Dr Doom. I'll show myself out.'

Rose stood and made a beeline for the door.

'You have the makings of an excellent detective, Rose.' Leach spoke quietly, apologetically – which was almost unheard of for him – but emphatically. 'But I need to be sure you can back up your colleagues.'

'Yes, sir,' she squeaked and left the office before her tears showed. She darted across the room, head down, aware of several pairs of eyes watching her. As she ran down the stairs, she used her sleeve to wipe her eyes, then she raced across the car park. Through the rear window, Monty was watching her, tongue out, ears pricked. He looked so happy to see her. She got in and burst into tears. Monty poked his head between the two front seats and nuzzled her neck. His whiskers tickled her. She leaned her face against his velvet soft ears.

'Oh Monty. They won't have me back.'

5

Rose sat at the kitchen table, her chin resting on her folded arms. Monty was at her feet, his muzzle resting on her knees. The warmth of his body was comforting. His whiskery jowl was splayed out either side of his muzzle, which made him look silly and endearing at the same time. He hadn't left her side since arriving home.

Rose ran a finger across a deep gouge in the table's surface that was stained a reddish-brown. Rose had been thirteen years old and cutting up carrots that Kay had just pulled from the garden. Rose had managed to slice the side of her second finger off. The knife cut deep into the wood and Rose's blood dripped into the wedge. It was funny how an experience that was so distressing at the time made her smile now. Kay had rushed her to hospital and they'd shared bowls of Rose's favourite ice cream when they got back home. She remembered Kay's loving hugs and soothing words.

If only Kay were here. She would know what to do. But Kay was gone and Rose felt her loss as a dull ache in her chest. It was ever present, but some days – like today – more pressing than others. Rose looked around the kitchen at the little things that reminded her of her aunt. The red and black ladybird egg timer that Kay had bought at Farley

Green's annual village fete. Kay's MasterChef apron which still hung on the back of the door – Kay had been an obsessive fan of the show. The small pots on the inside windowsill, brimming with mustard cress, basil, sage and mint. After the funeral, Rose had given Kay's clothes and shoes to charity, but she couldn't bear to part with anything else.

Rose considered calling her mum, Liz, but quickly realised it was a daft idea. Liz had been dead-set against Rose joining the police. In fact, she had been so horrified at Rose's decision she had refused to speak to her daughter for two years, and blamed her sister, Kay, for putting the idea into Rose's head.

Rain pounded the slate roof. The gutters overflowed and the downpipes gurgled. On the kitchen floor by the fridge was a galvanised steel bucket. A drop of water fell from the ceiling and landed in the pail with a *plip*. A few seconds later, another drop fell.

'Who was I kidding?' she said aloud. 'I'm in no fit state to work.'

Monty looked up at her, as if considering whether this statement was true or false. He sneezed, then went back to resting his jowl in her lap.

'That tickles.' She found herself smiling and leaned forward to give Monty a cuddle. 'I don't know what I'd do without you.'

She was stroking Monty's head when her phone rang. It was her mum. Had Liz's ears been burning?

'Hey, Mum, how are you?' Rose had her fake cheery voice on.

'Dreadful! Thanks to your wretched father.' Rose inwardly groaned. 'Honestly, he's the most boring man on earth. I mean, how did I end up married to him? I must have been out of my mind!'

'Come on, Mum. He just likes his quiet times. He's not like you.'

'There you go defending your bloody father as usual. What about seeing it from my point of view for once? He does nothing but sit at the computer. He refuses to speak to our guests. If it wasn't for me we'd be bankrupt.' Her parents ran a guest house in the quaint Cornish village of Mousehole. 'He's even stopped coming to bridge club which means I have to play with Constance Gwinnel and we all know what a stuck-up cow she is.'

Oh, dear. Liz was winding up for an extended moan. She could easily go on for an hour without ever seeming to stop for breath.

'Maybe Dad's not well?' Rose said.

'God, no. He's just boring. And he won't fix the doorbell. Seriously, I could wring his neck.'

Rose imagined her dad barricaded into his study with headphones on, listening to classical music while her mum yelled through the door.

'Have you thought about taking a break?' Rose suggested.

Such breaks were a regular event for Liz. The problem was that she somehow managed to upset her hosts. The circle of Liz's friends willing to have her to stay was ever-shrinking.

'My thinking exactly. I haven't seen Babs in a while. I'll give her a call.' Liz paused. When she next spoke, it was as if she were cooing at a baby. 'How are you, my poor darling? Those bastards paid you out yet?'

"Bastards" was how she referred to DCI Leach and the rest of her colleagues.

'They're paying for my sick leave, mum, and for the psychiatrist.' Rose tried not to let her irritation show. 'They've been very supportive.'

'Supportive? Those pigs?' Liz laughed. 'They work you like a slave and then when some maniac tries to murder you, they throw you on the rubbish tip. Bastards!'

This conversation wasn't exactly lifting Rose's spirits. 'I'm not on a rubbish tip. I'm on sick leave and trying to get past my panic attacks.'

'You don't have panic attacks, darling. That's psychobabble. Don't pay any attention to that psychiatrist of yours – Dr Death or whatever she's called.'

'Doom, Mum. She's called Dr Doom.'

'Just as bad. I mean, what a name! Anyway, shrinks want to brainwash you. They use hypnotism and can get you to do anything they like. Really. I saw it on YouTube.'

Rose rolled her eyes at Monty.

Liz hadn't finished. 'This is your chance to escape, darling. Resign. Come back to Cornwall. Help me run the guesthouse. It'll be such fun! Us girls together!'

It sounded like hell.

'I love being a detective, Mum. It's what I've always wanted to do.'

'I blame Kay. She knew how I felt about the pigs.'

Rose wasn't going to have this conversation again. She'd lost count of the times her mum unfairly blamed Kay for Rose going to Police College. 'My point is, I want my job back and nothing's going to stop me. If I have to see the psychiatrist, then I will. I've been stupid trying to avoid her. And she doesn't use hypnotism, by the way.'

'How would you know? What if she's already hypnotised you?'

'Good grief.' Rose sighed.

'Come home, darling. There are loads of gorgeous men in Cornwall. Get married and give me some grandchildren.'

'I'm not interested in a relationship right now. I want to focus on my career.' Rose searched for a way to end the conversation without being rude. Her only option was to tell a little white lie. 'Sorry, Mum, I have to go. I have to be somewhere. Talk soon.'

'But…'

'Bye Mum.'

Monty gave a little whine. He was staring at the ceiling. Rose looked up to see a new cluster of droplets forming near the back door.

'Oh rats!'

Monty's ears pricked up expectantly.

'No, not real rats,' she said. 'At least I hope not.'

Rose wiped the floor with a rag. Then a saucepan went under the leak.

'That should do it.' Rose picked up two hessian shopping bags. 'Time for a food shop.' The dog looked unimpressed. 'It's the best I can offer in this rain. At least you get to ride in the car. I might even buy you a treat.'

That got Monty's tail wagging.

 6

I've never been inside Sainsbury's. I do have dreams about it though. In my dreams I've been awarded the Sainsbury's Golden Bone, a prize for special dogs which allows the winner to eat anything they can take from the shelves. There's always a time limit. I can never remember what it is, but I know I have to be quick. So I dash straight to the meat fridges, drag a beef joint off a shelf, tear the plastic away with my teeth and feast on the delicious red meat. I then wake up salivating.

Rose has gone into the supermarket and left me pacing in the back of the car where the seats are flattened so I have a large space to myself. I press my nose against the glass and it steams up. The car park is vast. It has its own petrol station and even a bus stop. The rain has eased into a light drizzle. Water pools around clogged drains and hoomans dash about beneath umbrellas. Through the fogged glass, I see a man walking a British Bulldog that's wearing a Union Jack coat. The dog leaves a wee-mail on a section of the hedge near the bus stop, then moves on. The owner is heading for a housing estate that backs onto the car park.

I bark. 'Any news on the missing dogs?'

I have a loud and deep bark that easily carries. The Bulldog turns his head and stares. He can't see me because of the breathy fug, but he knows I'm in here.

'Word is they're targeting vet's now,' he barks back.

'Quiet!' the hooman says irritably.

The Bulldog rolls his eyes and follows.

Vet's? This is very bad indeed. It means the dognapper is targeting sick and vulnerable dogs. I need to warn Malcolm. Perhaps I can find a way to get Rose to drive by the Vet Hospital so I can leave a wee-mail? At least then the dogs coming and going will know to be on high alert.

I'm super fidgety. My paws won't stop moving. I'm now worried about Rose *and* the dognappings. This is a lot for a dog to cope with. I have no idea how long I've been waiting for Rose's return, but it feels like forever. Then I spy her leaving Sainsbury's with a trolley. I'm disappointed to see that the trolley doesn't have much in it. How is that possible?

'Excuse me!' a woman calls out as she chases after Rose.

She has long blonde hair. Her hessian bag is bulging with food which must be heavy because she leans the other way to compensate. Rose keeps pushing her trolley. She hasn't heard the woman's cries because she has little white blobs in her ears that she calls earbuds. I bark to get Rose's attention, but Rose is oblivious.

'Wait please!' The woman's voice has a note of desperation in it. 'Help me, please.'

I have to do something: the woman is clearly in distress. Rose never locks the car: it's so old, she says, that if somebody were to steal it, she'd thank them. But if I leave the car, am I breaking one of the Ten Dog Commandments? I sit and scratch an ear with my back paw as I think about this. Breaking a Commandment is a big deal. However, Rose didn't tell me to stay put. She simply told me to be a good boy. And a good boy would leave the car if a hooman needed help.

The decision made, I clamp my jaws down on the long door handle that resembles a turkey wishbone and pull it towards me. It's a slippery sucker but soon I get a satisfying clunk as the door opens a fraction. I use the top of my head to push it fully open and jump out. My paws hit a cold puddle and I enjoy the sensation for a moment, then run toward Rose.

'Look, Mum, there's a doggie!' a little girl in a pink plastic poncho says, pointing.

'Big doggie,' the mother says, taking the little girl's hand and walking away quickly, giving me nervous glances.

I suppose I am big for my breed and broad in the shoulders. Some hoomans find me scary. But I'm a lover, not a fighter. I can honestly tell you that the only time I have bitten a hooman was to defend my owner. Which, according to the Ten Dog Commandments, is the only time that a dog can attack a hooman. These laws were laid down by my wolf forefathers many centuries ago when the wolf nation made a pact to work with hoomans. The wolves who obeyed the Ten Dog Commandments became man's best friend. Like me. Of course, some wolf tribes refused to bow to hooman governance. They disobeyed the wolf elders and formed new packs. These are the wild wolves of today that have, tragically, been hunted almost to extinction. Dogs have learned to work with hoomans and we hide our true capabilities so our masters don't fear us.

Rose locks eyes with mine, sees me charging at her, and stops pushing the trolley. She tugs the earbuds from her ears.

'Monty! Whatever are you doing?'

I skid to a halt in front of Rose but look past her and bark. Rose turns and for the first time she notices her pursuer. The woman has a lineless face and is wearing metal bits on her teeth. I have only ever seen hoomans in their teens or twenties wearing these things called braces on their teeth. She smells of musky perfume, coffee and the vinegary smell of fear. Who or what is she afraid of?

'It's you, isn't it?' the young woman says to Rose. 'You're a detective. You solved that murder case. You and your dog.'

Rose shakes her head. She takes a step back. I can hear her heartbeat quickening. 'I'm not on duty,' Rose blurts.

The scent of Rose's anxiety is like burnt toast.

'I need your help,' the woman says. I bark encouragement. Isn't this exactly what Rose wants to do? To help people? 'Can I walk with you, please?'

Rose hesitates, then beckons the woman over, who glances nervously from side to side as if checking to see if she's being watched. Then she joins Rose, lugging her shopping bag with her.

'That looks heavy. You can put it in the trolley if you like. Save you carrying it.'

The woman smiles, revealing bits of metal stuck to her teeth. I now feel even more sorry for her. She's afraid and clearly being tortured. Why else would she have metal bits in her mouth?

Rose walks slowly to the car and the woman keeps pace. 'What's your name?'

'Zofia Nowak. You find people, yes?'

'Not exactly. I work in Major Crime. Has someone you know gone missing?'

'I d-don't know,' Zofia stammers. 'Maybe.'

Zofia fiddles with the clasp of her handbag which is slung diagonally across her body. She takes out her phone and, as she walks, scrolls through pictures. Then she holds the screen up. We are too far away to see it. 'This is my friend. I am very worried. She not come home.'

The photo is so small I only get a rough impression of the woman in it. She has brown hair and pale skin and has an arm draped over Zofia's shoulders. They look like close buddies.

Rose puts out a hand. 'Can I take a look?'

Zofia clutches the phone to her chest protectively. 'You've seen enough.'

'What's her name?' Rose asks.

Zofia puts her mobile away. 'It is difficult. Maybe she is okay. Then she will be angry with me.'

We reach Rose's car and stop walking. 'How long has your friend been missing?'

'She did not come home last night.'

'If you're worried, dial 101 and report her missing to the police.'

Zofia shakes her head vehemently. 'No! No policja! I want *you* to find her. No-one else.'

Rose is startled by Zofia's outburst. 'There's no need to be afraid. Look, I can go with you now, if you like. To the police station. Do you have a car?'

'No, no. This must be anonymous. I cannot be… You will keep this confidential, yes?'

'Yes, of course.'

'I pay you. I have fifty pounds.' Zofia takes a small purse from her bag. 'I give you more later. Please. Will you help me?'

She holds out a fifty pound note. That would buy a lot of dog food.

'I can't accept money, Zofia. I'll take you to Geldeford nick. You can report your friend missing.'

'No, I cannot do this.' A bus pulls up, the breaks squealing. 'I must go now.'

Zofia picks up her shopping and runs awkwardly to the bus stop. Rose watches in silence as Zofia boards and sits at a far window, her head turned away.

'That was odd,' Rose says as the bus pulls away from the curb. Rose's hair and the shopping bags are covered in a fine mist. She tilts her head and I see a brightness in her blue eyes that I haven't seen for a while. 'The 442. That one goes to the university. I wonder…'

Rose loads the bags into the back of the car and tells me to get in. 'No stealing, okay? That food is my food.'

Does she seriously mean it? I'm a dog in a confined space with all manner of delectable smelling foods. This is going to be a real challenge.

Rose gets in, then sits behind the steering wheel and stares out through the windscreen. She doesn't turn the ignition. Okay, now I'm getting fidgety. There's a loaf of freshly baked bread on the top of one of the bags and it's drawing me in like a magnet. I decide to take affirmative action. I nudge Rose's shoulder with my snout.

'I can't stop thinking about her,' Rose says.

Her? Does she mean Zofia?

Rose takes her mobile from her handbag and makes a call. The whole car smells maddeningly of fresh bread and I'm close to ripping off the packaging, which of course would make me a very bad dog. I'm saved from the shame of transgression by the sound of Big Man Joe at the other end of the line.

'So the boss said no then?' Joe says.

'Yes. Says he won't have me back until the psychiatrist says so.'

'I'm sorry to hear that. Maybe he's right, though?'

'I thought you were on my side.'

'I am. You know I am. But there's no point coming back until you're ready.'

There's an awkward silence. Rose has the fingers of one hand locked onto the steering wheel so tightly they are turning white. 'I need a favour, Joe,' Rose says eventually. 'Can you check on a missing person for me?'

Another awkward silence. 'Are you going to tell me why?'

Rose explains about our meeting with Zofia Nowak and her missing friend. 'I don't know the friend's name but she's likely to be late teens, early twenties, has brown hair and is possibly Eastern European. She could be a university student.'

'That's not much to go by, but I'll see what I can do.'

'Thanks, Joe.'

'But I need something in return.'

'Sure, what is it?'

'Can you meet me later? I finish my shift at three thirty. Outside Kelly's Cakes?'

'I'll be there.'

 7

We are on our way to meet Joe in town and I have my head out of the side window. There's nothing better than feeling the wind in my fur. The faster we go, the more my ears flap. It's like I'm flying. If I see a dog I recognise, I bark a friendly hello. I love riding in this car. It's like my very own stretch limo. The Honda Jazz is what Rose calls "second hand" and rattles like a pebble in an empty can and smells as if McDonald's had set up a kitchen in the back. Rose tries to mask the smell with an air freshener that dangles from her rear-view mirror. Thankfully, it isn't working.

The rain has stopped but the clouds are so dark it feels like night has arrived early.

We turn into the cobbled high street and the car labours up the steep hill. Rose pulls up outside a shop that has three headless people in suits in the window. I immediately bark an alarm, warning her that something is wrong. The hoomans I know generally have heads.

'Oh, you're right,' Rose says, peering around at me. 'I'm so used to parking anywhere I like. Not a cop anymore, am I? How did you know about double yellow lines?'

I stare at her blankly. I haven't the faintest idea what she's talking about. I bark again and stare pointedly at the headless hoomans in the window. Rose follows my line of sight.

'They're mannequins, silly. They're not real.'

Rose continues up the hill and parks in a multi-story car park. We then walk back down the high street. The pavements swarm with people like a new litter trying to get to their mother at feeding time. We pass a coffee shop: the scent of the coffee is overwhelming. Rose once told me that smugglers hide all sorts of things in coffee beans. No wonder. Even a super sniffer like mine would struggle with that stink. Then we pass a Marks & Spencer with its unmistakable smell of crisp cotton, creamy cakes and beef Wellington. I know about Marks & Spencer because Rose once went in there to buy some knickers and came out with a rainbow coloured five-pack, plus a meal of lamb shanks with honey-roasted vegetables, a bottle of wine and some chocolatey walnut whips, which Rose called a Meal Deal. When I'd looked at her imploringly, she'd said, 'Not for you. These are my special treat.'

Next is a shop full of nothing but shoes. I still can't fathom why hoomans put these things on their feet. I love the feel of wet grass under my paws and the bliss of squishy mud between my toes. Their loss, I guess.

Stall holders in the outdoor market are closing down for the day, putting their produce back in vans.

'Hopefully he hasn't closed yet,' Rose says, speeding up.

We arrive at the spot where the stall selling pet supplies normally stands, but they aren't there. The ground still radiates the heady aromas of liver treats, marrow bones and oily pigs' ears. I spot a Jack Russell tied to a lamp post. To be more accurate, she's run around and around the lamp post so that her leash is now so tight, her head rests against the post. She sees me looking. Yaps a hello and then proceeds to gnaw at her lead. I'm not surprised. With the absence of dog treats in the area, the poor creature must be famished.

'Never mind, there's a pet shop in Abinger Hammer,' Rose says to me. Rose is very particular about what she feeds me. She doesn't like the supermarket's dog food. I couldn't care less. I'll eat anything except lettuce. I mean, lettuce! What is the point of it? 'I've got enough to feed you tonight.'

Phew. That's a relief.

Rose leads me under an arch and into a narrow, cobbled lane. The buildings here are very old and very crooked. They have white walls and black timbers and Rose says they are Tudor, whatever that means. Metal chairs and tables line one side of the lane and tall heaters bestow warmth on the customers of Kelly's Cakes who are seated at tables huddled around them. They seem to be either smokers or dog owners. Joe is seated at a table beneath one of the heaters and waves at us.

'I ordered your favourite,' Joe says as Rose takes a seat. I squeeze between Joe and Rose.

'Black Forest Gateau and Yorkshire Gold tea?' Rose asks.

'You got it.' Joe turns to me. 'Hey, Monty, how are you, buddy?' He gives me a scratch under the chin. That's nice but my belly would like some attention. I lie on my back, legs in the air. Joe leans down and strokes my tummy. What a gentleman. I squirm with pleasure. Up a bit, left a bit, ah! That's it. My back leg twitches like Bambi's Thumper. Does this all on its own. Nothing to do with me.

Kelly, who owns the tearoom, arrives with the pot of tea and a huge slice of cake. There's got to be enough for me too, surely?

'I checked Missing Persons,' Joe says, shovelling a substantial slice of cheesecake into his mouth. Joe's my kind of guy when it comes to food. He doesn't mess around. 'Four young women have been reported missing in the last two weeks. None are Eastern European. Only one is a student, from Mumbai.' He produces a photo and hands it to Rose. 'Could that be her?'

'Afraid not.'

'You didn't get this info from me, okay? If the boss finds out, I'm stuffed.'

'Thanks, Joe. So what's the favour?'

'There's this lad I know. Seventeen. Got in with the wrong crowd. But he's a good lad and I want to help him. Maybe you need some repairs done around the house? Leaves raked. That sort of thing.'

Rose picks up the big cup of tea and sips. 'I suppose I could find something. But I don't have any cash to spare, Joe. It would have to be odd jobs.'

'Anything that gets him away from the Truscott Estate.'

Rose's forehead furrows. I don't blame her. I have been to the Truscott Estate and was chased by a very angry man.

'How do you know this boy?' Rose asks.

'Name's Oliver Fernsby, but he likes to be called Ollie. He stole a car. Funny story, really.' Joe chuckles to himself.

'Were you the arresting officer?'

'Yeah. You know gangs operate on that estate, right? Kids get coerced into joining the Blockers.'

'Jeez, Joe, they're seriously bad.'

'I know but hear me out. Ollie got pressured into it. He didn't want to, but he was scared. The Merc belonged to this woman who had left the engine on while she posted a letter. So Ollie jumps into the driver's seat and takes off. Then he discovers there's an eight-year-old boy in the back. You know what Ollie does?'

'I'm guessing you're going to tell me.'

'He drops the kid at school, even waits for the little guy to go inside to make sure he's safe, then abandons the motor with not a scratch on it. We found it easily because the lady left her mobile in it. Ollie didn't even nick the phone.'

'He really drove the kid to school?' Rose's frown softens.

'Yep. Caught him on the school's CCTV.' Joe studies her face. 'He's a good kid. Why don't you give him a chance?'

'Can I think about it?'

Joe glances over her shoulder. 'Ah there he is.' Joe stands up.

'He's here?' Rose turns in her seat.

Shuffling leisurely towards us is a lanky teenage boy in a faded olive bomber jacket. His curly hair adds a couple of inches to his height. Black-framed glasses dominate his chiselled face. His hands are wedged deep into the pockets of his baggy jeans that do little to disguise his pipe cleaner legs. When Joe raises an arm and waves, Ollie stops in his tracks and mumbles something. He hurries over.

'What ya think ya doin'?' Ollie says to Joe. 'I can't be seen wiv ya. You're a cop.'

8

It is gone midnight and Rose is asleep upstairs. I am curled up on my bed in the kitchen, my chin resting on my way-too-clean fluffy yellow duck. At least my bed carries my doggy aroma. The smells that come with me to bed at night are the memories of that day and they rub off on the bed cover. When I sniff my bed, all those memories come flooding back. Wash my bed and the result is olfactory amnesia. A terrible affliction.

Today has not been a good day for Rose, so my bed smells sad tonight. It holds the salty sweet smell of Rose's tears – for which I blame the Leach – and the musky perfume, coffee and vinegary smell of the mysterious Zofia. I shift position and rest my head on a front paw. Then I hear a gnawing noise and open my eyes. It's coming from a small hole in the skirting board to the right of the larder. I lift my head and sniff. That hole belongs to my friend, Betty Blabble, a former Eurotunnel rat. I haven't seen her for a while. Has she returned at last?

I trot over to the hole to get a better sniff. There's a length of pizza crust protruding from it that has hooman teeth marks in it. It carries a residue of the pepperoni, cheese and ham topping. Rose has this strange habit of leaving the pizza crusts behind. Betty must have rummaged in the bin and found them; if it is Betty that is. I breathe in deeply and inhale the smell of rotting fruit, greasy food wrappers and a hint of hot metal, engine oil and rubber, much like the trains she uses to get about.

There's a crunch and the crust kicks up like a leg.

'Betty!' I woof as quietly as I am able, so as not to wake Rose.

The pizza crust zips into the hole and disappears from view. Then Betty's head pokes out, her black ball-bearing eyes as shiny as ever, her pink nose twitching. 'Hey, Mith-ter Monty, I'll be out in a jiffy.' Her cheeks bulge with tiny pieces of crust, making her lisp.

Headfirst, she begins to squeeze her rotund body through the hole. It has always been a tight fit, and she appears to have expanded.

'Who made thith hole thmaller?' she mumbles.

I watch patiently. When her body is about half-way through, her progress stalls.

'Do you need some help, Betty?' I ask.

'No thank you, Mith-ter Monty, I've got thith.'

Her back claws scratch the floor as she pushes herself forward. With one final effort, she pops out into the kitchen like a pebble fired from a slingshot and comes to a halt when she hits my leg. *Boof!* She jumps up and brushes down her fur. Her stomach looks like she's swallowed a cricket ball.

'I've missed you,' I say, settling down on the floor next to her.

'Mithed you too, my friend.'

I rest my head between my front paws so that I can look *at* her rather than *down* at her. 'I was worried about you. You left so suddenly. Where did you go?'

'A retreat. Needed to recover, see? I mean, it's not every day you get flushed down a toilet. I thought I was a goner.'

I should make it clear that Rose didn't do the flushing. It was the hooman who broke into our house. Betty would have drowned if she wasn't such a strong swimmer. And it helped that the sewer pipe had a crack in it, which she escaped through.

'You're looking well.'

'It's the diet,' Betty says, sending crumbs flying out of her mouth. At surprising speed given her huge stomach, she dives at each crumb and sucks it back in as if she were a vacuum cleaner. 'Part of my recovery program. It's called the Pizza Diet and it's working wonders. Mind if I finith me thupper? I won't looth weight if I don't keep eating.'

My ears twitch in confusion.

I've never been on a diet and never intend to be. But I'm pretty certain what she's just said doesn't make sense. However, I've learnt that contradicting Betty is never a good idea. She can be fearsome when she wants to be. 'Go ahead,' I say.

She swallows some of the crumbs in her cheeks. I watch the bulges either side of her nose gradually diminish.

'Where was this retreat?' I ask.

'In Brighton. Easy to get to by train which, as you know, Mister Monty, is my favourite way to travel. Brighton is a happening place, I can tell ya. Lots of nightlife and more rubbish that I can poke a stick at. All the fish and chips, see? Although those bleedin' seagulls can be a pain. Bloody thieves, they are.' She tuts disapprovingly.

Betty pokes her head back in the hole and drags out the long piece of crust she was gnawing earlier. She takes a bite.

'So you're feeling better?' I ask.

Her head snaps around, her fur bristles and her stunted tail slaps the floor like a whip. How Betty lost half her tail I don't know and don't ask, just in case it's a touchy subject. I imagine it had something to do with a mouse trap. 'I wath never ill, okay? And don't you go around thaying anything different, all right?'

I decide to change the subject.

'When did you get back?'

'Today. Thought you might be lonely.' I'm never lonely as long as I'm with Rose. But I did miss my night-time adventures with Betty. 'Howth our Rose doing?'

I suddenly realise Betty doesn't know that Rose is on sick leave.

'Oh Betty,' I shake my head. 'Something is wrong with her and I don't know what to do.'

'Tell me everything.' Betty gets comfortable against one of my outstretched paws which she uses as a back rest. 'The word in the sewers is that you saved Rose from that crazy woman.' Betty balances the crust on her belly and waits for me to begin.

'We saved each other,' I say.

Flashes of memory buzz around the inside of my head like angry wasps but I can't, or maybe I don't want to, relive that terrifying night.

'I need my bed, Betty. Come with me.'

But Betty doesn't budge. 'I'm nice and comfy here,' she moans and then sits up. 'Oh I see. You need your memory bed.'

She nods sagely and gets onto all fours to follow me, the crust clenched in her jaws. I swear her belly touches the floor as she waddles along.

I lie down on my bed and Betty, a little breathless, sits with her back against my paw. I press my nose into the soft padding of my bed and inhale. The buzzing inside my head clears. I remember.

'Rose hasn't been the same since the night we both almost ended up in a furnace.'

'Yeah, that can really mess with your head,' says Betty.

I tell Betty all about that terrible night with the furnace and the knife and how we both almost died. Betty interjects with an 'oooh!' then a 'sounds nasty.' I tell her how Rose and I worked together to capture the people responsible for my old master's death. When I stop talking, Betty claps her front paws together.

'Blimey! That's some story.' She then jumps up and does a little jiggle, wobbling her bottom from side to side. 'What a team you two make! You caught the killers! Oh yeah! Oh yeah!'

'We did.' I nod proudly.

Betty's dance doesn't last long. She plonks down with exhaustion. 'You're a hero, Mister Monty, you know that, right?'

My ears droop and I hang my head. 'But Rose is different now. She's…she's…'

Betty grips my paw. I feel the sharpness of her claws. 'She's what? Spit it out!'

'She's anxious and doubts herself a lot. She doesn't think she's a good detective.'

Betty pauses, one claw raised. She's having a light bulb moment. 'It's that bleedin' boss of hers, isn't it?'

'He's put Rose on sick leave. Says she can't return to work until the psychiatrist says she's got over something called PTSD.'

'What have peas got to do with anything?' says Betty.

'Not peas. PTSD. It's what her doctor calls it.'

'It's The Leach! I bet he's given her a hard time. I'll punch the bleedin' daylights out of 'im.'

Betty is up on her hind legs, shadow boxing. She swings a particularly energetic punch and falls flat on her face.

'That's not a good idea, Betty. He'd probably kill you.'

'Good point.' Betty frowns. 'What's this PPSP thing?'

I don't correct her. 'All I know is that she has nightmares most nights. Wakes up terrified. When she's in danger, she freezes. She blames herself for putting me in danger.'

'Poor, poor Rose,' Betty sighs. 'We gotta help her.'

'How do we do that?'

Betty paces, her stunted tail flicking excitedly. 'I know. She needs to solve a crime. If she solves a crime, then her confidence will come back.'

I wag my tail. 'In that case, I have good news. Rose is looking for a missing person.'

Betty's eyes shine like black diamonds. 'Then we have to make sure she succeeds.'

9

Rose woke at four in the morning, a strangled scream caught in her throat, her legs kicking. Her flannel pyjamas clung to her sweaty body. For a second or two she didn't know where she was. Then a damp nose sniffed her face. Monty wasn't supposed to come upstairs but she was grateful he sometimes knew when to break the house rules. She groped for the bedside lamp and turned it on. Monty jumped onto the bed and lay next to her. Stroking his fur was soothing.

'Maybe I do need help,' Rose said as she cuddled him. 'I have to get better.'

When her heart rate had returned to normal, she changed into fresh pyjamas and donned her dressing gown. There was no point pretending that she would fall back to sleep. Every time she closed her eyes she saw the furnace flames. She headed downstairs to make a cup of tea.

The house was freezing, so as soon as she entered the kitchen Rose headed for the boiler which was hidden inside a cupboard. She wasn't going to wait two hours for the heating to come on so she flicked the manual override switch.

There was a click but nothing else. She peered through a little gap to check for the blue flame of the pilot light. It wasn't on. She tried again.

To her relief, this time there was a *poof* followed by a *clunk*. Soon the old pipes, feeding the radiators, rattled under the floorboards. Rose made a mental note to phone the boiler man. The old boiler was on its last legs.

Rose opened the back door to let Monty out for a wee, then made herself a super strong cuppa. She opened the bag of dry dog food, only to discover there was barely enough left for a meal. She had some raw chicken wings in the fridge so she added three of them to Monty's bowl. Lord knows how, but he must have smelt the chicken from out in the garden because he came racing in, tail up, smacking his lips.

Rose closed the door and told Monty to sit. It made her smile that he always sat to attention as though on a parade ground. At her word, Monty got stuck into his meal.

What shall I do now? Hours of boredom loomed ahead.

Rose picked up her laptop and wandered into the sitting room. She sat cross-legged on the sofa with a blanket over her, switched it on and began searching for Zofia Nowak. *Why not?* she thought. She had nothing else to do. And besides, she couldn't forget Zofia's plea for help.

First, Rose tried the 192.com directory. There couldn't be many Nowaks in Geldeford. She found just one: Hirek Nowak lived seven miles from the university in the village of Heston – an unlikely place for a university student unless she was related to Hirek. Rose would have to wait a couple of hours before she could phone him.

Monty strolled into the sitting room licking his muzzle and plonked down between the sofa and the coffee table.

Next, Rose tried Google, searching for Zofia's name along with Geldeford University. This was more promising. The university had a Polish Society, which in turn had a Facebook page. On it Rose found photos from a pub lunch. Rose immediately recognised the blonde-haired Zofia.

This confirmed two things: Zofia was Polish and she was a university student. Rose checked if Zofia had her own Facebook profile. Bingo. Lots of photos with friends, but nothing that identified where she lived. The student did, however, moan about her tax law examination. Through Facebook Messenger Rose would be able to contact Zofia and ask to meet.

Most cops didn't have any social media presence and Rose was one of them. It was too easy to be targeted by trolls. However, if Rose wanted to contact Zofia, she needed a Facebook account. It didn't take long to set one up. Only once she had jumped through all the hoops did she discover the twenty-four-hour waiting period before the account would be activated.

'Bums!' Monty looked up at her with sleepy eyes. 'Don't mind me,' she said, stroking the top of his head. 'We might be visiting the Faculty of Law later. Fancy being a legal beagle?'

Monty's tail wagged.

10

Ollie had asked to be picked up at a bus stop on the outskirts of Geldeford, which suited Rose because it meant she avoided the torturously slow traffic through the town's centre.

Ollie was leaning against the corner of the bus shelter, arms folded, a beanie pulled down low over his ears, his chin tucked inside his jacket's collar. She pulled up and waved through the windscreen at him.

'All right?' Ollie said, jumping in and slamming the door as though it was a getaway scene in a movie.

As he clipped on his seatbelt, his gaze swept back and forth like a radar dish. Rose guessed he didn't want to be seen getting into a copper's car. Kids from the Truscott Estate who got into police cars were usually either snitches or on their way to the nick.

'What's up, Ollie? Are you all right?' Rose asked.

'Yeah, yeah. Can we go now?' He was jittery. His shoulders were so tense they were up to his ears.

Rose set off and Ollie began to relax. Monty stuck his head between the two front seats and sniffed his coat.

'Watcha, Monty. How ya doing, mate?' Ollie gave Monty a scratch under the chin. 'You're a big fella, aren't ya?'

Monty wagged his tail. He clearly liked Ollie, which made Rose feel a little better about having him in her home. And Joe had vouched for Ollie, so if she could help a young offender onto a new path and a better life, she was happy to do her best.

'Joe says you got some jobs for me.'

'I've been trying to clear the attic of junk,' Rose said, glancing at Ollie. 'I need your help getting stuff down and then sorting what goes to charity and what goes in the bin. And there's furniture up there too.' Kay's furniture and memorabilia. Ollie nodded. Rose continued, 'The leaves need raking too and putting on the compost. Lots to do.'

'I don't want to get me trainers dirty.'

Rose regarded the expensive-looking Nike trainers on Ollie's feet. 'What's your shoe size?'

'Men's seven.'

'Kay had big feet. I might have some Wellies that'll fit.'

They lapsed into silence. Ollie gnawed at a fingernail.

'How old are you?' he said.

'That's a bit personal, Ollie.'

'I can't believe you're a copper. No offence, but you look my age.'

This happened a lot. It was a right pain, especially when people thought it meant they didn't have to take her seriously. 'I'm old enough.'

He stared at her. 'Why a copper?'

'Because I want to stop people from being hurt. That's a copper's job. That's *my* job.'

Ollie gawped at her as if she'd just revealed that she was an alien.

Rose slowed to a stop at some traffic lights. Monty stuck his head out of the window and barked enthusiastically. Rose followed his line of sight and saw Malcolm walking a Cavalier King Charles Spaniel puppy. The pup was doing her best to bite the lead. Malcolm turned towards the barking, recognised Monty, smiled, and waved at Rose. He picked up the spaniel and jogged over. Rose lowered the passenger window and Malcolm leaned in.

'Hi Malcolm, who's is the cute puppy?' Rose asked.

Monty had his head out of a rear window and sniffed the puppy, who lunged forward and bared her sharp little teeth. Monty pulled his head in, his ears back, looking very put out by the rebuff.

'This is B,' Malcolm said. 'Well, actually, it's Lady B. She was left in a box outside my practice last week. The note said she was aggressive, and they couldn't bring themselves to put her down so could we find her a new home.'

'That breed isn't normally aggressive. How strange,' Rose said.

'I know. She's a bit snappy, but nothing some training and TLC won't cure. I've adopted her.'

He held her aloft so Rose could see her better. The spaniel had brown patches around her eyes which made her look as if she was wearing an eye mask. Ollie reached out through the open window and stroked B. She didn't snap at him. Quite the opposite. She leaned into his hand as he stroked her.

'You're the first person she hasn't tried to bite,' Malcolm said.

'This is Oliver,' Rose said. 'He's helping me with a few jobs around the house.'

'I could do that for you,' Malcolm offered.

Rose was taken aback. He was her vet. She didn't really know him. 'Oh, um, that's very kind, but Ollie is…' She was saved from the awkward situation by Monty who barked at B. B yipped back, but less belligerently this time. It was like they were having a chat. Then the traffic lights turned green. 'I have to go,' Rose said. 'Bye!'

Rose turned onto a slipway that led to a dual carriageway. 'Dogs like you, Ollie.'

'I like them,' said Ollie. He looked around him. 'Joe said you live at Farley Green.'

'I do.'

'Then aren't we going the wrong way?'

'A quick detour,' Rose said. 'There's something I have to do at the university first.'

Eventually Rose pulled up outside the Faculty of Law. It had been difficult to find. When the university was built in 1970, a mind-boggling decision had been made to identify the streets numerically, and non-sequentially, rather than give them names. Add to that the problem of missing street signs, no doubt thanks to students who thought it a laugh to steal them.

'Do you mind waiting in the car?' Rose said to Ollie, then craned her neck to look at Monty. 'You too, Monty. I won't be long.'

'What's this about?' Ollie asked.

'Someone I'm trying to track down.'

Ollie shrugged and pulled out his phone.

Rose got out of the car. Monty stuck his head out of the window and gave a little whine.

'I won't be long. Stay with Ollie.'

The Law Faculty was a concrete, three-storey, Brutalist building with tinted windows, desperately in need of a facelift. To the right of the entrance was a scissor-lift aerial work platform being used by window cleaners, one of whom was whistling a tune. Students came and went in a constant flow.

Rose found her way to the faculty office. Initially, she was intending to leave a message for Zofia, but on entering the building, she changed her mind. Time was of the essence in a missing person's case. Rose held up her warrant card. She technically shouldn't use it because it wasn't police business – yet. But the university wouldn't give her Zofia's contact details otherwise.

'Oh, I'm not sure what to do,' said Sally, who had short spiky hair. 'Is Zofia in trouble?'

This response told Rose she was in the right place.

'She might be able to help with an enquiry. Is she in the building?'

'Let me see.' Sally went to her computer. 'Not today, no. She has a tutorial at ten tomorrow with Professor Lingley.'

Rose didn't want to wait another twenty-four hours. The longer Zofia's friend was missing, the less chance they'd find her. 'I need her contact details.'

'I'll have to check with HR. Aren't you supposed to have a warrant for that?'

Rose inwardly groaned. Sally was right. But if she involved HR, this was sure to get back to DCI Leach, who would not be happy. The last thing Rose wanted to do was give him an excuse to keep her on leave.

'No problem. I'll come back tomorrow.' Rose turned to leave, then turned back. 'Can you direct me to the Polish Society building?'

Sally came out from behind her desk and kept her voice down. 'You might find her there now.' She winked at Rose. 'It's walking distance. Follow the main road in. First left and you'll see a café. Behind it is the Student Union. The Polish Society meets in one of the meeting rooms.'

When Rose returned to her car she found Ollie and Monty playing chase on a patch of lawn in front of the building. Monty had his bum in the air and his front legs flat on the grass, tail wagging, which was the universally accepted dog signal for Chase Me. Ollie ran at Monty who ran off, followed by Ollie who was laughing so much he didn't stand a chance of getting close. Rose watched while they were unaware of her presence. It was good to hear Ollie laughing.

'Hey, guys, fancy a walk?' she called out.

Monty immediately raced over to her, tail wagging. Ollie leaned forwards, his hands on his knees, catching his breath. 'Why not,' he said. Monty walked between Rose and Ollie. 'Where we going?'

'The Polish Society.'

Ollie stopped dead. 'Why we going there?'

Rose and Monty stopped too. 'What's wrong?'

Ollie shoved his hands in his jeans pockets and stared at the pavement. 'Nothing.'

'Come off it, Ollie. Something's wrong. Do you know someone in the Polish Society?'

He shook his head. 'It's embarrassing.'

'Go on.'

'Did part of my Community Service at the Student Union. Cleaning away graffiti. Loads of stuff about Eastern Europeans. Real nasty.'

'Good for you,' Rose said. 'That's nothing to be embarrassed about. Come on.'

The café in front of the Student Union building had benches and tables which only a couple of smokers were using. A man in his early twenties drew Rose's attention. Tall, with a flat face and wide-set blue eyes, he paced up and down outside the café entrance trying to shove leaflets into the hands of anyone who would take them. His face seemed familiar. Had Rose seen him in one of Zofia's Facebook photos?

'This way,' she said to Ollie.

The man saw them coming and switched on a smile which he directed at Rose. 'Pub crawl, tomorrow night. Come and make Polish friends. We start at the Tudor Rose.' He then glanced at Ollie, as if checking him out.

Rose took the proffered leaflet. 'Maybe I will, thanks. Is Zofia going?'

'I don't know.'

'Is she in the Student Union?'

His smile faded. 'How do you know Zofia?'

'I met her the other day. I'm Rose. What's your name?'

'Kacper. President of Polish Society.'

'Then I'm sure you can help me. I've lost her mobile number. Do you have it?'

'No.'

Rose's hands and feet started to tingle. He was lying.

He turned his back on them to walk away. 'Wait, Kacper.' Rose pulled her warrant card from her pocket. 'DC Sidebottom. I need to talk to Zofia Nowak. Tell me where she is.'

Kacper jutted his neck forward so his face was close to hers. His mouth was a sneer. 'Piss off, pig!'

'Hey, mate!' said Ollie trying to wedge himself between Rose and Kacper. 'No need to be like that.'

Monty produced a low rumbling growl and approached Kacper from the other side.

Kacper shoved Ollie hard in the chest. Ollie was at least a couple of stone lighter than Kacper, and he stumbled backwards. Kacper wagged a finger in her face. 'Leave Zofia alone.' Monty released a ferocious bark. Kacper backed away. 'And keep that dog away from me.'

Kacper stomped up the ramp to the Student Union building and didn't look back.

'Pleasant fellow,' Rose said. 'Ollie, are you all right?'

'Yeah, 'course I'm all right,' but his voice was shaky. 'You going after that prick?'

Rose knew Kacper's type. He hated cops and she'd have to move heaven and earth, or more likely have something on him, to get anything out of him. And Rose couldn't risk making a scene. She'd wait until tomorrow morning when Zofia had her tutorial.

'He's not worth the aggro,' Rose said. 'Come on, let's go.'

They wandered back to Rose's car. 'Thank, Ollie, for stepping in. Not that I needed it, but it was nice of you.'

Monty nudged Ollie's hand with his nose. She was pretty sure Monty was thanking him too. 'I'll make us some lunch when we get home. You hungry?'

'Always.' He grinned.

11

I'm dreaming I'm chasing rabbits through a flowery meadow with clover flowers as tall as lamp posts and buttercups that melt like butter left in the sun. A ringing noise intrudes. Maybe it will go away? It's fun in my dream world and I want to stay there. I concentrate hard on the bouncing white ball of a tail that is a few centimetres from my snout. I'm so close now. But the ringing is getting louder, and the rabbits are getting further and further away until they suddenly disappear.

The floor jolts.

I open one eye. Where am I?

I see faded carpet and take in the smells that tell me I'm at home in Duckdown Cottage. I'm not on my bed in the kitchen where I normally fall asleep. I'm at the foot of the stairs so that if Rose cries out in the night, I can reach her without delay. It's pitch-black outside and Rose has switched on the stair's light. I lift my head as Rose steps over me.

'Hinchley Wood?' she says into her phone.

Rose is talking to Big Man Joe. I hear the tension in Joe's voice as I follow her into the kitchen.

'Thanks for telling me,' I hear Rose say, 'I hope to God it isn't her.'

Rose clicks on the kettle then slumps into a kitchen chair and covers her face with her hands. 'Dear God!'

I nudge Rose's leg. She drops her hands. They lay limp in her lap. I give her a tentative lick and can taste her sadness.

'She's dead, Monty.'

Who's dead? Zofia? Or the missing woman? Not her mum, surely? Liz had sounded very alive when they last spoke.

I stare into Rose's eyes, seeking answers.

'Why didn't I do something?' Rose asks me, shaking her head. 'I feel terrible.'

I hear a squeak coming from the hole in the skirting board beneath the larder. 'What's up?' Betty asks.

Rose doesn't hear her, and I can't answer. Barking when Rose is sad would be wrong.

Rose springs out of her chair. 'I have to do something. I should be there,' Rose says, pacing. I follow her, first one way across the length of the kitchen, and then back the other way. 'Maybe I can identify her?' She turns back the way she came. 'But they won't want me there.'

I think this is what hoomans call a conundrum.

The kettle gurgles and shoots steam out of the spout, then clicks off. Rose ignores it.

'Oy!' squeaks Betty, demanding my attention. 'Rose needs to solve this case! Get your furry arse moving!' I catch a glimpse of Betty's face poking out of the skirting board. She shoos me away with her front paws.

Betty is right. Of course, she's right. It doesn't matter what The Leach says. Rose and I will find the killer. When Rose solves the case, she'll get her job back and she'll be happy again. All I have to do is get her over to Hinchley Wood. But how do I do that?

A cockerel crows in the distance. I look out of the window at the dawn sky, then at Rose's Wellington boots and coat by the kitchen door, and at my lead hanging from a hook. I have an idea. I trot over to where my lead hangs and tug it down, then carry it in my mouth and present it to Rose.

'Not now, Monty. I need to think.' Rose opens the kitchen door. 'If you need to wee, off you go.'

I don't move, even though I really would like to wee. It's been a long night. I give the lead a shake, then snuffle her hand holding her phone. Her look of confusion shifts into a smile. 'Oh I get it. You want to walk in Hinchley Wood.' Rose nods. 'It's open to the public. There's nothing stopping me walking there. Clever boy!'

Rose races back up the stairs, two steps at a time. 'I won't be long,' she calls out.

I check my food bowl. I'm an optimist at heart, so it's always worth the chance. But just as I thought. Nothing there. The old boiler clanks and then whines as the hot water makes its way through the old pipes upstairs to the shower. Which reminds me. I head out of the back door and have a long pee on a flowerpot with a dead geranium in it. Much better. I look over my shoulder to the kitchen door. I can still hear the shower running. Rose will be a little while yet. So I creep as quietly as I can towards the pond, inhaling the smell of poultry poo, mud, and rotting reeds. I spot a matronly Mallard called Henrietta fast asleep, her beak tucked into her wing feathers and she's perched on one leg. Inside my head she morphs into a bull's eye on a board and I dart forward, nose down and tap her. She topples over with a screech.

All hell breaks loose. The other ducks and the two geese wake, and the gentle melody of the dawn chorus is drowned out by a cacophony of honks and squawks. I manage to topple a Shoveler named Denis before I run for it. Denis comes after me, his huge spatula bill swinging from side to side as if he's going to slice me in half.

'Young hound,' he bellows, his yellow eyes blazing from his green feathered head, 'You have gone too far!'

Denis speeds up, beak slashing the air like a scythe, and I pick up my pace. This is exactly the reaction I was looking for, of course. Then I notice that Henrietta is gathering an army.

'Girls!' she yells like a sergeant major. 'Get in formation.'

Six Mallards, a female Shoveler and two Gadwalls form two neat rows. The male Mallards and the two Egyptian Geese – who turned up in Farley Green one day seeking asylum – watch quietly from where they sit.

'My money's on Henrietta,' the goose named Nile says in a honking tone.

Thanks a bunch, I think.

'Charge!' cries Henrietta.

By now I'm being chased by Denis around and around the great oak tree. The battalion of ducks descending on me divides in two. In a classic pincer movement, one group led by Henrietta goes clockwise around the tree and the other group, led by the female Shoveler, attacks anticlockwise. I know when I'm beaten. I bolt, my tail tucked between my legs so the ducks can't nip it.

'We'll get you next time!' Henrietta screams after me as I scramble through the doorway, then use my body to shove the door shut.

Rose appears wearing the smart grey suit and wool coat she used to wear when she worked Major Crime. There's a look of determination in her eye. She tugs on her red Wellington boots, which kind of ruins the business look but they are understandably necessary, given the rain we've had.

'Ready?' she asks me.

Invigorated by my skirmish with the ducks, I give Rose a big doggy grin. I'm ready! I've never been to Hinchley Wood. I hope there are lots of rabbits.

 12

Through the drool-smeared rear window of Rose's car I watch trees and houses and people race by. Or perhaps that's because Rose is driving very fast, I'm not sure which. I long to poke my head out of the side window, but Rose says it's too cold for that. At least the window isn't completely closed, so I can savour the mingling of town and farm smells as we enter countryside. Even though the heating system pumps the car full of a plasticky-smelly-sock odour, I can still detect the splendid stink of cow pats and the straw-like bouquet of horse droppings rising from the fields as we pass. Soon we are bouncing up a hill on an unmade road, the loose stones clanking against the car's underbelly and the town's aroma left far behind.

We come to a halt at the top of a hill that's covered in a circular thicket of mature oak, birch and ash – Hinchley Wood. I paw at the door, keen to explore. But we are not alone. Hoomans, some in police uniform, some in plain clothes, mill about. Perimeter tape, wrapped several times around various tree trunks like corsets, cordons off a section of the trees. There are marked police cars and a van.

'Forensics are here already,' Rose says. She takes a deep breath. 'Here goes.'

Rose lets me out of the car but holds me tightly on a short leash. We're on the western side of Hinchley Wood, where the lower slopes are paddocks with horses. I point my nose at the trees and inhale the scent of rabbit which is just like marshmallows. I pant in anticipation. There's also fox, squirrel, mole, badger, hedgehog and others, too. I can hardly contain myself and my paws dance up and down as if they have a life of their own. Have I mentioned? They do that. There's a sharp wind coming from the east that carries the grassy, sweet and slightly sour scent of sheep. My eyes bulge. Sheep!

'Whoa there, Monty,' says Rose, holding me fast. 'We've got work to do, remember?'

Okay, the sheep will have to wait. I leave a wee-mail on the nearest tree trunk warning about a dognapper targeting vets. Yesterday, when Rose stopped the car to chat to Malcolm, I managed to warn his puppy, Lady B, that Malcolm's practice might be targeted. She seemed unperturbed and told me she was perfectly capable of defending Malcolm, thank you very much! She might be young, but she's a brave little thing. The problem, though, is that Malcolm doesn't know of the danger.

The first hooman we come upon is Big Man Joe. He's unrolling some blue and white tape and winding it around another tree at the edge of the wood. When he spies us, he drops the roll of tape and strides over.

'You can't be here,' Joe says, looking over his shoulder to where other uniformed officers loiter. 'Leach will know I told you. He'll have my guts for garters.'

That doesn't sound pleasant. I decide there and then that if the Leach tries to take Joe's guts, I will have to take offensive action, which may involve digging my teeth into the Leach's leg. Which I have to confess doesn't appeal. I once tried to lick a slug, which I've been told is not unlike a leach in texture, and it tasted so bad I had to gulp down loads of water and then chew sticks to get rid of the foul aftertaste.

'I'm walking my dog, Joe. That's all.' I peer up at her, confused. Is this what she calls a little white lie?

'Go home, Rose, please. This isn't your business.'

'It is my business. It could be Zofia's friend in there.' She nods at the wood.

Joe shakes his head. 'I can see you're not going to take no for an answer. At least don't let Leach or Pearl see you.'

Does he mean Detective Pearl? The man I call the Prancing Pony? He's pretty and has a blond mane he likes to flick back and forth, but his eyes are spiteful. My lip curls up at the edge and from deep in my throat comes the start of a growl. A wicked thought enters my head. Now she's no longer officially working with Pearl, does that mean I can do what I've been so close to doing many times before? Can I finally pee on his trouser leg?

'Where is the body?' Rose asks.

'East side of the wood. I'll pretend I haven't seen you.' Joe looks down at her red wellies. 'Although it's pretty hard to miss you.'

We walk around the perimeter of the wood until the taped off zone ends, then we follow a path through the trees. It's darker in here and the trail is redolent with mushroom, leaf litter and loam smells. I try very hard to ignore the delicious scent of rabbits and it takes all my willpower not to lunge at rabbit holes as we pass them.

I sense the trees are very old on Hinchley Wood and imagine my ancestors running through here, hunting their food. I pause at the trunk of a beech with thick roots like enormous claws digging deep into the earth. Dogs have left wee-mails on the exposed roots. I sniff. The most recent is from a Border Collie called Pepper who must have found the dead woman. Pepper is clearly very scared:

I thought it was a bone. How was I to know it was hooman? I didn't kill her, honest.

Poor Pepper is terrified she'll be accused of murder, which, if it were true, would mean banishment. No tail wags, no sniff exchanges, no games in the park. Thou Shalt Not Kill a Hooman is the number one Dog Commandment.

There's movement up ahead. People milling around one spot. The sun, though weak, is directly in our eyes which makes it hard to make out who they are, but I can smell The Leach and the Prancing Pony from a mile away. The Leach always smells like the interior of boxing gyms, and Pearl wears an overpowering lemongrass aftershave that always makes me want to wrinkle my nose to try and stop the stink from getting in.

Rose suddenly stops. My lead snaps tight, jolting me to a standstill.

'I can't,' Rose says under her breath. Her heart rate is racing. 'Oh God, what am I doing?' She looks like she's about to cry.

You're going to solve this crime, I want to say. You're a very clever detective. But I can't speak. Instead I pull on my lead, hoping to drag her forward.

Ahead of us, The Leach turns his shiny, snooker ball head towards us. Perhaps he heard us coming. 'Bloody hell,' he growls.

Pearl spins around and his eyes narrow in his fake-tanned face. 'I'll sort it, gov.'

'No. Leave it to me,' Leach pats Pearl on the shoulder. 'Get a statement from Daimon Clark, will you?'

Leach strides over to us, crushing any wildflowers and bracken unfortunate enough to be in his path. 'What are you doing here?'

'Hello, Craig,' Rose says. The Leach blanches, I'm guessing because he's not used to Rose addressing him that way. I think Rose is trying to sound casual but The Leach doesn't like it. 'Just walking my dog.'

The Leach shakes his head. 'Come off it, Rose. We both know that's not true.'

'What's going on over there?'

He takes a step forward. I do the same. If he's spoiling for a fight, then he can deal with me. He glances down at me, undeterred.

'This must be hard for you, I get that,' he says, his voice softening. 'You miss solving cases. But you have to focus on getting well. Go home, Rose.' The Leach then glares at me. 'Don't you dare let this dog mess up my crime scene.'

'He won't, sir.' Rose clears her throat. 'Is the victim nineteen, twenty?'

Leach's small eyes bore into hers. 'Why do you say that?'

'Over here, sir!' shouts Pearl, who stands away from the crime scene, a notebook in his hand.

With him is a distressed-looking man in a bobble hat, clutching the lead of an even more distressed Border Collie that is shivering. Bobble Hat must be Daimon Clark.

Leach shouts back, 'Give me a minute!' Then he snaps at Rose, 'Spit it out, I don't have all day.'

I can see Rose's confidence deflating like a balloon. *No. Don't give up. Show them what you're made of.* I nudge her hand with my nose. *I'm with you, buddy.*

'Do you know who she is?' Rose's voice is getting quieter as her confidence wanes.

'Not yet. Why?'

'I may know her. Please, sir. Just a glance?'

Leach eyes Rose for a moment. 'Cover your shoes, then come find me.'

Rose pulls from her pocket some elasticated blue booties which she puts over her red Wellies.

'You just happen to have those in your pocket, huh?' Leach says, amused. 'Come with me.'

He leads us to where two people in white coveralls are working. The taller one is kneeling. She looks up, her mouth hidden behind a mask, but her eyes are smiling.

'Jenny. Good to see you,' Rose says.

I've overheard Rose talk to Jenny Pinto on the phone, but we've never met. Jenny is a Ghanaian basketball player who gave up a promising sporting career to study corpses in the U.K. and decided to stay. She joined the forensics team about the same time as Rose became a copper.

'Rose will take a look at the victim,' Leach says. 'I'll hold the dog.'

He holds my leash very tight. I watch Rose step closer to a patch of leafy ground where a woman is partially buried in a shallow grave. It looks as if the rain has washed away the top soil. Her grey face is only just visible and her long chestnut-brown hair is clogged with dirt. The tips of three fingernails poke through the soil. They are painted purple. I put my nose to the ground and sniff. I pick up hints of a Lilly of the Valley fragrance and red wine. And new leather.

I need to be closer. There are subtle scents I'm missing from this distance.

Rose crouches down. 'The marks on her neck. Strangulation?' she asks.

There is a brownish-red mark encircling the girl's neck.

'Looks like it,' Jenny says. 'Blood vessels in her eyes have burst. Could be due to suffocation.'

I whimper. It makes me sad to see someone so young has died.

'Well?' says The Leach to Rose. 'Can you ID her?'

Rose stands up slowly. She has her back to us. She raises her hand and appears to wipe an eye. 'I'm not sure–'

'Yes or no?'

There's a pause. 'No.'

'Boss?' says Pearl, suddenly appearing next to Leach. 'Can I have a word?'

'Take your dog and move along, Rose.' Leach holds out the lead.

Rose accepts it and before she can say another word, Leach and the Prancing Pony are headed into the trees towards Clark and his dog.

'Call me, okay?' says Jenny. 'Have a drink one evening, yeah?'

'Yeah,' Rose says, but I can tell she doesn't mean it. Rose is embarrassed about her PTSD.

Rose walks away then tears off her blue booties.

Betty will be furious with me. I can hear her telling me to find a way to stop Rose leaving until she's solved the case. I try to think of something to delay us. All I can think of is to stop and sniff everything: every tree trunk, fern frond, rabbit hole and fox burrow. Twigs crack behind us and I look around. It's Clark and Pepper. They must be walking home after their chat with Leach and Pearl. This is Rose's chance, so I drag her towards them. Thankfully she, too, sees the opportunity.

'Excuse me,' Rose calls out.

Clark looks harrowed. 'Yes?'

Pepper eyes me nervously and hides behind her owner's legs.

'It's not your fault,' I bark at Pepper, trying to comfort her.

'Hush, Monty,' says Rose. She then asks Clark, 'You found the body?'

He nods. 'Ay. The poor wee girl.'

A Scottish accent. I recognise it from watching the TV crime series, *Shetland*, with Rose. Yes, I do watch TV, as do many dogs, especially when we're left alone during the day. My favourite crime show is *Inspector Rex*. But my all-time favourite is David Attenborough's conversations with animals and birds and insects. Even fish. I love barking at all the animals he meets.

Rose stays quiet. It's a trick she uses. People don't like silence. They try to fill it with words. The man tells Rose how Pepper started digging and found a foot without a boot.'

'Is the boot nearby?'

'No. It's gone.'

'Did you see anything suspicious on your walk? Someone leaving in a hurry?'

'You're asking me the same questions he asked. I don't want to keep talking about it. The poor girl.' He doubles over and vomits into some bracken.

Pepper whines, 'I didn't do it.'

I reply, 'I know. You did a good thing finding her. Tell me about her smell.'

'Leather. An oily cream. Lilly of the Valley perfume, and dogs,' Pepper barks.

'Shut up, Pepper,' the man says, then cleans his mouth with a cotton handkerchief.

'Are you all right, sir?' Rose asks. 'Do you need a lift home?'

'No, I'm okay. It's the shock, you see.'

The man and his dog walk away. 'I'm not sure, Monty,' Rose says to me. 'She could be our missing girl. Or someone else entirely.'

'Look what the cat dragged in.' Unmistakably, DI Pearl. He flicks a blond curl away from tanned skin that looks more orange than brown. I find my teeth are bared and I'm edging towards his legs. 'If that mutt even tries to bite me, I'll have it put down, you got that?'

'He only bites criminals,' Rose says fiercely. 'And we're leaving.'

I take one last longing look at his legs and promise myself. Next time.

 13

Rose trudges back to the car park, looking very hangdog. Maybe if I can get her to McDonalds, she'll feel better. We always eat our Big Macs in the car, getting the meaty juices and the runny cheese all over our faces. I start to drool just thinking about it and then pull myself together. Before we leave Hinchley Wood, I have work to do. I cock my leg and leave as many wee-mails as my bladder can sustain.

Contact Monty if you know anything about the dead girl in the woods.

I hear the rustle of clothing. Someone is walking fast, kicking up leaves. Jenny overtakes us, a camera hanging around her neck.

'I need something from the van. Want to walk with me?'

'Love to,' Rose replies.

Walking with Jenny isn't easy for two reasons: her very long legs and the narrow path.

'This isn't a coincidence, is it?' Jenny asks. 'You're here because of the girl.'

'It's that obvious, huh?'

'Totally obvious.' Jenny grins at Rose. 'My friend, you've never been good at subterfuge. Come on, tell me what's going on.'

Rose tells Jenny about Zofia Nowak. 'Look, I know this is a big ask, but can I have a photo of the victim?'

Jenny folds her arms over the bump of her camera 'I shouldn't, but I'd have tossed this job in a dozen times if you hadn't dragged me down to the pub and never stopped telling me I was good enough.' She fiddles with buttons on her camera. 'I sent you a close-up. Did you notice the small scar across her right eyebrow? Should help with an ID.'

'Yes I did, and thanks Jenny. Have you an estimated time of death?'

'She's been dead at least forty-eight hours.'

'So she was killed, what, Tuesday?' says Rose.

'I can't say until I've done the post mortem.'

I try to remember which day Zofia spoke to us in the Sainsbury's car park. I think it was Tuesday because Rose routinely does her grocery shopping on that day. Zofia said her friend didn't come home the night before…that would be a Monday.

Ahead, a car door slams. We've reached the edge of the wood. Blue and white tape bobs in the wind like ribbons from a maypole.

'She's missing a lace-up ankle boot,' Jenny says. 'Black leather.'

'Maybe she lost it trying to escape her killer.'

'Maybe. I must get a move on. Good luck, Rose.'

Jenny darts off to a police van, opens the double doors at the rear and starts rummaging through one of many drawers inside.

'Time to leave,' Rose says to me.

We head for her car on the other side of the car park.

That's when I catch it. Just a hint. The sour tang of red wine mingled with the sweetness of Lilly of the Valley. I drop my nose to the muddy, flinty ground. No. Not here. I lift my nose and move my head from side-to-side. It's coming from beyond Rose's car. I set off, forgetting I'm on a leash and end up dragging Rose along behind me.

'Keen to get home, huh?' Rose says.

But I don't stop at her car. I keep going.

'Stop, Monty.'

I lurch a few more paces, then drop my nose. No, not in the grass. A marked police car has parked on the verge. It's coming from beneath the car. I crouch down low and poke my head into the shadows. Something leathery and covered in mud sends me into olfactory overload. Clay soil.

Lilly of the Valley mixed with an oily residue. Maybe she liked to rub what Rose calls moisturiser into her skin. The oily residue must have infused the inside of the boot. On the boot's toe, I detect a drop of red wine. The boot definitely belonged to the murdered girl. On the sole, there's a myriad of new aromas: dust, cigarette butts, the acidic stench of vomit, cow poo and dog urine. There are a couple of short brown dog hairs stuck under the boot's tongue. The dog in question must be very young because there is no strong hormonal signature. Perhaps the dead girl had a puppy?

Rose kneels next to me and peers under the vehicle. 'Oh my God!' says Rose, staring at the ankle boot.

She takes my collar and pulls me backwards. I lie still, my nose pointing at the boot.

Rose shouts and waves, 'Jenny! Over here! Monty's found the boot.'

Jenny runs over, looks under the car. 'Don't touch anything.' She takes several photos, then carefully removes the boot and bags it.

'Clever dog,' she says. Rose looks down at me, her face serious but her eyes gleaming and alive. My tail swishes once or twice in the grass behind me.

'Hey! What do you think you're doing?' calls out The Leach, stomping across the car park.

'Sir, look at this,' Jenny says, holding up the transparent evidence bag. 'This could be the missing boot. Rose found it.'

'Did she now?' Leach muses with a smile.

 14

It seems The Leach has given up on trying to get rid of us. He's given us permission to watch the crime scene proceedings from a distance. This makes it difficult for Rose to hear what they are saying. Luckily, my hearing is better than Rose's, so I catch most of what Leach, Pearl and Jenny discuss, although I don't understand much of it. Leach keeps referring to the girl as Jane Doe, so I guess he's worked out her name. Rose sits on a wooden stile that straddles a wire fence. Sheep are grazing on the other side.

Rose calls me over. I sit. Give her my undivided attention.

'I want you to remember the dead woman's smell. Okay?'

I bark once in the affirmative.

'I'll take that as a yes.'

Perfect, that's exactly what I mean.

Rose continues, 'If you smell her scent anywhere, you bark once, then lift your paw, got that?'

I bark once in the affirmative. Ears pricked. Ready, willing and able.

'Shall we practise? Monty! Bark once and lift your paw,' she commands.

This is too easy. I do exactly what she says.

'Good boy.' She gives me a cuddle.

I make a mental note to rub my muzzle all over my bed tonight so that Jane Doe's smell stays a strong memory. I wish I could explain about the dog smells on Jane's boot and the chocolate brown dog hairs, but I expect Jenny will discover the hairs sooner or later.

An old elm tree's gnarled branches sway in the wind above us. Rose pulls her coat tightly around her. After last night's fierce winds, Hinchley Wood is a smorgasbord of sticks. I select a short chunky one, grip it between my front paws, tilt my head to one side and get stuck in, using my back teeth to crack it. I love that sound!

Snap. Crack. Chew. Swallow.

Snap. Crack. Chew. Swallow.

High up in the branches above me, there's the sound of claws scraping wood and the whoosh of a tail flicked very fast. I hear someone humming the *Mission: Impossible* theme tune. To a hooman it sounds like a series of repetitive *eeks*. But to animals like me there's no mistaking the tune and I've only ever known one creature to hum it – Nigel the squirrel, our local Animal Neighbourhood Watch representative. Squirrels are notorious busy bodies, but Nigel has perfected snooping to the point that if it were an Olympic sport, he'd win gold.

I pause in my stick chewing in the hope that Nigel won't notice me lying on the leaf-strewn grass, far below him. The *eeks* stop. I take that as a good sign. He's scampered away. I open my jaw and position the stick between my upper and lower molars then bite down. *Crack!*

'I say,' Nigel calls out, flicking his bushy tail aggressively. 'You there! Dogtective!'

His voice grates like fingernails dragged down a blackboard. My ears twitch with irritation. But I've never been called a dogtective before. My pride gets the better of me and I make the mistake of looking up.

'Finally!' Nigel huffs, blowing out his cheeks. 'For a moment I thought you were trying to ignore me.' He clears his little throat. 'Now I have your attention, I'd like to point out that we haven't had the chance to clear up the small matter of your breach of the peace.'

'I'm sorry, what are you talking about?'

The squirrel jumps down to a lower branch, then another. He now sits on a branch that's not much higher than Rose when she's standing. I crane my neck to peer up at him.

'That squirrel's brave,' Rose says to no-one in particular, 'What on earth is it doing?'

Telling me off, by the sound of it.

Nigel chatters on. 'Don't play innocent with me, young hound.' He tuts at me through four grey, prominent, front teeth. 'I thought you a dog with integrity. Perhaps I am mistaken?'

'I am,' I say, licking my stick. 'I honestly don't know what you're accusing me of.'

My stick, juicy with saliva, pulpy and broken, is calling to me. I rip at the bark, peel it off and chew. Collateral bits of bark go flying in various directions.

'This is a serious matter,' snaps Nigel, stamping a clawed paw on the branch which causes it to bounce. 'Stop that chewing at once,' he commands, his huge eyes glistening with fury.

I swallow. A bit of bark sticks out from the side of my jowl. My tongue curls around it and pulls it into my mouth. I swallow. 'Okay, what exactly have I done?'

'Monty, don't be so mean. Stop barking at the poor squirrel,' Rose says.

Oh great. Not only do I lack integrity, I'm now mean, too.

The squirrel taps a long claw against one of his front teeth. 'Barking at night. There have been complaints.' Barking at night? The only time I do that is when I'm chatting to Betty and I always try to keep my barks as quiet as I can. Nigel continues, 'And then there's the bigger issue of duck toppling.'

Ah, now I can guess who has made the complaints. Henrietta the Mallard or Denis the Shoveler. 'It's just a bit of fun, Nigel. Nobody gets hurt.'

'It's just not neighbourly, young hound. It has to stop.'

'But they are just so tempting.'

'Do it again and you'll force me to call an emergency Neighbourhood Watch meeting.'

I consider this for a moment. 'What happens then?'

'I have no idea. I've never called one before, but it's very serious.'

'It is?'

'Oh yes. Indubitably.'

I've lost interest in my stick. I spit out a few loose bits of pulp which have now taken on a bitter flavour. 'I'll do my best, Nigel. That's all I can promise. My memory isn't the best, so I could forget.'

Nigel taps his nose. 'I'll be watching,' he says with a sinister tone, then scampers up to the higher branches.

Feeling a little fed up, I wander to the wire-mesh fence and sniff a ewe that's grazing on the other side. She looks up, busy chewing grass, oblivious to my presence until she actually looks me in the eye. Then she lets rip with an ear-splitting bleat.

'It's the wool-af! It's the wool-af!'

All the sheep in the field look up from their grazing and scream, 'It's the wool-af! It's the wool-af!'

'I'm not a wolf,' I bark, trying to reassure them.

The ewe nearest to me runs away, setting off a stampede that has the flock darting to the other side of the field.

'Monty, what's got into you today?' Rose admonishes. 'First the squirrel, now the sheep. What's the matter?'

I hear the pounding of hooves and discover the sheep have followed the fence line in a circle, which means they are all heading back towards where I'm standing. This makes no sense at all. However, they are sheep. I watch them through the wire-mesh as they charge closer, like cotton wool balls on muddy stick legs.

'Right, that's it!' Nigel says, having clambered down to the lowest branch above my head. 'I'm issuing you a formal warning. This is a second disturbance of the peace. One more and you're out.'

'Out of what?' I ask.

'Out of favour, of course,' Nigel replies.

The sheep are about to run past us when one of them spots me at the fence and bleats a warning. This propels them back to the other side of the field. It's like that movie I watched with Rose, *Groundhog Day*. Watching them is making my head spin so I turn away leaving a wee-mail asking dogs for information on the murdered girl.

'Ah-hem!' Nigel has followed me, scampering through the tree canopy.

'Nigel, please leave me in peace.'

'Monty, I should inform you that—'

'I'm just wee-mailing, Nigel. I'm not breaking any rules.'

Rose stands up. 'That's enough barking. Time we went home.' She sounds cross. I didn't mean to make Rose cross. She pulls my lead from her coat pocket.

'No, but–' Nigel points a claw at the field of sheep.

'They'll calm down soon, Nigel.'

Nigel hangs upside down from a bouncing branch which drops down to my face level. 'Over there! A hooman is watching you. Do you see the glint?'

I turn my head and see it. A flash of sunlight on glass. I see a hooman hiding in a thicket of hazel trees on the other side of the field. He's using binoculars.

'He was here earlier,' Nigel says, 'watching the police.'

'Did he kill her?' I bark.

Rose leans over me with the intent of clipping the lead to my collar.

'I don't know,' Nigel replies. 'But he's been there a while. Best be quick. Or he'll run away.'

I bark frantically at Rose and point my nose in the direction of the man spying on us, just like Pointers do.

'I really don't know what's got into you,' Rose says, shaking her head.

I zip away from her so she can't leash me. Why would a hooman hide in bushes and watch a crime scene? What if he is the killer? If I jump the fence, Rose will follow me over the stile and across the field.

The fence is only a little taller than me. I do a big circle, followed by an exasperated Rose, then run at it, and spring through the air. My back left paw clips the top of the wire but not enough to impede me. I land on the muddy grass.

'Stop!' Rose shouts.

It's a direct command. I look back at her. How can I tell her we are being watched, possibly by a killer? I don't know what to do. Should I keep running or obey her?

Rose squints off into the distance. 'What's that?' she says, peering at the line of tree where the hooman is hiding.

I bolt. The sheep panic and bleat frantically, running in circles and colliding with each other like dodgem cars. I have to weave my way through them, which slows my progress. The glint disappears. He has moved, but not far.

'Monty!' Rose calls as she vaults over the stile. 'Come back!'

If I go back, we'll never know if he's the killer. I speed up, my legs burning, my tongue lolling, panting hard. Suddenly there's a boom. Birds scatter into the sky screeching. Rose yelps in shock. I try to stop, but the back half of me wants to keep going, and I topple end over end in the grass, mud splattering over my coat and muzzle. I stay down, panting. I don't like guns.

'No!' screams Rose, from somewhere far behind me. 'Don't shoot. Police officer!'

The sheep are now head-butting the fence, trying to escape. I see the man retreat into the trees. Do I run after him or protect Rose? The answer is simple. Rose always comes first. I shake myself off as best I can, mud spattering everywhere, and sprint back to her. There are no more gunshots. She grabs me in a tight embrace. 'Oh my God, Monty, I thought he was going to kill you.'

Me too!

Big Man Joe, followed by another PC, jumps the stile. 'I heard gunshots,' he says, gasping for breath.

Rose nods. 'Someone shot at us. From that clump of hazel trees,' Rose says, pointing.

'Could be the farmer,' Joe suggests. 'Maybe he thought Monty was bothering his sheep.'

'Who owns this land?'

'That'll be John Clapper. His family's farmed this land for centuries.'

15

Rose was white-knuckled with frustration. The shooter was nowhere to be seen and Leach wasn't interested in finding him.

'I've got a murder to deal with,' he said, still wearing his crime scene coverall. His booties were caked in mud. 'And a farmer has the right to shoot an animal attacking his sheep. You should consider muzzling that dog.'

Her heart was still hammering from the terror that had run through her like an electric shock when the gun went off. Beneath her coat, her blouse was soaked with perspiration. At the same time, though, she felt elated. She had purpose. She had found the victim's boot. She had seen someone hiding in the trees, watching the detectives. Surely, Leach would see that she was ready to return to work?

'Sir, he was using binoculars,' said Rose, chasing after him. 'He might know something important. Or he could be the killer? You know, gloating?'

Leach turned to her like a bull confronting the matador. He flared his nostrils. Not a good sign. 'Go home, and that's an order. If I find you interfering in this case, I'll have you transferred to Traffic.'

Traffic Offences was the elephants' graveyard of policing.

'But, sir, I found the victim's boot. That has to count for something.' She looked down at Monty. '*We* found it.'

'That was good work, sure,' he said. 'But you're on sick leave. You could compromise this investigation. Now get out of here.'

It was now or never. She hesitated. What if she was wrong? What if Zofia was mistaken about her friend? *Just tell him*, she said to herself. *Just say it!* 'I might have a lead on her identity.'

Leach screwed up his eyes. 'But you said you didn't recognise her.'

Rose felt Monty nudge her hip with his head, as if to say, *Spit it out!* 'Yesterday, a woman named Zofia Nowak approached me, worried about her missing friend. She wouldn't report it. She seemed afraid.'

'Where can we find Nowak?'

'All I know is that she's studying Law at GU.' That's what locals called Geldeford University. Rose checked her watch. 'And she has a class at ten. I was going to go find her.'

He stabbed a stubby finger at her. 'Don't you dare. That's our job.'

She watched Leach head back to the car park where Pearl and Varma were waiting.

'Come on, Monty,' Rose said. 'We have a farmer to see.'

Polsted Lane was riddled with potholes and Rose's car bucked and bounced in and out of them like a flighty yearling. At the end of the lane was the entrance to Clapper's Farm. It wasn't a welcoming site. The red brick wall and electronic wooden gates were tall enough to block any view of the farm. The jagged glass along the top of the wall, the security cameras and the large Private Property Keep Out sign, made it very clear that John Clapper did not welcome visitors.

Rose wound down the window, stretched out an arm and pressed the call button on an intercom.

And waited. No answer.

She tried again, pressing the button longer this time. 'It's a busy farm,' she said to herself. 'There's got to be somebody about.'

'Yes?' said a man over the intercom.

Rose tried to ignore the nervous butterflies in her stomach. 'John Clapper?'

'Yes.'

'DC Rose Sidebottom.' She held her warrant card close to the camera, then pocketed it. She imagined Leach, puce in the face, yelling at her for interfering. She pushed the image in her head aside. This was personal. 'Somebody on your farm shot at me and my dog. Can I come in?' Rose said.

'You're mistaken. Try Bocketts up the road. It's pheasant season.'

'Mr Clapper, please open the gates.'

There was no response, although she could hear the man's noisy breathing.

There was a clunk and the gates opened in the centre and swung inwards. Rose drove through. Monty got up and stuck his muzzle out of the gap in the side window and sniffed. With all the security measures, Rose had expected a mansion. What she found was an asphalt drive, a rickety barn with a corrugated iron roof and the doors hanging wide open like an unbuttoned shirt, the interior piled high with bales of hay, and a workshop crammed with dirty farm machinery. The thatched farmhouse was as bent as a bow-legged old man. Through the gaps between the buildings she could see an apple orchard, the trees gnarled and bereft of fruit, then fields of sheep all the way to the crest of the hill. There was a dip in the land beyond the sheep fields, but she could just make out the tips of what must, from the size and shape of them, be poplars. The ground then sloped up until the hill levelled out at Hinchley Wood. If John owned all the land between the house and Hinchley Wood, the shooter had to be John, or someone known to him.

Before she had even switched off the engine, a man in his sixties wearing a khaki green padded vest, dark olive moleskin trousers and a tweed flat cap, exited the house with the biggest Rottweiler that Rose had ever seen. It wasn't on a lead. Monty barked frantically through the gap in the window, clawing at the car door. The Rottweiler responded with a low rumbling growl.

You're in the car. You're safe, she said to herself. But she felt short of breath.

'Shut up, Tank!' John said sharply, and the Rottweiler, a young male, flinched and went quiet. The dog's rapidly blinking glance at his master made Rose suspect it was afraid, despite its size and fearsome appearance.

Rose twisted around in her seat. 'Monty, quiet,' she said, breathily. 'It's okay.'

Monty stopped barking but his tail, his wide stance and the raised fur down the length of his spine told her he was on high alert.

Rose focused on calming her breath. *Breathe in, breathe out. You're safe.* She rolled down her window. 'John Clapper?'

'Of course I am. And you can't be a day over eighteen. What the hell is happening to our police force?!'

Rose ignored the jibe. 'Sir, you need to put your dog on a lead or put him inside.'

'Tank can be a bit intimidating.'

Rose guessed that was the point. She waited until he had ordered the dog inside and shut the front door.

When she was satisfied it was safe, Rose opened her car door. Monty pressed his nose against the window but as she had commanded, he stayed quiet. Just then, she heard barking, way off in the distance. Too high pitched to be Tank. Then a squeal. She froze, one foot in the car, the other on the drive.

'How many dogs do you have, Mr Clapper?'

John's puffy face was riddled with broken blood vessels, especially on his cheeks and nose, which gave his skin a reddish-purple hue. Often an early sign of alcohol abuse.

'A couple. They're safely shut away.'

Rose felt a sharp pain in her hands and feet. He was lying.

'Are there any more guard dogs loose on your property?'

'No, now what do you want?'

Rose left the car but stayed close to it. 'Does the boundary of your farm border Hinchley Wood?'

'Yes, why?'

'Somebody fired a shotgun at me and my dog, not twenty minutes ago. I'd like to speak to them.'

'Wasn't us. Look, there's a public footpath across my land. We get idiots chasing the sheep, taking pot shots at rabbits. It could have been anyone.'

'How many men work for you?'

'Depends on the season. We get a lot of casuals. Two, full-time.'

'Women?'

'A cleaner. And…what's this about?'

Pins and needles again.

'And you, Mr Clapper? Were you in the top field twenty minutes ago?'

'No, I wasn't, and this is bloody ridiculous. What were you doing in Hinchley Wood anyway? Having a picnic?'

'There's been a murder, Mr Clapper.'

'Good God!' He took a step back. 'That's...dreadful. What happened?' If he was the man with the binoculars, he would already know about the murder. He seemed genuinely shocked.

'We don't know yet, sir.'

Rose toyed with the idea of showing him the victim's photo. But she would be stepping on Major Crime's toes and that would enrage Leach. They were bound to interview people in the surrounding area and this man would be one of them.

'If there's nothing else...' He paused. Rose shook her head. He touched the brim of his cap. 'Please excuse me, I have an appointment. The gates will open as you leave. Good day.'

16

I breathe a sigh of relief as we leave Clapper Farm. There was something very wrong about the place. Tank reeked of fear. I didn't catch what the other dogs were saying, because they were too far away, but like Tank, I could tell they were afraid. I'm so thankful I live with a kind and loving owner.

I hope Rose is taking us home. I need to imprint on my dog bed the smells from Jane Doe's boot because Rose has asked me to remember them. Lily of the Valley. Red wine. Leather. Something oily. Cigarette butts. Vomit. Cow poo. Dog urine. As smells go, that's an unusual combination.

Rose turns onto a winding road that goes through the village of Abinger Hammer. I immediately start to salivate. There are three reasons we come to this village and they all involve things I can eat. The first is the pub, the Jolly Farmer. It allows dogs inside. Rose and I sometimes spend Friday nights there, me under the table, while Rose quietly feeds me tasty morsels. The smells of wood smoke, old beams, steaks and sausages and the yeasty carpet are heaven. The second reason we come to Abinger Hammer is the Tin Shed café, which does the world's best bacon butty. I kid you not. There's even a sign outside that says exactly that, and Rose agrees. The third, and my particular favourite, is the pet shop, Pawfect Pets. I could happily live there, with Rose, naturally, and I would eat my way around the shop until there was nothing left. Although I might miss Henrietta and her gaggle.

Please don't tell her I said that.

Rose parks in a bay outside the post office and we get out. I cock my leg on the red postbox:

Murder of young woman in Hinchley Wood. Any information to Monty at Duckdown Cottage.

With my last dribble I add, *Dogtective.*

'I'm starving,' Rose says.

Me too!

We cross the road and enter the Tin Shed café and Rose orders the best bacon butty in the world, and a latte. I'm a little disappointed she hasn't ordered me one – chasing shooters is exhausting work. My stomach rumbles.

'That was loud,' Rose says to me. 'The pet shop is next. I'll get you something there.'

A big lorry roars past, and the café's windows, along with every cup and saucer and plate and mug, shakes like there's been an earthquake. Nobody seems to care. Two mums with babies in prams are having coffee at one table and an old man with rheumy eyes and wispy white hair tucks into a full English breakfast at another table. My legs move of their own accord towards his table. Rose tugs me back but my snout and stomach are in the driver's seat now. All I can smell is the bacon and sausage. And I'm HUNGRY.

'Come on Monty,' Rose says under her breath, 'Professionalism at all times.'

I don't remember agreeing to anything of the sort, but there again, I do have selective hearing.

'Hungry, is he?' asks the old man. He gives Rose the kind of smile men give to women they particularly like. 'Here, he can have this.'

He picks up a half sausage and offers it. I literally drag Rose to his table. He lowers his hand and I take the sausage piece gently and swallow it whole. Then lick my lips.

'So what's a gorgeous lady like you doing in a place like this,' the old man says, jiggling his white eyebrows.

Rose laughs nervously. She's saved by Carol, the pretty lady who runs the café. She says with a cheeky grin, 'Oy Harold! Don't be rude. My place is lovely and don't you forget it.'

Harold chuckles and continues with his breakfast.

Rose leaves with her bacon butty and coffee and sits on a bench under the branches of a grizzled yew tree in the churchyard opposite the pub to eat her breakfast. The paving stones near her feet very quickly get slick with my slobber. Rose treats me to a little bit of bacon. The salty smokiness, still smeared with butter, was worth the wait.

She smiles at me. 'This morning was great. We make a great team.'

Her skin glows. She's happy. I wag my tail. Betty was right. Rose is happy when she's solving crimes.

'Now we get *your* breakfast,' she says, and we head for Pawfect Pets.

In the shop window are two Perspex boxes, each big enough to fit me in, with shredded newspaper at the bottom. One has nothing but the newspaper in it. In the other is the saddest puppy I've ever seen. He's a chocolate Labrador that can't be more than five weeks old. He hangs his head and even when I press my snout against the window, he doesn't look up.

Rose is too busy reciting a shopping list to notice the little fellow.

'In we go, Monty.'

There's a bell above the door that tinkles as we enter. The pet shop is crammed to the brim with huge bags of animal feed, tins piled up on shelves, dog and cat bowls, collars, leads and toys of both the fluffy and chewy variety, coats and bedding, shampoos and flea treatments, cat boxes and litter trays, bird seed bags and bird tables, fish tanks and fish feed, hamster cages, and at the very back, a counter with a till. The friendly girl who usually sits behind the counter reading a book isn't there.

The aisles between the merchandise displays are so narrow that Rose has to go first, and I follow. My tongue accidentally wraps itself around a rawhide chew which somehow ends up clamped between my teeth. This can easily happen when the treats are at dog-height.

'Put it back,' Rose whispers.

I'm understandably reluctant to give up my prize, so Rose has to pull it from my mouth. I wag my tail with pride at the saliva and teeth marks all over it.

'Looks like I'm buying this,' she sighs, as we head for the dry dog food section.

A woman with a wrinkled face like a walnut and hair that is too yellow to be real is using a small net to lift a goldfish from a tank. I've only ever seen her once before. She owns the shop. She drops the fish into a red bucket of water where it joins several others. The tank is empty of fish and there is a sponge in her other hand, so I'm guessing she is about to clean the fishes' home. I can't work out if she is old or young or somewhere in between, but she has no problem jumping down from her two-step ladder.

She emanates heady smells – cigarettes, pubs, puppies and fish food. And something else – a musky perfume, and she's wearing way too much of it, perhaps to mask the animal smells. I sneeze. And sneeze again.

'You try, you buy,' the woman says, her voice harsh and loud like a coffee grinder.

She runs her tongue over her cherry red lipstick as if she is about to eat us. I take a step back. Where is the nice girl who likes books and always gives me some liver treats?

'Of course,' says Rose, blushing.

'Over there.' The woman points.

As we squeeze between fish tanks on one side and dangling dog leads on the other, I notice a transparent plastic bag next to the bucket, sealed at the top, inside of which is a solitary goldfish with big bulbous eyes, who watches us intently as we pass. I give the bag a good sniff.

'Why's that fish in a plastic bag?' Rose asks, frowning.

'Punishment,' says Walnut Face.

'Punishment? What for?'

'Trying to escape. Keeps leaping out of the bucket. The stupid thing will kill itself and then where will I be? Can't sell a dead fish.'

The woman screws up her already wrinkled face into a puzzled expression, as if she is wondering if she could actually get somebody to pay for a dead fish.

Rose parts her lips. Is she going to object? I think she should. Poor fellow will suffocate in a sealed bag. Instead she kneels down and studies the bags of dry dog food.

'Just this brand?' Rose asks Walnut Face.

'Just the *best* brand. Basil's Pet Food. Locally made.' She gives me an appraising look. 'Nice looking dog. Where did you get him? From a breeder?'

'I'm his second owner.'

Walnut Face peers into my eyes then runs a finger down my back. 'Nice lines.'

'Thanks,' Rose says, dropping my lead so she can use both hands to pick up a bag and read the ingredients.

I'm deeply uncomfortable about Walnut Face poking me about. Luckily, her phone rings, which distracts her.

I trot to the front of the shop. The sad puppy whines, so quietly only a dog can hear him. He has no pals. No toys. Just a water bowl.

'Hey little guy? What's the matter?' I ask as quietly as possible.

The little fellow lifts his head and lets out a high pitched, 'I want my mummy!'

My ears prick up. Poor little guy. I look behind me at Rose whose head snaps around and her eyes widen. She leaves the food bag behind and comes over. 'He doesn't look very happy.'

'He'll be alright,' says Walnut Face, ending the call. 'The last of the litter. Missing his brothers and sisters.'

Rose studies the puppy. Frowns. 'How old is he?'

'Six weeks.'

I'd say more like five at most. He should be with his mother. He can't learn the skills he needs in life if he's taken away too young.

The puppy gets up on wobbly legs and head-butts the Perspex wall. 'I want my mummy,' he wails again. It's heartbreaking.

I whimper. Lift a paw and tap the Perspex in solidarity.

'Want to hold him?' the woman asks Rose. 'I'll give you ten percent off.'

Before Rose can answer, Walnut Face has grabbed the puppy by the scruff of his neck. It pees itself in terror. She then plonks the trembling pup in Rose's hands.

'Poor little thing looks terrified. There's no need to be so rough,' says Rose, clearly annoyed. She strokes the little mite, trying to sooth him.

I give the puppy a reassuring nudge, then a sniff.

I smell mother's milk and his fear. But what causes me to jump back like a scalded cat is the other scent on his fur: the smell of our Jane Doe.

My rear bumps into the wall-mounted display of collars and leads.

They jangle like little bells. A lead falls down and clanks when it hits the floor.

'Oh Monty, you're not jealous, are you? The poor little guy needs some love.'

What? Can't she smell it? No, I always forget. Our noses are a 100,000 times more sensitive than hoomans' noses. Rose keeps stroking the little pup while Walnut Face gives me a hard stare. How can I make Rose understand that this puppy was recently held by the woman who was lying dead in Hinchley Wood?

I lift one front paw a faction, then the other, like I'm doing a slow trot on the spot. I do this when I'm frustrated. What do I do now? Suddenly, I remember Rose's instructions: bark once and lift my paw if I detect Jane Doe's scent. I gaze at the trembling little Labrador in her hands. I have a deep bark and don't want to scare him, so I go for a half-bark and a paw lift. The puppy panics and tries to wriggle out of her grasp.

'You *are* jealous,' says Rose clutching the little fellow close to her chest. She doesn't notice my front paw is lifted. 'Shame on you.' With her free hand she gives me a playful tap on the bridge of my nose.

No, that's not what I mean. I fidget, lifting alternating front paws again.

'Looks like your dog wants a playmate. Why don't you take him?' urges the pet shop lady, with the look of a fox about to snatch a hen.

Rose hesitates, then gently places the puppy back in the transparent box. He squeals when she lets him go. 'I'd love to, but I've already got this one. I can't look after another.'

I bark once again and lift a paw. Louder this time.

'Okay greedy-guts, I haven't forgotten you.'

I'm frantic. I'm not thinking about food which, I admit, is rare. I leap up so my front paws rest on the side of the puppy's box.

'Get him down, he'll scratch it,' says Walnut Face.

Rose takes my collar and pulls me down, then clips the lead on. 'Changed your mind, have you? Sorry, Monty. I just can't afford another dog.' Rose turns to Walnut Face. 'I'd like to buy the pup a toy. Something to keep him company.'

'Sure.' The woman's face brightens.

Rose chooses a fluffy rabbit no bigger than her hand that is super soft and has a squeaker in its tummy. The moment she places it next to the puppy, the little fellow sniffs it then rests his head over it. She gives him one last stroke then turns towards the dog food aisle.

I lock my front legs, refusing to budge, and point my nose at the puppy. I bark once.

'Stop it, Monty' Rose admonishes.

I have to find a way to get Rose to understand. Her phone! The picture of Jane Doe is on the screen. It's in Rose's coat pocket. I'm not sure if I can fit my snout into her pocket but if I can get her phone out and drop it inside the puppy cage, maybe then she'll guess I'm trying to tell her something.

I snaffle her pocket, but my attempt to squeeze my large muzzle into the small space fails. 'What's got into you?' says Rose, pushing my face away.

She hurriedly grabs a bag of beef and vegetable dry food and a couple of tins of Chum, pays for them, the toy rabbit, and the rawhide chew in her pocket, and leaves.

'Poor puppy,' Rose says, 'I feel like I'm abandoning him.'

I twist on my lead to peer back at the pup in the window, who watches us go. I hear him whining for us to come back.

17

Ollie was a no-show.

Rose had arranged to pick him up at eleven at the same bus stop as last time. It was now twenty past and she'd already texted him to check that he was on his way. Sloppy chewing noises distracted her. In the back, Monty was working his way through the rawhide chew he'd nabbed from Pawfect Pets.

'Enjoying that, are you?' Rose said, watching Monty through the rear-view mirror.

Monty wagged his tail but the big chew, shaped like a knobbly bone, stayed firmly gripped between his front paws and his jaw didn't stop grinding away.

Had Ollie changed his mind, Rose wondered. Was he ill? Or had he simply forgotten? If so, why didn't he text back? Rose dialled his mobile. It went straight to voicemail. She left a message asking him to give her a call. Then she called Joe.

'Ollie hasn't turned up today. Is this normal or should I be worried?'

Joe laughed. 'He's a teenager, Rose. They forget stuff.'

'Suppose so. Still, he seemed keen to meet again and he's not answering my calls.'

'I'll see if I can get hold of him.'

Rose waited until eleven thirty, then turned the ignition. No contact from Ollie. No news from Joe. Maybe she should just go home. She turned left out of the side road and followed the signs for the dual carriageway. She wondered if Major Crime had spoken to Zofia yet. Was the murder victim Zofia's missing friend? Her fingers itched to dial Joe again and ask, but she didn't want to hassle him.

Her thoughts returned to Ollie. She made a split second decision and veered away from the dual carriageway slip road and headed for the Truscott Estate where Ollie lived.

She hadn't been at the estate for a while and this would be her first time without another officer. Coppers only went onto the estate in pairs. Drugs were sold openly and vandalism, muggings and turf wars had made it the most crime-ridden residential area in the county. Plenty of law-abiding citizens lived there, but they kept themselves to themselves for fear of retaliation if they reported anything.

The estate was divided into four blocks of flats, built in a cheerless grey breeze-block. Each building was four levels high with stairwells at either end. The lifts hardly ever worked. As soon as they were fixed, they were vandalised again. There had once been a little parade of shops, including a mini supermarket, a newsagent and a hairdresser, but they had long since been boarded up, the walls covered in graffiti. The green space between each block of flats was strewn with litter. A discarded mattress leaned against block B, and a ragged sofa faced the street as it slowly decomposed. A gang called The Blockers, unimaginatively named after the four blocks they regarded as their territory, controlled the illicit drug trade there, and woe betide anyone who tried to muscle in on their operation.

Rose parked in a vacant spot near Block C, next to the burned-out wreck of a Vauxhall Corsa. Two teenage boys, one black, one white, one in a puffer jacket, the other in a hoodie, leaned against a waist-high metal fence and gave her the once over. A third male, a few years older than the others, sat on a milk crate, smoking. He stared at her from behind a fringe of wispy hair.

Rose felt a buzz of panic. The last time she'd visited the estate, a gang of boys had thrown glass bottles at her. Saying that, Joe had been in uniform at the time. The problem wasn't so much that she was alone, because she wasn't – she had Monty – and she had been trained to handle herself in dangerous situations; it was more that she didn't trust herself anymore. If she was threatened, would she freeze?

Rose took a couple of jerky breaths, then hastily took Monty from the back of the car and locked the doors. He must have sensed her trepidation. It was as if Monty had puffed himself up to look bigger. His stance was wider. His tail was up and curled into a tight question mark. He watched the youths intently. His jowl quivered as he emitted a low rumbling growl like a racing car on the grid, ready to leap into action.

The group stayed put, but she could feel their eyes on her as she scanned the door numbers looking for flat seven, the address Joe had given her when she agreed to keep an eye on Ollie. She set off, Monty walking to heel.

A boy of around eleven appeared from nowhere and followed them on a bicycle, no doubt sent to spy on them. Anyone new to the estate aroused interest.

The kitchen window to flat seven had lace curtains and on the inside sill were black plastic pots with herbs growing in them. Rose pressed the doorbell but it didn't ring. She tried knocking. The boy on the bicycle went around in circles, brazenly watching her. The lace curtain was flicked back by a woman with the same dark hair and dark eyes as her son.

'What do you want?' she called out.

'I'm Rose, a friend of Ollie's.'

'Oh.'

Ollie's mum briefly disappeared. The deadbolt turned, the security chain was unlatched, and the front door opened. The woman flicked a nervous glance up and down the pavement, clocked the boy on the bicycle and beckoned Rose inside. She slammed the door shut quickly.

'I'm Brenda. Joe told me about you. Come through.'

Brenda led Rose down a narrow hallway and showed her into a Spartan but neat lounge room. 'Ollie talked about you.' She nodded at Monty. 'And the dog. He's always loved animals, you see. Went on and on about your ducks and geese.'

Monty was sniffing the air as if his nose was a radar dish scanning for Ollie.

'Monty's really taken a shine to your son,' Rose said, 'which is why I'm here. I was hoping he'd help me out again today. Is he home?'

'I don't know what's got into him. Won't come out of his room.'

'Can I talk to him?'

'Be my guest. His room has the "Geek Zone. Do Not Enter" sticker on it. Don't be offended if he won't open the door. He's in a real mood. Like a cuppa?'

'Yes, please, that would be lovely.'

The kitchen was at one end of the living room. Dated laminated cupboards and an electric cooker that was old but clean. Brenda clicked on the kettle. 'Thanks for what you're doing for Ollie. This place is poisonous. I'm scared to go outside my door. The more time Ollie spends away from here, and Nat, the better.'

'Who's Nat?'

'Nathan Hill. He's the one that got my son caught up in that car business. Nothing but trouble. Lord knows why Ollie has anything to do with him after he killed Ollie's pet rat. Ollie was devastated. He loved that rat so much.'

Brenda handed Rose a mug of tea that said "Keep Calm and Carry On" on it. Rose smiled inwardly. That advice was way too close for comfort.

Brenda perched on the arm of her sofa. She was clearly up for a chat. 'His father died six years ago. Things would be different if he was still around. I wouldn't be working two jobs, for a start.' Brenda sipped from her own mug. 'Ollie spends too much time alone, cooped up in his room. Not healthy for a young lad. I encourage him to apply for jobs but it's not easy. The thing with the car...well, you can imagine, can't you?' The dark semi-circles under Brenda's eyes, the worry lines around her lips, and the unflattering baggy leggings and sweatshirt were testimony to a life under siege.

'I can only pay Ollie for odd jobs now and again but I'll put the word out and see if anyone else can offer him work.'

'Ta very much.'

'I'll go see him now.'

Rose led Monty to Ollie's bedroom door and knocked.

'You'll have to be louder than that,' Brenda called out. 'He's got headphones on. Here, I'll have a go.' Brenda hammered on the door and shouted, 'Ollie, you got company!'

There was a rustling sound then Ollie opened the door. The room's interior was dark, the only light from a computer monitor. It didn't help that the walls were painted black and the curtains drawn. A video game was frozen mid-frame. Almost abutting the swivel chair was a single bed. The space between the two was littered with dumped clothes.

'Shit! You have to go.' Ollie didn't even notice Monty, who was wagging his tail. Ollie ran his fingers through his hair which made it stick up on end. 'Oh man, this is bad.'

'I was worried when you didn't turn up today.'

'Yeah, look, sorry, I can't, okay.' He saw Brenda hovering in the background. 'What?'

'You gotta stick with it, love. It's paid work. And maybe Rose can get you some more.'

'Muuuuum,' Ollie moaned. 'Stop nagging.'

The room smelt of dust and body odour. Brenda shouldered past them, pulled back a curtain and opened the window. She nodded at shelves on metal brackets above his desk.

'Show her your inventions, Ollie,' Brenda urged. 'Go on, love.'

Ollie stepped back from the door so that Rose and Monty could enter. He stared at Brenda until she got the message and left. Ollie shut the window as soon as she'd gone.

On the shelves was a small drone with a camera attached to it and a remote control. Next to that was a device that resembled a miniature GoPro camera attached to a tiny harness with Velcro straps. Scattered around the device were plyers, a couple of circuit boards, a soldering iron, loose batteries, a roll of electrical wire and various bits and bobs that Rose didn't recognise.

'I'm working on a device that can recharge mobile phones in fifteen seconds. If it works, I'll be rich.'

'That would be really useful. My phone takes ages to recharge. Drives me nuts.' Rose's eyes were drawn back to the GoPro-like camera and harness. 'That looks interesting.'

Ollie shrugged. 'No point finishing it after Cody died.'

'Who's Cody?'

'My rat. Named him after the first Brit to fly a biplane. It was going to be a Rat Cam. I trained Cody to wear it and we recorded video.'

'So it records video in small spaces, like under floorboards?'

'Yeah. It was pretty cool.' He started to explain how he synchronised the video with his phone and could stream it in real time. As he did, he became more animated.

'This is incredible stuff, Ollie. Have you thought of going to college? You could do this kind of thing for a living.'

'Nah, I messed up my GCSEs.'

Male voices outside the window stopped Ollie in his tracks. 'I can't help you no more. Please go.'

Someone kicked an empty can across a hard service.

'Got anything to do with the boys outside?'

Ollie shook his head, but his eyes didn't meet hers.

'If you change your mind, just call me.' Rose headed for the door with Monty in tow. If she pushed Ollie too hard, she might never see him again. 'I don't know what's going on in your life, Ollie, but I do know you have a great future if you stop listening to people who want to drag you down. I can help you, but you have to want to be helped.'

18

The stars tonight remind me of a particularly sparkly dog collar at Pawfect Pets. As I peer out of the kitchen window at the clear night sky, I think back to the lonely Labrador puppy that was too young to be separated from his mum. I should know. I was separated from my mother at six weeks and the memory of that terrible day still haunts me.

'So tell me again, Mr Monty,' Betty says, tugging at the feathery fur on my elbow to get my attention. 'Are you saying the puppy is a clue?'

Betty is up on her hind legs, nose twitching, her eyes shining with eagerness. I have filled her in on the day's events: the dead girl in Hinchley Wood, the boot I found at the crime scene, the sad puppy at Pawfect Pets, and how disappointed I am that Ollie won't come to visit us anymore.

'Yes,' I say. 'Rose doesn't know what I know: that the puppy in the pet shop smells of Jane Doe. If we could find out who handled the little guy and where he came from, perhaps we'll find the killer. And besides, I can't bear the idea of the pup so alone and afraid. I wish we could get Rose to adopt him.'

Betty snickers. 'Mate, Jane Doe isn't the girl's name.'

'Yes it is. I heard Rose's boss say so.'

'Take it from me, Jane Doe is what them coppers call a dead woman they can't identify. I should know. Seen a few dead hoomans in my time in the Eurotunnel. Those trains go real fast so the bodies can get very messy. You know what I mean?'

'So The Leach doesn't know who she is?'

'That's right. Unless Zofia has identified her.'

'Betty, the problem we have is that Rose isn't allowed to investigate the case. I heard The Leach say so. How is Rose going to believe she's a good detective if she can't do her detecting?'

'Good point, Mr Monty.' Betty taps her front teeth with a claw. 'Only you and me know the puppy is a key witness, right? He could help us find the killer.'

'Agreed.'

'And the poor puppy definitely needs some TLC, right?'

'Agreed.'

'It's simple,' Betty says, pointing a claw up to the sky. 'We rescue the little tyke. Tonight.'

'What?' I sit up. 'We can't do that.'

'Why not? We bring him here. He can help us solve this mystery. Plus, we'll cheer him up.'

'Because it's so far away and because I can't disobey Rose and because the hoomans will think we're stealing him and that's a crime,' I pant.

Betty strokes my paw. 'Calm down, Mr Monty. I can get us to Abinger Hammer. Easy-peasy. I know them trains like the back of me paw. And as for all that nonsense about committing a crime, it's actually Pawfect Pets who is doin' the crime. They shouldn't sell dogs that young. We're saving a puppy and finding him a home. We're doing the right thing.'

Her logic makes sense, but I know in my heart I'm being a bad dog.

'I can't do this, Betty. I'm breaking so many rules.'

She peers up at me. 'You mean those commandy things?'

'The Ten Dog Commandments, yes.'

She scratches her head with a claw. 'Remind me what they are again.'

I recite them. They are drilled into us by our mothers.

1. Love your master.
2. Obey your master, who is pack leader.
3. Defend your master.

4. Never embarrass your master.

5. Never appear smarter than your master.

6. Never show you understand hooman language.

7. Never be seen using hooman technology.

8. Cooperate with other creatures for peaceful purposes.

9. You may abandon a master if ordered to kill another animal for entertainment or profit, or another hooman, unless your hooman's life is at risk.

10. If in doubt, play dumb and wag your tail.

'I would be breaking commandment two and maybe five as well,' I say.

'Poppycock,' says Betty, wagging a claw at me. 'You are following rule eight, as in you're cooperating with me. Plus, you're showing how much you love your master by risking your neck, which covers rule one. Plus, if Rose is angry when she finds the pup at home, then you can always go with number ten and play dumb.'

I nod. Betty can be very persuasive when she wants to be. 'But what about the hooman laws?' I say. 'Stealing a puppy is breaking the law.'

Betty taps the side of her head. 'You're not thinking straight, Mr Monty. It's not breaking the law when the pup in question wants to be taken. The poor little bugger's gonna have problems when he grows up unless he finds a good home. You mark my words. Whatever the rat community may say about me, I never abandoned my pups. Never!' Betty shakes her head. 'I was a good mum, I was. That certainly can't be said of their fathers. Bastards, all five of 'em.'

Betty has had five litters and I know she misses her offspring terribly. I contemplate the little Labrador, alone in the pet shop, with nothing but the toy rabbit Rose gave him as comfort.

Betty clinches the deal with, 'And besides, you're helping Rose catch a killer.'

I can't argue with her logic. She's right.

'I'll have us back before dawn and Rose will never know you left the house.'

'But Rose doesn't sleep well these days. She often comes downstairs in the night.'

'No problem. Find me a cushion. We'll stuff it under your blanket and Rose will never know you're not there.'

I think Rose is not that easily fooled but then I see in my mind's eye the poor little puppy, his face pressed against the Perspex, crying out for his mummy, and I cave.

We follow the train tracks that run at the back of Duckdown Cottage. The nearest station is Milford, about a mile away, and we're intending to take the first train of the day to Geldeford.

'Remember to stay away from the live rail,' Betty says, panting like she's run a marathon, although we only left the house a moment ago. I'm concerned she isn't going to make it to Milford and without her help, I won't be able to rescue the puppy.

Our progress is slow because Betty has to stop every so often to catch her breath. Underfoot everything is covered in white frost. I hear a fox's cry, which always make me flinch because it sounds like a hooman screaming, but she's just challenging another fox to stay out of her territory. A Tawny Owl swoops down and tries to grab Betty, his talons glinting in the moonlight. She squeals and darts underneath me. The big bird's wing feathers brush my back.

'Twit,' says the owl, landing on a branch, its huge eyes very much focused on me. 'Tewoo.'

At least he isn't quoting Shakespeare. It seems that every owl I come across hurls a quote from Shakespeare at me as if it were a barbed weapon.

'Betty's a friend. Now let us pass.'

The owl swivels its head and blinks. 'Truly, thou art damned like an ill-roasted egg, all on one side.'

I'm guessing that's Shakespeare. I have no idea what he's talking about.

'Leave us be,' I say. 'We're doing detective work.'

'Twit!' he repeats, then flies away.

I get the message and to be truthful, I'm beginning to wonder if I am a twit. But it's too late now.

'Get on my back, Betty. I'll get us there quicker.'

'All right then,' she says, scampering up my leg. Her claws tickle until she settles down in a spot between my shoulder blades and grips my collar like a bridle. 'I'm ready.'

Soon my strides get longer and I'm in a full sprint. I know we're almost at Milford Station when we reach a tunnel, a cutting through a hill. Inside, it's blacker than a Doberman's coat, so I slow down and hug the wall so we don't stumble onto the live rail. Once we're back out in the open air, I hide in a tangle of bramble bushes at the far end of Platform One and wait for the train. Betty stays on my back.

'I'm hungry,' Betty says. 'Just as well we're heading for a pet shop full of food.'

'Please don't, Betty, I already feel bad enough stealing the pup.'

Betty sulks. 'Spoilsport.'

I feel the rumble of the train approaching even before its headlights appear like eyes glowing in the blackness of the tunnel. It roars and screeches, filling the air with the smell of rubber and grease and hot metal. As the train slows, I count three carriages. Milford is a local line that connects a myriad of villages to Geldeford. Apart from the driver, I spot two men in the first carriage, six people in the second, and the third looks empty except for a woman whose eyes are closed. We sneak out of our hiding place just as the train doors open with a beep. Betty holds on tightly to my collar as I jump into the third carriage, just as the doors close. Once inside, I duck between two seats and lie low. The sleeping woman hasn't moved. The train jolts as it leaves the station.

'That's the easy bit,' squeaks Betty.

I daren't answer for fear of waking the woman. The bit I'm dreading is when we arrive at Geldeford Station, which has lots of platforms, bright lights and, even at this hour, plenty of staff keeping a vigilant eye on the trains.

In no time at all, our train pulls into Geldeford. 'You know what to do,' says Betty.

The sleeping woman wakes and presses the button to open the doors. With Betty on my back, grasping my collar like a little jockey, I dart out of the carriage, brushing past her legs, causing her to gasp. I dart through a ticket-reading machine. A British Rail employee exclaims, 'Bugger me, is that a dog?' I race across the concourse, dodging several attempts to catch me, with Betty screaming at the top of her voice, 'Woohoo!'

Trains don't go to Abinger Hammer. Our plan is to get to our destination courtesy of the Royal Mail.

Geldeford's Post Office depot is right next to the station. We sneak silently past the boom gate while the security guard sips his tea in his little hut. I then hide amongst the red postal vans that nuzzle up to the loading bays like puppies at their mother's teats.

Betty clambers down my leg to the ground. 'I'll find out which one's going to Abinger Hammer. Stay here.' She scampers off in the direction of a big warehouse with a raised loading dock. I wait and watch sacks of mail being loaded into waiting vans. In no time at all, Betty is back.

'Follow me.'

I keep my head down as we weave between parked vehicles. Then we observe the driver of one van, a young man, tall and scruffy like an Irish Wolfhound, take a large white sack from a burly guy wearing a post-box red vest with reflective stripes around the middle.

'That's all of it, Fred,' says Red Vest Guy.

'I'll distract him,' says Betty to me. 'You jump in the back.'

Before I can argue, Betty scampers over to the van, climbs up the wheel and stands on top of the right-hand side mirror, squeaking aggressively at Fred.

'Shit!' Fred says. 'It's a bloody rat!'

The man in the vest races to join Fred, to see what the fuss is about. Betty keeps up her high-pitched racket.

'I've never seen anything like it,' Red Vest Guy says. 'Big bastard, isn't he.'

Betty hisses. I'm not surprised she's upset. Isn't it obvious she's female?

I charge for the back of the van unnoticed, jump in and hide behind the piles of mailbags.

'Stay back,' Fred says in a faltering voice. 'Could have rabies.'

'Don't be daft. We don't have rabies here.'

'It's gone mad, look at it.'

Betty hears me in the back of the van, leaps off the wing mirror, slides down the bonnet like a slippery dip, and once on the ground, darts into the vehicle's chassis.

Fred peers under the van nervously. 'Where'd it go? Don't want it attacking me when I'm driving.'

I hear Betty mutter from somewhere beneath the floor, 'Enough of the *it*.'

'Nah, it's gone,' says the other man.

'You sure?'

'Yeah, course. Now get moving. If you ain't noticed, there's a queue behind you.'

Fred reluctantly shuts the van's rear doors and gets into the driver's seat. Through the metal mesh separating me from the front seats, I see him peer into the footwell, presumably checking for rats, then he turns the ignition and drives off.

Fifteen minutes later, Fred pulls up outside The Tin Shed café in Abinger Hammer. He waves at Carol through the café's window and she waves back. She seems very pleased to see him. Fred gets out. Carol pokes her head out of the door.

'Got something hot and delicious brewing for you upstairs.'

Strange. I thought the café was on the ground level and Carol lived upstairs.

Fred is about to remotely lock the van when Betty climbs up the outside of his trouser leg. He is so startled, he screams and drops the key on the frosty pavement. Betty jumps down and scoops up the round, black key fob in her strong jaws. Fred stumbles backwards, yelling, 'Get away!' Then his face turns red with fury when he realises Betty has run into the van with his keys.

'Right! That's it. You're dead.'

He storms into the café and demands a broom, startling Carol who is looking very alluring in a silk dressing gown. Meanwhile, Betty uses her claws to grasp the mesh barrier separating the front and back of the van and feeds the key fob through a gap to me. I take it between my teeth, drop the key and stamp my paw on the fob. The back doors are supposed to open. They stay shut.

A broom head smashes down on Betty who releases the mesh and disappears between the two seats.

'What the–?' says Fred, having noticed for the first time there's a large dog among the sacks of mail. Time for me to exit. I stamp on the key fob again. Nothing happens. Okay, this isn't good.

'Get out!' yells a puce-faced Fred.

I stamp on the key fob so hard it's painful. There's a clink and the two rear doors spring open. I push them wide open with my head and jump to the ground. Fred tries to grab my collar, but I'm too quick for him. I bolt down the street and disappear into the darkness.

Betty and I regroup outside Pawfect Pets. Betty is breathless but elated. She does a little jig. Her big belly wobbles.

'We are so cool. What a team!' she squeaks.

She insists we high-five. I lift my big paw and her tiny one slaps into mine. Then, while Betty catches her breath, I jump up and place my front paws on the glass of the shop window. The fish tanks light the interior in an eerie turquoise glow. The Perspex boxes are still in the window. I see the toy rabbit Rose bought for the puppy lying in the middle of the second box. I sniff hard. His scent is weak. Very weak. I shift position, to get a better look. Maybe the little fellow is curled up, deep in the shredded newspaper. I sniff again.

'Oh no. He's gone. We're too late.'

19

It was eight o'clock on a Friday morning and Monty was still in his bed, which wasn't like him at all. Maybe he'd had a bad night. Did dogs have bad nights, Rose wondered. For once, she had slept soundly, and felt better than she had in a long time. As she ate her eggie soldiers, she checked on her new Facebook account. It was active. She could now contact Zofia through Messenger. As Rose dunked a thin slice of toast into the egg yolk and bit into it, she considered the risk of annoying Leach, because contacting Zofia was certainly treading on his toes.

Monty opened a bleary eye, lifted his head for a moment and then, as though it was all too much effort, slumped back into the cushion, eyes firmly closed again. So, what was she going to do today? She needed a plan. She grabbed a notepad and pen and jotted down a list.

Contact Zofia?
Finish cleaning out attic? No Ollie. Ask neighbour?
Cook an exotic dish. Will need ingredients.
Clear piles of books from study floor. Rose sighed.
Clean house. Rose yawned.
Take dog for walk. Monty didn't look as if he wanted to go for a walk.
Find who killed that poor girl.

Rose stared at the last item on the list and then the first item. All she wanted to do was help solve the case, even if she wasn't supposed to. Rose phoned Joe. It went to voicemail and she left a message. Seconds later she received a text message in return.

In a briefing. Talk later.

Joe was true to his word. As Rose was washing the drizzles of yolk from the side of her egg cups, he rang back. She dried her hands and put her phone on loudspeaker.

'You're going to hate me for asking, but I can't get that poor girl out of my head.' She paused, half-expecting Joe to cut her off. The briefing from Leach would have just ended and he'd be on his way out.

'Kind of gets to you doesn't it,' Joe said.

'Have you ID'd her?'

Joe dropped his voice. Rose could hear a car engine starting and people in the background talking. He must be in the car park. 'Not yet.'

'What did Zofia Nowak say?'

'Come off it, Rose, you know I can't tell you.'

'Please Joe, just tell me if she's been contacted.'

'Not yet.'

'The uni's not being helpful?'

'You got it.'

'So you're having to get a warrant?'

'Yup.'

Rose sat down at the table and grabbed the notepad. 'Has Jenny done the post mortem yet?'

'Yup and you know I can't go into that.'

'Please Joe. I promise I won't ask again.'

'You never give up, do you?' Joe sighed heavily. 'You owe me. Big time.'

'Okay.'

'You have to promise. If I call in a favour, you'll do it. Now promise.'

'I promise, Joe.'

'Okay. Time of death – Tuesday, between 1am and 4am.'

That fitted with what Zofia had told her in the Sainsbury's car park.

'Jenny confirmed death by strangulation. There was cow and dog poo as well as dog hair on her boots.'

'That would be kind of weird for a law student. Maybe the victim worked on a farm.'

'Yup, I'm door-knocking dairy farms all day.'

'What about dog walkers and kennels?'

'They'll probably be next. I'm just a PC, remember? I do as I'm told.'

'Anything else?' Rose asked, scribbling notes.

Joe cleared his throat. 'This is really sad. And you can't breathe a word of this to anybody. The boss is keeping this one out of the media.'

'I understand,' Rose said.

'She was pregnant. Twelve weeks.'

'Oh no. That's terrible.' Rose felt sick. The killer had taken two lives.

Joe said, 'Varma is talking to local GPs and the hospital, but it's slow going as you can imagine. Client-patient confidentiality and all that.'

'That means the victim had a partner or lover,' Rose said. 'What I find really puzzling is that he hasn't reported her missing. Why?'

'That's a really good question.'

As soon as Rose ended the call she used Messenger to ask Zofia to contact her. She reminded Zofia that she had approached Rose in the Sainsbury's carpark about her missing friend.

Then she switched on her laptop and searched for female dog walkers and kennel owners in the Geldeford area. Rose put together a list and then worked her way through it, leaving messages if she couldn't speak to them. She imagined Leach, fit to burst with fury at her interference. But if Rose succeeded in identifying the victim, he'd have to forgive her, surely?

Harriot of Canine Capers was the eleventh dog walking service she phoned. When Rose explained the reason for her call, Harriot went very quiet.

'Harriot? Has someone you know gone missing?' Rose asked.

'I…I may do. It could be nothing. I assumed she'd changed her mind.'

Rose sat up straight and stared hard at the image of Harriot on the Canine Capers' website. She wore glasses with transparent frames and a crooked but warm smile. At her feet were seven dogs of various shapes and sizes.

'Changed her mind about what?' Rose asked.

Down the line, a small dog yapped. 'Give it to me,' Harriot said. 'Jock, I can't throw the ball if you won't let me take it.' More yapping. 'Sorry about that. I've got four dogs with me. Can you repeat the question?'

'You thought someone changed their mind. Who?'

'A potential dog walker. I'm looking for an assistant. She came on a trial walk with me and she was great, so I asked her to take out a group the next day. She never turned up.'

'What was her name?'

'Libby, err, something. I'd have to look it up.'

'How old was Libby?'

'I'm guessing eighteen.'

'How do you know her?'

'I don't. She approached me. Said she wanted part-time work and loved dogs.'

'Which day was she due to walk with you?'

'Yesterday. My nine o'clock group.'

The morning the body was discovered, Rose thought. 'Do you have her phone number?'

'Sure, but I can never work out how to get to my contacts list while I'm using the phone. Can I do this later?'

'Harriot, this is urgent. I need Libby's contact details.'

'Right. Okay. Let me get these crazy hounds back in the van so I can concentrate.'

Rose stared at her phone, willing Harriot to call back. A minute went by. Then another. She searched the Canine Capers Facebook page to see if Harriot had posted a photo with Libby. All she could find were pictures of dogs playing and running.

Her phone beeped with the contact details for one Libby Jones. Rose immediately dialled the number. Libby answered.

'This is Detective Constable Rose Sidebottom. Am I speaking to Libby Jones?'

'Yes. Why? What's happened?' She sounded young.

'I'm investigating a missing person. Do you know Harriot from Canine Capers?'

'Yes. Is this because I didn't do the walk? I had the worst cold. It wasn't my fault,' Libby moaned.

Disappointed, Rose apologised and got off the phone quickly. For a while there, she thought she was on to something. Oh well, there were plenty of other dog walkers on the list.

Just then, she received a call back.

'Hi, you left me a message. I'm Debbie's Dog Services.'

Rose explained the reason she had called Debbie.

'Give me a sec,' said Debbie. 'Baxter's just done a giant poo. Have to pick it up.' There was a sound of rustling. The slam of a bin lid. 'Right. Now I can talk. I don't know about any missing girls, but I do know a new dog walker turned up on my patch and I wasn't happy. Out of the blue. A young thing, she was too, and bloody stroppy.'

'Your patch?'

'Yes. Everyone knows I get first dibs on dogs in the St Martha's area. This bloody girl turns up with two Golden Retrievers I recognised. I gave her a piece of my mind I can tell you.'

Rose hadn't realised that dog walking was so competitive. 'Can you describe her?'

'Oh I don't know. Twenties, maybe. Brown hair. Bad teeth. I couldn't help noticing how stained they were.'

Did Jane Doe have bad teeth? Rose couldn't tell from the crime scene photo.

'What was her name?'

'Anna something-or-other unpronounceable.'

'Please, Debbie, this is important. Try to remember her surname.'

'It sounded Eastern European to me. Those bloody people come over here taking our jobs–'

Rose cut her off. 'The surname, Debbie?'

'Sirbanksa or something like that.'

Rose googled Polish surnames on the off chance Anna was Polish, like Zofia. 'Czubinska?' she offered.

'That sounds about right. What's she done?'

Rose ignored the question. 'Do you know how to contact her?'

'I don't, but the owners of the Golden Retrievers should know. I can give you their address.'

Rose scribbled down the details and thanked Debbie.

Her heart was pounding. Was the murder victim Anna Czubinska? Rose had to be sure before she contacted Major Crime. Her chair scraped on the lino as she almost leapt to her feet. Monty lifted his head, ears pricked, looking at her for an explanation.

'Come on, Monty, we're going to St. Martha's.'

20

The nineteenth century church perched atop St Martha's Hill stuck out above the fog like a lighthouse above a sea of white caps. Rose knocked on the door of a modern bungalow at the foot of the hill. She stamped her feet, trying to get her circulation going. The freezing fog had seeped into her body despite her puffy coat. From within the house, two dogs launched into frenzied barking. Next to her, Monty wagged his tail.

The front door was opened by a grey-haired man in a navy V-necked jumper and caramel corduroy trousers. Two young Golden Retrievers jostled excitedly for the chance to poke their heads around the door.

'Ah,' said the man, 'You have one too. What's his name?'

'Monty. And yours?'

'Biscuit and Lolly. My grandkids named them.'

The dogs squeezed past the man's legs and were busy sniffing Monty, who was very happy to sniff them back.

Rose showed her warrant card and asked for Anna Czubinska's phone number. Derrick Pocock was more than happy to oblige. 'She was supposed to walk these two Tuesday afternoon but didn't show up. I left her a message. I have to say I was a tad annoyed. My wife and I had gone out for the day and left the dogs in the house. There was a little present in the kitchen when we got back. Not their faults of course. They must have been desperate.'

Monty barked in a friendly way and both Retrievers barked back, eyes bright, tails swooshing the air.

'Inside, both of you,' said Derrick, taking the dogs by their collars and steering them back into the house. 'I'll get her number.'

Moments later he returned with a phone number jotted down on a yellow Post-it Note. 'Is Anna all right?' he asked. 'I'm afraid I left her a rather stroppy message.'

Rose thought it best to avoid answering. She wasn't supposed to be working the case. She held up the photo on her phone of the woman found in Hinchley Wood. 'Is this Anna Czubinska?'

He squinted. 'I think so. It's hard to tell. Why's she lying on the ground?' Rose watched his lips part as the realisation set in. 'Is she de—'

'Thank you for your time, Mr Pocock. You've been most helpful.'

Rose and Monty left quickly. When they were back in the car, Rose dialled Anna's phone number. Listening to the girl's voicemail greeting was heartrending. Rose had to clear her throat before she was able to speak.

'This is Detective Constable Rose Sidebottom. Please call me back on this number as soon as you can.'

Rose couldn't yet be certain that Anna Czubinska was the victim, so she had chosen her words carefully. If Anna was dead, her phone could still be out there somewhere. Perhaps the killer had taken it. If Rose could locate it, then she might also catch the killer. Normally she would contact the telephone service provider and ask them to track the phone. For that, she would have to complete paperwork and get the DCI's approval, none of which she could do. Was there another way to track a mobile phone? She dialled Ollie. He was into technology, surely he would know. To her relief, he answered.

'I need to find the location of a mobile phone. Can you help me?'

'Piece of piss. There's an app. If you have the number, it finds the phone's location in real-time.'

Ollie told her which app to download. 'Thanks Ollie. You're helping solve a murder.'

'You're joking, aren't ya?'

'Not at all. And remember. If you need my help, give me a call. Any time.'

Rose downloaded the app and then added Anna's mobile number. A map appeared on her screen. The university. A little purple icon shaped like a mobile phone appeared over the Student Union building. That was where the Polish Society met and someone with Anna's phone was there right now.

'Buckle up, Monty,' she called over her shoulder.

Rose parked on the other side of the road to the Student Union building and the café. She had a good view through the café's windows and of the courtyard out front. Only smokers clutching mugs of coffee were brave or desperate enough to sit on the benches outside in near freezing temperatures. She checked the location finder for Anna's phone: she was definitely in the right place. Then she dialled Anna's number, hoping someone in the cafe or the courtyard would pull out a phone. There was no answer.

'Let's go,' she said to Monty, zipping up her coat.

They entered the Student Union building, which consisted of narrow corridors and poky rooms in cream-painted brick. She asked a passing student where the Polish Society met and was directed to a meeting room towards the back of the building. Rose hovered outside. Chairs were arranged in rows and about fifteen of them were occupied with students.

Kacper Kowalski was perched on the edge of a table at the front of the room, his gaze fixed on the attractive young woman he was clearly flirting with.

Rose dialled. A phone rang inside the room.

Kacper pulled a ringing phone from his jeans' back pocket. He glanced at the screen, touched the end button, and pocketed it again.

Kacper had Anna Czubinska's phone.

Rose led Monty away from the open door. A little voice in her head kept saying, *What if you're wrong? What if Anna isn't Jane Doe? You'll have egg all over your face and Leach will think you an incompetent fool.* Her head was spinning. She was heating up, her face and neck blotchy and red. Monty peered up at her and whimpered. He must have sensed her agitation.

Should she confront Kacper? No, she should call it in, do things by the book. DI Varma was the best officer to tell. He had always been supportive. Maybe he'd help pave the way with Leach. Rose dialled Varma's number.

Just then a girl exclaimed, 'Oh what a cute doggie!'

Kacper recognised Rose and Monty. He dived through a door in a partition wall to his left. Seconds later he darted out from the adjoining meeting room and ran. Rose released Monty from his lead.

'Go!' she ordered.

Monty took off after Kacper, ears back, weaving between students as if he were in the giant slalom. Rose followed, dodging stunned students in the corridors.

'Out the way! Police!'

Kacper led them out of the Student Union and into the courtyard, where he almost sent a smoker flying as he headed for the road where Rose had parked. Monty lunged at his leg and clamped his jaws down on the hem of his jeans. Kacper tumbled and landed face-first on the pavement. Monty tugged and snarled, jerking the man's leg. Kacper kicked out at him with his other foot but Monty easily dodged it, giving Kacper's leg another tug to keep him off balance.

Rose caught up. Students stared.

'You can't do this! I have rights!' Kacper seethed.

'And I want the truth.' Rose kneeled so she could see Kacper's face. 'Why do you have Anna Czubinska's phone?'

'I say nothing to Policja.'

'Suit yourself. I'll put you in the back of my car with this dog and you'll be interviewed at the station. How would you like that? Or we can talk now. It's up to you.'

He spat at her shoe and said something in Polish that Rose had no doubt wasn't at all complimentary.

Rose held her phone up to his face. 'Kacper,' she said sharply. 'Is this Anna Czubinska?'

He reluctantly looked at the photo. Then his mouth contorted into a sneer. 'What is this? You're playing tricks.'

'Just answer the question, Kacper. Is this Anna Czubinska?'

'Yes. Yes. What's wrong with her? Why she look like that?' His body went limp. 'Oh no.'

'Monty, stop!' He let go of Kacper's jeans and stood next to Rose, panting.

'Get up Kacper, we need to talk. And don't think of running. Monty will catch you.'

But the fight had gone out of him. He staggered as he stood, then sat heavily on a bench.

'Anna is…dead?'

'Yes, and you have her phone.' Rose sat next to him. Monty positioned himself right in front of Kacper and stood guard. 'You better start talking fast.'

'We had argument. It is my phone. I wanted it back.'

'Is the phone registered in your name or hers?'

'My name.'

'Why?'

'I live in England three years. She arrive here six months ago. She had no fixed address. She could not get contract for phone. I don't know why I help her. She was stupid bitch.' He shook his head.

Clearly Kacper was recovering quickly from the shock and his acerbic tongue had returned.

'When did you last see Anna?'

'I do not know. Maybe Monday.'

'Where?'

'I can't remember.'

A sudden tingle in both her arms and legs. It was his first lie. 'Oh I think you can. Where did you see Anna on Monday?'

He shrugged, 'Maybe it was here.'

Rose felt even stronger pins and needles. Lying again.

'Is she a student?'

'Yes.'

'What is she studying?'

'Chemical engineering.' He gave her a sly look. 'She think she can do man's job.'

Was he trying to provoke her?

'Where does she live?'

'I don't know.' The sting of pins and needle was unbearable. Rose rolled her feet from heel to toe to try and calm the painful sensation.

'I think you do. Anna is dead, Kacper. And you're obstructing a police investigation. That won't go down well.'

'Number twenty-four Dorset Street. I want a lawyer.'

Rose dialled DS Varma and asked him to come right away. She gave Varma the victim's name and address. Varma said he would be with her in ten.

She turned her attention back to Kacper.

'Why didn't you report her missing?'

'Why should I care? I am not her boyfriend. You talk to Zofia. She lives with Anna.'

'Zofia Nowak?'

'Yes.'

Rose should have been happy. Her hunch had worked out. She had tracked down Anna's phone and confirmed the victim's identity. And yet she had secretly hoped Zofia's friend was still alive. She didn't envy the detective who would have to break the terrible news to Zofia and to Anna's family.

 21

Rose and I loiter across the road from 24 Dorset Street with DS 'Gentleman' Varma. In the back of Varma's unmarked Vauxhall Insignia is Kacper Kowalski, who glares at us. A police officer sits with him. Kowalski is not the only one unhappy with us. Pearl stomps over the road in our direction.

'I'll arrest you for stalking,' Pearl snaps at Rose. 'Now bugger off.'

He hasn't even thanked Rose for discovering the victim's name and address. He really is insufferable.

'It's a public street,' Rose responds, crossing her arms.

You go, girl! I hold my head up high, feeling very proud of her.

He gives Rose a stay-where-you-are glower, then stomps back to number twenty-four.

'Is Leach furious too?' Rose asks Varma.

'No. He's pretty impressed to be honest. You did well, Rose,' Varma says, very dapper in a grey pinstripe suit, pink shirt and pink stripy tie. He nods toward the retreating Pearl. 'Pearl's got his knickers in a twist because he thinks you made him look bad. He takes these things personally.'

'Are you testing Anna's phone for fingerprints?' Rose asks.

'Yes, and we'll go through her calls and messages. Right now, Kacper is our prime suspect. He knew the victim. Had her phone. Has a temper. But what's his motive?'

'Crime of passion?' Rose suggests.

'Perhaps.' Varma wanders across the road and joins Pearl.

Pearl hammers a fist on the front door. 'Police, open up!'

There are three overflowing bins against the front wall of the semi-detached house where Anna lived and the aroma of discarded lamp chop bones has me drooling onto the pavement. It must be time for a snack. I look up at Rose hopefully, but her eyes are fixed on Pearl and Varma. She chews her lower lip nervously.

'Go around the back,' Pearl directs Varma.

Pearl then puts his thumb on the doorbell and keeps it there. An upstairs casement window is flung open and a young woman, who isn't Zofia, leans out and yells, 'Piss off!' She has pale skin and light brown dreadlocks.

'Police!' Pearl says, holding up his warrant card. 'Are you Zofia Nowak?'

'I don't give a toss who you are.' She shuts the window, ignoring Pearl's question.

Of course, Rose could tell him the woman at the window isn't Zofia, but he doesn't ask. Pearl puts his thumb back onto the doorbell.

A face appears in the window of another bedroom. I recognise Zofia's long blond hair and the delicate features. I bark once to alert Rose.

'I've seen her,' Rose says. She lifts her hand and waves at Zofia.

Zofia disappears back into the room.

I listen intently and hear the two women having a heated conversation. A few seconds later the front door opens a few inches, still on its security chain, and the woman who told Pearl to go away glares at him through the gap. 'Do you have a warrant?'

'Do we need one, Miss?' Pearl asks, still simmering.

'This is not a good time. Come back later.'

'And who are you?'

'Mila De Vries.' She shoves long fingers into her baggy dungarees' pockets. She has a clipped way of speaking. 'And who are you?' she throws back at him, mimicking his delivery.

'Detective Inspector Pearl from Major Crime.' He pauses, perhaps expecting some kind of awe from Mila.

'So?' Mila shrugged, like she couldn't care a less.

'This is a murder investigation, Miss De Vries. I can come back. With a warrant. Better still, I'll serve the warrant when you're in a tutorial. Would you prefer that? The university wouldn't be happy, I'm sure of that.'

'Who is dead?' Mila is nothing if direct.

I'm guessing Mila doesn't yet know Anna is dead. Varma arrives, dirt on his shiny Oxfords from his reconnaissance of the back garden.

'I want to talk to Zofia Nowak,' Pearl says. 'Is she home?'

'Zofia is upset. She will not talk to you.' Mila looks across the street to where Rose leans against the side of her car, with me sitting next to her. 'She will only speak to Rose,' she says loud enough for Rose to hear.

I like Mila already.

'*Trainee* DC Sidebottom isn't working this case. Zofia will talk to me.'

Mila shakes her head. 'No, she won't. Rose or nobody.'

I swear I can see steam coming out of Pearl's ears. I also think I see Varma smirk, but he does a good job of concealing it. 'That's not possible.'

'She trusts Rose.'

Pearl looks over his shoulder at us, then back at Mila. He lets out an exasperated sigh.

'Okay, she can join us, but I ask the questions.'

Mila shrugs then cups her mouth with her hands and hollers across the street, 'Rose, Zofia wants to talk to you!'

Pearl frowns but he doesn't argue.

'Okay, Monty,' Rose says to me as we cross the road, 'Best behaviour, no matter what Pearl says.'

I walk to heel, determined to be a good dog. I will be good. I will be good.

'Not the dog, for Christ's sake,' Pearl says. 'Put him in the car.'

I can't restrain myself any longer. I lift a quivering back leg and aim for Pearl's trouser leg.

'The dog comes in,' Mila says. 'Zofia likes him.'

Just in time, I drop my leg. A dribble of wee hits the pavement but

Pearl's trousers remain dry. For now, anyway. The four of us follow Mila into the house.

'Are you a student?' Pearl asks Mila.

'I study Business Management.'

The house smells of stale beer, cigarettes, and smoked sausage. Never had smoked sausage but I'm game to try it.

We find Zofia in the sitting room, seated on one of two, unmatched, sagging sofas. One is a floral print, the other is pretending to be suede. Zofia is in knee-length boots, black woolly tights, a mini skirt and a pale pink roll-neck jumper. On a bamboo coffee table is a glass ashtray almost full to the brim with cigarette butts. Zofia holds a lit cigarette in a trembling hand. Mila sits on the fake-suede sofa's arm so that she is near Zofia.

'Are you Zofia Nowak?' Pearl asks, smoothing down his wavy hair, having no doubt noticed that Zofia is a very beautiful hooman. If she were a dog, she'd at least win her group at *Crufts,* and maybe even have a shot at Best in Show.

Zofia nods but looks past Pearl at Rose, who hovers a few feet away. 'You have found Anna?'

Rose moves closer to Mila and I stay close at heel. 'I'm so sorry, Zofia. We've found a body in Hinchley Wood.'

Pearl steps around us and sits next to Zofia on the fake suede sofa. 'I'm Detective Inspector Pearl. I'm in charge of the investigation. We haven't formally identified the deceased, but we have reason to believe she could be Anna Czubinska. I'm going to show you a photo. I need you to tell me if it is Anna.'

Pearl holds out his phone. On it is a different image to the one Rose had. Hers is of Anna part-buried in soil and leaves. Pearl's photo is of Anna lying peacefully on a metal table.

Zofia's face collapses and she drops the cigarette onto the bamboo coffee table. Varma picks it up and leaves it smoking on the edge of the ashtray. Zofia leans forward, clasping her stomach. She wails as if she is in agony, tears running down her cheeks. I want her to know I am sorry she has lost her friend, so I rest my chin on her hand and whimper. Zofia puts her other arm around me and sobs into my fur.

Zofia mutters between sobs. 'If only I had reported it.'

I feel wet, hot tears on my skin as they trickle through my fur. Her whole body trembles. Her grief reminds me of when I lost my mother, Summer. One day she was with us – me and my six brothers and sisters – and the next, she was gone. I was the first born and, I have to confess, the naughtiest. I wanted to explore everything: the house we lived in, the garden and the world beyond. I was only six weeks old when I escaped through the fence and almost got run over by a truck. Summer picked me up in her mouth and ran, narrowly avoiding being struck by the monstrous thing herself. At night, when the family was asleep, she would teach us about the ways of our forefathers and our roles, today, of hooman companion and working dog. The night before she disappeared, I was asleep, curled up between her muzzle and her chest, cosy and warm and protected. I'll never forget the regular beat of her heart and her smell which was like her name, summer.

'I'm very sorry to have to ask,' says Pearl, 'but is the woman in the photo Anna Czubinska?'

Zofia releases me from her grasp and sits up slowly but she doesn't have to answer because Mila speaks for her. 'Yes, it is Anna. We share this house.' Mila dabs her eyes with a tissue, but they look dry to me. 'Oh Zoffy.' Mila places an arm around her housemate.

'This must be very upsetting, Ms Nowak, but I have some questions. When did you first notice Anna was missing?'

Mila butts in, 'I can answer your questions.'

There is a tightening around Pearl's jaw, and he pauses before speaking in a surprisingly calm voice. 'Miss de Vries, can you please go with my colleague, DS Varma, who will ask you some questions.'

'I wouldn't mind a cup of tea,' Varma says. 'How about we chat in the kitchen?'

Mila hesitates, squeezes Zofia's shoulder, then leads Varma out of the room.

More tears run down Zofia's face. She looks across the coffee table at Rose. 'Please, come sit with me.'

'I must insist–' Pearl begins.

'Rose, come sit with me,' Zofia persists. 'Please Mr Pearl. I want to speak with Rose.'

I'm up and leading her to take Pearl's place. Pearl glares at Rose but retreats to the opposite sofa. Rose holds Zofia's hand.

'I wish I'd told you more,' says Zofia. 'Maybe Anna would be alive.

Everyone said not to worry. She's with her boyfriend, they said. Having a good time.'

Rose hands Zofia a fresh tissue from a box on the table. 'Tell me about Anna's boyfriend.'

'I do not know him. It is a secret.'

I watch Rose carefully. If Zofia is lying Rose will rock her feet from heel to toe and may also clench and unclench her hands to get rid of the stinging she feels whenever anyone doesn't tell the truth. But Rose's legs and arms stay still.

'Why is he a secret?'

'I don't know. Maybe he is married.'

'Who told you she had a boyfriend?'

'She did. She was so happy. She said he was smart. Treated her like a lady. Gave her gifts.'

'Do you have any idea where she met him?'

'No.'

'What was her relationship with Kacper Kowalski.'

Zofia looks down at her hands. 'We know him from Polish Society.'

'Okay, but what was her relationship with him?'

'She did not like him, but she had to be nice to him.'

'Why didn't she like him?'

'He flirted with her all the time. She did not like this.'

'Just flirted? Was there more?'

'He wanted more but had no chance. She was in love with her boyfriend.'

Pearl cuts in. 'Zofia, when did you last see Anna?'

Zofia closes her eyes. 'I can't think.'

'Take your time,' Rose says, squeezing her hand.

'Monday, around, I don't know, seven.'

'Morning or evening?' Pearl asks.

'Evening.'

'Where was she heading?' asks Pearl.

'To see her boyfriend, I guess. She did not say.'

'Does she own a car?'

'No. She takes the bus.'

'Did you see her board a bus?' says Pearl.

'No.'

'Did she have a part-time job?' Rose interjects, earning a withering stare from Pearl.

'Job?'

'Yes, in a restaurant, bar, something to help pay her tuition fees.'

Zofia looks away. 'I don't know.'

Rose's feet fidget. She flexes her fingers. Her lie-detector is working. Why would Zofia lie about Anna's job?

'I can't answer any more questions.' Zofia bolts from the room and up the stairs.

'I'll deal with this,' Pearl says, getting up. 'You've done enough damage.'

Rose and I wait. I think we both know that Zofia is hiding something. Rose's phone rings.

'You remember that favour you owe me?' Big Man Joe says.

'Yes.'

'I'm calling it in. Tonight.'

'Babysitting?' Rose is thinking of their one-year-old, Daniel.

'Not exactly.'

22

I lie on my belly in the kitchen of Duckdown Cottage and wonder why Rose is staring at the hot-water boiler and tugging at her hair.

'I don't believe it,' she mutters, flicking the boiler switch up and down, on and off. 'Of all nights.'

Betty pokes her head out of her hole.

'What's all the racket about?' she whispers.

I can't answer. If I do, Rose will hear me barking and she's already stressed.

'You smell lovely,' Betty says to me, her nose twitching. 'Let me guess. Ooh…cow manure?'

I nod.

Is Rose upset because I rolled in cow manure on our walk this afternoon? She threatened to shampoo me, which is my idea of total hell. Luckily, she only gave me a spray with the garden hose and then a towel dry. Betty and I know cow manure is more tenacious than that, even if Rose can't detect it with her hooman nose.

'How am I going to wash my hair without hot water? I can't go out like this,' Rose says, looking over her shoulder at me in my dog bed, as if I should have the answer. I could suggest she use the hose she just used on me, but she'd just tell me to stop barking. So I wag my tail and hope that will suffice. Commandment number ten always helps.

Rose races up the stairs mumbling something about a cold shower and catching pneumonia.

Once Rose is out of earshot I say, 'Rose was a champion today.'

I fill Betty in on the day's events while my friend nibbles on half a digestive biscuit. Lord knows where she found it, but Betty is a master at finding tasty morsels. Her back is propped against the wall and she methodically works her way around the biscuit in a clockwise direction.

'Do you think The Leach will give Rose her job back now?' I ask.

'Maybe. But coppers are as slippery as slugs, so who knows.'

'Rose is a copper and she's not slippery,' I say, feeling I should defend Rose's vocation.

'Yeah but Rose is different. She's a good egg. Most of 'em are as rotten as hell.'

From the bathroom, Rose shrieks. I trot over to the foot of the stairs. Listen. No more screams. I trot back into the kitchen and plonk down next to Betty, who is making good progress on her biscuit. The outer rim now has bite marks all the way around. It looks a bit like a flower.

'What's got you so jumpy?' she asks.

'I'm worried, Betty.'

'Wath about, my friend?' A crumb pops out of her mouth but she snatches it up in no time.

'Rose is going out without me tonight. I won't be there to protect her.'

'Who's she meeting?'

'Big Man Joe and his friends.'

Betty pauses in her nibbling and lets the biscuit rest against her stomach. 'Whath wrong with that? Ith about time she had some fun. She's been down in the dumps for far too long.'

'But I go with her everywhere. Why won't she take me with her?'

Betty stares at me with a toothy grin. 'Well, bless me if you ain't jealous.'

I lift my head, shocked at the idea. 'I'm not jealous. What if she gets into trouble?'

'Nah, you're jealous, my friend. And that's understandable, given what you've both been through. You two's been to hell and back with all those crackpot killers. But it's like this, see,' Betty says, wagging a diminutive claw at me, 'When you love someone, the hardest thing to do is let them go. Take it from me. It broke my heart each time I said goodbye to my pups when they left my nest. I fretted something rotten. But I had to let them find their own way.'

'You're saying I've got to let Rose find her own way?'

'Sorta. More like you gotta let her have a life beyond just you.'

I drop my chin to the floor, crest-fallen. Rose is my bestest buddy. If she finds her own way, what happens to me?

Upstairs, the sound of running water stops. That was the shortest shower I think Rose has ever had. I can hear her making strange *brrr* buzzing noises like a bee, which are soon drowned out by the whine of a hairdryer. I look down and find Betty has put her biscuit aside and is hugging my paw.

'There, there, Mr Monty. Why don't you fink of something else, like finding that Labrador pup. Poor fella. He's a clue, an' all.'

I stare at her blankly.

'He smelt of the dead girl, remember?'

I jerk my head up, suddenly remembering my chat with Biscuit and Lolly at St Martha's village. 'I got a lead today.'

Betty rolls off my paw laughing. 'Good one, Mr Monty.'

I have no idea what she's laughing at and decide to keep going. 'The Retrievers told me an Airedale Terrier pup went missing a few days ago from the village. They heard him barking, calling out for help, but they were shut in the house and there was nothing they could do. They said they saw a white van racing away from the village.'

Betty has her serious face on. 'That's terrible news. But what's that got to do with the Labrador pup?'

I blink a few times. 'I don't know. It just popped into my head. It means the dognappers are active again.'

Rose spits out a tiny crumb into her paw. 'You what? Dognappers? When were you going to tell me about them?'

'Sorry, Betty, there's so much going on, my head is too full to remember everything.'

'Well go on then, who are these dognappers?'

'We don't know. The wee-vine is buzzing with rumours and

speculation. But young dogs are disappearing from homes and even from vet's. Word is that my vet is going to be hit soon.'

'Does Rose know about this?'

'It's been on the news but she doesn't know that Malcolm could be next.'

'Right, this requires planning.' Betty stamps on her biscuit and it breaks into four pieces. She separates them. 'Okay, this piece is Anna. Our job is to make sure Rose solves the case so The Leach will have to reinstate her. Right?'

'Right,' I say.

She points to the second piece of biscuit. 'This is the chocolate Labrador. He's a clue, so I'm moving this piece close to Anna.' She does exactly that. 'This third piece is the dognapping. I'll put it over there because it's a separate case. Seems to me we need to warn your vet to be on the lookout.'

'I've warned his dog.'

'Good but, with dognappers, that might not be enough. So we have to warn your vet.'

'How?'

'No idea. You?'

I ponder this. 'Rose listens to the radio a lot. When there's a story about the dognapping I could hold up something to make her think about the vet. You know, so she links the two things – the vet and the dognapping.'

Betty nods her little head slowly. 'What you got that will make her think of the vet?'

'A box of nasty tablets he gave Rose for me to take. There are some left and she kept them.' I trot over to a corner countertop where Rose keeps some cookery books and my tablets and a bottle of what she calls Vitamin C. I look around to make sure Rose isn't watching me. Then I put my front paws up on the counter edge to make sure I can reach the tablets. I give them a nudge with my nose then drop back down and give Betty a grin.

'Good work, Mr Monty.'

'What about the fourth bit of biscuit, Betty?'

'Let me see, are there any other clues we should follow up?'

'Hold on a tick, I'll sniff my bed.' I push my nose into the soft padding and inhale deeply. The smells resonate in the way the sound of Big Ben lingers after it's struck. Everything that has happened over the last week comes flooding back. I lift my head. 'John Clapper. He lied when he said he didn't recognise Anna. And the hooman who shot at us was on Clapper's land. That can't be coincidence, can it?'

'Now that's an important clue, Mr Monty. Could John be Anna's secret boyfriend?'

'I don't know, but he's a grumpy old man so I can't imagine what Anna would see in him.'

'Money, maybe? Sometimes we make terrible mistakes when it comes to the males in our lives. I did. Five times. Bastards. All of them.' She shoves the fourth piece of biscuit next to the one she christened as Anna. 'John Clapper is another clue that must be investigated.'

'You're right, Betty. But there's the not insignificant problem of Tank.'

'Tank?'

'A Rottweiler. He guards the place. Big and dangerous.'

'Oooh! Nasty.' Betty taps a claw against her chin. 'One thing at a time. We can't warn Rose about the dognappers until there's a story on the radio. But we can find out what John Clapper is hiding. Because he's definitely hiding something.'

'Clapper's Farm is even further away than Pawfect Pets. How are we going to get there?'

'I can't believe I'm about to say this.' She shakes her head.

'What is it?'

'We could ask Mr Snooty-Pants to take a look. Fly over the farm, like them drones do. Although I was hoping I'd never have to see that strutting, stuck-up pain in the proverbial again.'

23

The White House pub sat on the bank of the River Wey in the heart of Geldeford and, as you might expect, was painted white. In summer, revellers sat outside on benches, much to the delight of the ducks that pecked at scraps and the occasional hot chip tossed their way. Given it was a brisk winter's night, a log fire was burning and the drinkers were all ensconced in the cosy interior.

Since Rose's social life had dwindled to almost zero over the last few months, the pub's refurbished interior came as a surprise. It was now a gastro-pub with butchers' paper on the tables, bentwood chairs and a high-backed, button-upholstered banquette along one wall. Joe and Rose sat near the bar in a booth that was large enough to seat six. Rose had already gulped down her first glass of chardonnay to calm her nerves. She now wished she hadn't, because she felt a little light-headed.

'I can't believe you talked me into this,' she said.

Joe threw back the last mouthful of his pint. 'Oh come on Rose, you make it sound like I've asked you to wrestle a python. I invited a few mates along. Nice guys. Malcolm's coming. You know Malcolm.'

Yes she knew her vet. Malcolm invited her to tonight's gathering, but at the time she'd thought it was a boys' night. At least she could chat to him about his work if she got stuck. And at least he wasn't going to try to chat her up. She was worried about the other guys, though. She had a sneaking suspicion Joe was trying to set her up with one of them.

'You know I find this sort of thing excruciating. I'm not good at small talk. Or with people I don't know.'

'You'll be fine. Just an hour or two. That's all I ask, okay?'

She nodded. 'What's Sarah doing tonight?'

'Got her friend, Edwina, round for a night of wine, popcorn and romance movies.'

Rose tried not to let it show that she'd much rather be joining Sarah and Edwina. 'I know you mean well, Joe, but I don't need a boyfriend.'

In fact, a boyfriend was the last thing she needed. She was putting her all into trying to impress Leach. Which reminded her, she had an appointment with the psychiatrist on Monday. She'd have to make sure she had the right answers to Dr Doom's questions.

'I'm not trying to find you a boyfriend. Honest.' Joe's cheeky grin said otherwise, as did the tingling in her feet and hands.

The pub was packed and getting increasingly hot. Rose tugged at her black cowl-neck jumper. Joe was one of the few people who knew that she took medication for her anxiety.

'I'm not ready for this.'

He put an arm around her shoulders. 'Come on, mate. This'll be fun. Look, there's George now.' Joe stood and waved.

Two men, both with crewcuts, weaved their way through the press of people to their booth. Joe had mentioned one of his mates was on leave from the Army.

'Mate, good to see you,' Joe said, shaking the darker man's hand, then he introduced her. 'Rose is a detective. Rose, this is George Ricci, or should I say Corporal Ricci?'

George was short and stocky with dark stubble around his chin. He shook Rose's hand. 'Good to meet you.' Then he gestured to the man with him. 'Lance Corporal Steven Bartlett. He's kipping at my place for a couple a days. Didn't think you'd mind if he tagged along.' He rubbed his hands together. 'Up for a big session, are we?'

Steven was tall with startling green eyes. Rose thought he was the most stunning man she'd seen in a long time. He took her hand, leaned forward, and kissed it. 'A pleasure to meet you, Rose.'

Rose's heart felt as though it was leaping out of her chest. Nobody had ever kissed her hand before.

George winked at her. 'Watch him, he's a real charmer. Right. Who's up for a pint?'

Joe was habitually affable, but Rose briefly caught him looking darkly at the uninvited guest. 'I was going to the bar,' Joe said. 'What's your poison?'

Joe took everyone's order and then he and George headed for the bar, which was four or five deep with patrons trying to do the same. This left Rose with Steven. He sat next to her, the warmth of his thigh touching hers.

'How do you know Joe?' he asked.

Rose blinked at him like a mole emerging into the light of day. *Say something, for goodness sake!* 'Police college. We trained together. We now work Major Crime. And you? How do you know him?'

'I don't. George dragged me along. Glad he did.' He smiled. Rose gazed at his perfect teeth. 'We're on leave for a week. Got bored at me parents place, so I sprung a surprise visit on Georgie.'

It was her turn to say something. Oh God! 'Where was your last tour of duty?' At least it wasn't an idiotic question.

'Ukraine.' Steven regaled her with a couple of hair-raising stories and Rose was happy to listen. It meant she didn't have to think of something funny or intelligent to say and besides, he was a good storyteller. Before long she found herself laughing. Perhaps Joe was right after all about getting out of the house?

'Er, hello, Rose.'

She tore her attention away from Steven. She hardly recognised Malcolm. Had he had a haircut? His wild hair was mostly tamed. He wore a leather jacket instead of his usual Barbour. He smiled nervously, then flicked a glance at Steven.

'Hello, Malcolm. Good to see you,' Rose said. 'Joe's at the bar. If you hurry, you might still be able to get an order in.'

Malcolm's gaze hopped from her to Steven. 'Hi.' He shook Steven's hand. 'Well, I'll…I'll just get a drink then.'

He swivelled on his heels, took a step towards the bar, then turned back. 'You look lovely, Rose.' He then darted off to the bar.

She gawped after him, wondering why he was behaving so oddly.

'Anyway,' said Steven. 'There we were in this bar and we had no idea what they were gassing on about and…'

George and Joe returned clutching pints and a glass of white wine for her. But no Malcolm. 'Did you see Malcolm? He was on his way to the bar,' she asked.

'No. It's like a mosh pit,' Joe said.

Joe and George sat and they all clinked glasses. Rose took a small sip.

'So, a detective, hey?' said George, after a gulp of his Guinness. 'I bet you meet some real freaks.' For the next few minutes George quizzed Rose about her job. Malcolm finally rejoined them, clasping a pint of Old Speckled Hen. He took off his leather jacket and sat next to Joe.

'You a copper too?' Steve asked Malcolm.

'Vet.' He cleared his throat. 'Sorry I'm a bit late. Had an emergency. Dog got hit by a car.'

'Oh no,' said Rose. 'Is he all right?'

'Lost a leg but he should recover well. How's Monty?'

'He's fine. Managed to roll in a cow pat this afternoon, which stank to high heaven. Very proud of himself, too. I had to hose him off when I got home. How's little B getting on?'

Malcolm leaned back and seemed to relax. 'She's a funny one. Patrols the surgery at night as if she's a guard dog. Unusual behaviour for a Cavalier King Charles.'

'What are you doing with a lapdog, you big girl,' says George, playfully punching Malcolm in the arm.

'She was abandoned. Maybe that explains why she's edgy, like someone's going to come and take her away.'

'She's probably got abandonment issues,' suggests Rose.

'Come off it,' said Steven. 'Dogs don't think like us. They're just dumb animals.'

Rose blinked rapidly with embarrassment. Malcolm spoke, 'Many dog breeds are highly intelligent. They sniff out explosives, guide blind people across roads, even detect cancer. And Rose's dog is in a league of his own. There's a special connection between them. It's like he anticipates what she wants.'

Rose blushed. She didn't like being the focus of attention.

'Come off it, mate,' said Steven. 'I was brought up on a farm. The sheep dogs obeyed commands. That's all. There was no telepathy.'

'It's true,' said Joe. 'Monty saved Rose's life.'

'Yeah and that's just obeying a command,' argued Steven.

'No, I didn't tell him to do it,' said Rose, wishing someone would open a window. It was way too hot in here.

'I reckon, well, you two have this special relationship,' said Malcolm. Steven chuckled. 'Oh yes?'

Rose flushed as though she was standing right in front of the fireplace. Why was Malcolm doing this? It made her sound like some kind of weirdo. She looked at him, imploring him to drop it, but he was staring at his pint glass.

'It's like. I don't know, I mean it's like you're bonded in a way, like a mother and child or something.'

Rose caught her breath sharply. She had no desire to marry, let alone have kids. Why was Malcolm saying Monty was a child substitute? Why was he embarrassing her like this?

'No, he's my dog. I love him, but he's my dog.' Rose glowered at him. 'Can we please change the subject now?'

'Oh no, I didn't mean to…your relationship with Monty is great. It's like…you know, with single parents, sometimes they become very close to their kids.'

'So I'm a single mum, now! Well, I'll have you know I like being single and I most definitely don't mother Monty.' Rose stood, grabbed her coat. 'If you'll excuse me, I have to be somewhere.'

She dived for the exit. Joe called after her, but she ignored him. She threw the door open and gulped down the chill air.

'Wait! Rose!' Malcolm ran after her. 'I'm so sorry. It came out wrong. Don't leave.'

She rounded on him. 'All my life I've been an outsider. The weirdo. Nobody wanted to be my friend, Malcolm. You know why?' She didn't give him a chance to reply. 'Because I know when people lie to me, and people lie all the time. It does my head in knowing how fake everyone is. My dog, and only my dog, understands me. He's my best friend and you made that sound weird and creepy.'

'I didn't mean to. It's the last thing I meant to do. I like you, Rose, I really—'

'I can't talk to you.'

Rose ran away.

 24

I grip the handle of a torch in my mouth and point the brilliant beam into the leafless upper branches of the oak tree in the back corner of the garden. The torch's smooth handle and my drool do not go well together. It slips from between my teeth and lands on the ground, narrowly missing Betty, who sits close by.

'Careful, Mr Monty,' she says.

I pick up the black metal torch again and lean it against a flowerpot so that the beam points up at the night sky. I gently let go. It stays put. I'm hoping the light will attract Dante's attention, although I can't know for certain if he's in the neighbourhood. One thing I am sure of, though, is that Dante loves bright shiny things and the torch beam can be seen from afar.

Betty scampers into the winter-flowering heather and hides there.

'I won't let him eat you,' I say.

In reality Betty is too big for a bird like Dante to carry away.

'He's tried before.'

'And I stopped him. I'll look after you.'

In the distance, I hear a sound like a lawnmower that won't start even though somebody repeatedly pulls the cord. The noise comes from the sky. Moments later, movement fractures the torch's beam. Blueish-green feathers glisten like gems. A white belly lights up like a star. Black eyes glisten with indignation. Dante, a magpie, swoops across the beam again, then lands next to me.

'How dare you disturb my rest?!'

Dante rears up, his wings extended to their full reach. He puffs out his white chest, which gleams in the glow of the torch. I take a step back. Dante's beak is sharp and he has been known to stab it at creatures he dislikes, not just those he wants to eat.

'We need your help, Dante,' I say.

'I am not bloody Batman!' Dante says, folding his wings.

'Don't flatter yourself,' mutters Betty, hunkered down in the heather.

Dante's sleek black head reminds me of a hangman's hood. He swivels it to look at Betty. 'Ah, Ratty. I thought you were dead. What a shame.'

Betty sits up on her hind legs. 'Don't call me Ratty. It's derogatory.'

'Big word for a little rat,' Dante mocks.

Betty has clearly forgotten her fear because she waddles over to stand in front of Dante. 'Don't you go all high-and-mighty with me. I may be a rat but I ain't no thief, let alone a dumb thief at that.'

Dante spreads his wings again and shrieks. It's deafening. Thank goodness Rose isn't home. Unfortunately, the ducks are startled out of their sleep and rush around in circles, quacking. Henrietta shrieks, 'Run for your lives!' which only makes matters worse.

'Henny!' I say. 'He's here for a chat. That's all. Please calm down.'

The ducks charge for the water where they feel safest. They will probably spend the next few hours conspiring against me for bringing a magpie into the garden. In fact, I'm surprised Nigel hasn't arrived to issue me another warning.

Dante towers over Betty. 'I am not just any thief, my dear Ratty. I am this country's most renowned jewellery thief.' A shiver runs through him as he revels in his own notoriety. 'I am so clever that hoomans think I'm hooman. They can't believe a magpie can do what I do.'

Betty squints at Dante. 'Bless my soul. You're wearing pearls.'

'What?' Dante looks down at Betty, and then cranes his head. With his beak, he taps the rows of pearls looped around his neck several times. 'Ah. Forgot that was there.' He looks at me coyly. 'Looks good on me, doesn't it?'

'You vain bugger,' Betty says. 'It's a wonder you can ever drag yourself away from the mirror.'

'At least I am deserving of admiration.'

'Please stop, both of you,' I say. 'This is going nowhere.' I wait for Dante and Betty to look at me. 'We called you here, Dante, because we need your help. Do you know about the murdered hooman in Hinchley Wood?'

'Of course.'

'We want Rose to solve the case. If she does, she'll get her job back. So we're helping her.'

'I wasn't aware she had lost it.'

'Only temporarily. Anyway, we think there's something fishy going on at Clapper Farm.'

'How so?'

'Rose asked John Clapper if he knew the murdered girl and he denied it. But he was lying.'

'I see. And what do you require of me?'

'Reconnaissance. John is hiding something, I'm sure of it. We want you to fly over his farm, look in windows, eavesdrop on conversations and report back.'

'And what exactly am I looking and listening for?'

'Evidence he knew Anna Czubinska. A young woman, brown hair. Maybe she worked there?'

Dante goose-steps up and down as he considers my request, his long claws glistening in the torchlight.

'You do realise John Clapper has a shotgun and enjoys nothing better than killing birds like me.'

'Yes, I know. Someone, and I suspect John, shot at me the other day,' I say. 'But I don't think he'll be outside shooting at night, do you?'

'One never knows. I'll need insurance,' Dante says.

'Insurance?' I scratch one ear in confusion.

'You may call it payment, if you like.'

Betty stamps her paw. 'Friends don't ask for payment.'

'What on earth makes you think I'm your friend?' he replies. His nasal tone drips with derision.

'No, you're too bloody full of yourself, ain't ya, Mr I'm-named-after-a piss-boring-poet!'

'Ratty, you're showing your ignorance. Dante's *Divine Comedy* has been revered throughout the ages.'

'Bloody stupid name for a magpie, anyway,' Betty grumbles.

'Can we get back to talking about Clapper Farm? Dante, what do you mean by payment?' I ask.

'I haven't decided. You will owe me a favour.'

Betty is suddenly tugging at the fur on my front leg. 'Don't do it. It's a deal with the devil. Once you owe a magpie, they own you forever.'

'Oh hush Ratty. You're being melodramatic,' says Dante.

'Now look here, Dante,' Betty says. 'You have to be specific about what you want from Monty, or there's no deal.'

Dante nods. 'The boy, Oliver Fernsby. I've seen you with him. He has something of mine, and I want it back. You, Monty, will get it for me.'

'Ollie?' I say. 'Wears glasses?'

'That's the one.'

Betty and I stare at each other. What could the boy possibly have that Dante would want?'

25

A car crawls up the drive, crunching gravel. I am immediately awake. Is Rose back already? I leave my dog bed and dash into the sitting room at the front of the house. I press my nose against the window, my breath instantly condensing on the frigid glass. Hares, caught in the headlights, are momentarily dazzled, then leap out of the way, somersaulting into bushes like a furry Cirque du Soleil troupe. I know it's Rose's car from the sound of the engine.

I race through the kitchen and out of the back door, bolt down the side passage and greet Rose as she steps out of her car. She crouches down and takes me in a tight hug, resting her cheek in the fur of my back.

'You're always so pleased to see me, aren't you, my friend?'

Oh yes, *super* pleased. My tail wags, well actually it's really my tail and whole bottom doing the wagging, and I nuzzle her jumper, picking up the smell of beer and crisps and the scent of hoomans I don't know.

'I wish I'd never gone.' A hiccup in her voice tells me she is upset.

I walk with her into the house. I catch a whiff of Big Man Joe and then Malcolm the vet. They are both nice hoomans, so why is Rose upset? I dive at my bed where my fluffy toy duck lies, still warm from when I rested my head on it. I pick it up and offer it to Rose, who is switching on the kettle.

'Is that for me?' she asks. I nudge the toy duck against her thigh. She takes it. 'A bit gooey but thank you.' She then stares at my gift for a while with a faraway look. 'Am I a weirdo because I talk to you?'

That's like saying I'm a weirdo because I talk to Betty. I sit and bark twice which is me saying no you are not.

'Oh well, I am what I am.' She ruffles my ears. I love it when she does that. 'And you know what else?' I tilt my head to one side, waiting for the answer. 'I love you and I don't care what people think and I'm going to have another glass of wine and I don't care if I feel like crap tomorrow.'

I like the feisty tone of her voice. She sounds much more positive.

She takes a half-full white wine bottle from the fridge, pours a large glass and takes a gulp as if she's really thirsty.

I catch a glimpse of my prescription medicine: a box containing a blister pack of tablets from the Geldeford Vet Hospital. Now's not the time. It has to be when there's a news story about dogs disappearing, otherwise she won't make the connection.

Rose takes the bottle and her glass into the sitting room and collapses into the sofa. She kicks her shoes off and tucks her feet beneath her, then pulls a blanket over her. She picks up the remote control and switches on the TV, flicking through the stations. She lands on a repeat of the local six o'clock news. The Leach appeals for anyone who knows Anna to come forward. 'I bet you John Clapper won't come forward,' Rose says, then peers at me. 'We both know he knows her, don't we?'

I bark once. You bet we do!

The next story is about the Airedale Terrier that disappeared from a back garden in St Martha's. I get up so fast I knock the coffee table with my rump and the wine bottle wobbles. Rose lunges forward and grips the neck of it.

'Whoopsy!' she giggles.

I race to the kitchen, rear up, place my front paws on the countertop and grab the box of tablets. I race back to the sitting room and hold the box so she can see the label.

'Out the way, Monty, I'm watching TV.' A breeder is on screen talking about her prize Cavoodle that was stolen last week.

I drop the packet in Rose's lap.

'Don't remind me,' Rose says, staring at the box as if I'd dropped a dead mouse in her lap. 'I don't want to think about him.'

Does she mean Malcolm? This could be a problem.

Rose throws the box across the sofa. It ends up wedged between two cushions. She tops up her glass. 'And anyway,' she says, slurring her words, 'I like being single. You, me, this place and my job. That's all I want. Just get my job back, then life is perfect.'

Plan A isn't working. I need a Plan B. I sit and scratch my ear while I think. I don't know if it helps, but it feels good. Ah, that's it. I trot into the study, which is always somewhat fraught because of the precariously stacked piles of books on the floor and the tendency of my tail to do whatever it pleases. Fortunately, I navigate my way to Rose's desk without toppling any books. There are papers on top of it. She keeps my vet bills in a blue folder. I hope she hasn't put them away yet.

If you're wondering how I know that the blue folder contains invoices from Geldeford Vet Hospital, I need to tell you where I came from and my unusual training.

I was born into a litter destined to become Guide Dogs. My mother, Summer, had the calm temperament, patience and intelligence to be a Guide Dog and she was selected to deliver new Guide Dog puppies into the world. She was suddenly taken from us when we were six weeks old so my brothers and sisters and I were given to various foster parents who would prepare us for our Guide Dog training. I went to the Collum family in Windsor and my foster dad, John, was a gardener at the castle. Anyway, I didn't make it through Guide Dog School, to my eternal shame, and a lovely professor, Patrick Salt, adopted me. This was before I met Rose.

Paddy, as he was known, was fascinated by how insects and animals communicate within their species and cross-species. I became his guinea pig – at least that's what he said, although I'm pretty sure I always stayed a dog. Anyway, he taught me the basics of hooman language. I don't mean commands like sit, stay and stand; we all learn those. I mean the hooman alphabet and what words mean. Patrick taught me to read some basic words, which is how I can recognise "vet" on the piece of paper I need to show Rose.

I carry a vet's bill in my mouth and try not to crumple it too much.

I present it to Rose. She's slumped into the back of the sofa, her lids heavy with drowsiness. The glass she was drinking from is empty. I bob my chin on the top of her thigh, tapping it, and her eyes spring open.

'What is that?'

Rose takes the invoice and seems to have difficult reading it because she squints. The TV story about disappearing dogs has ended. Now there's an overly cheery woman on screen predicting stormy weather.

'I've paid it.' She drops it on the coffee table and yawns.

I pick up the piece of paper and stand in front of the TV and wave it about.

'I don't know what's got into you Monty,' she slurs, 'but I need my bed.'

Rose struggles to get up. After several attempts she stands.

I watch her climb the stairs, clinging to the rail as if she were climbing a mountain and it was her lifeline. Within minutes she is snoring her bedroom. Even my Plan B has failed.

I fall asleep at the foot of the stairs, hoping that Malcolm's puppy is as ferocious as she likes to think she is. Because she's all that stands between dognappers and the poor dogs recovering from surgery at the vet hospital.

26

Rose likes to sleep in on Saturdays. Last night, she left the back door ajar so that I don't have to wake her for my morning pee. I wander to the front gate post and sniff for new wee-mails. There's plenty of fearful chatter but no leads on who the dognappers are or where they come from.

I wander back to the house, using every ounce of self-control I have to ignore the ducks. I find a comfortable spot at the foot of the stairs and curl up to wait for Rose. I don't need a clock to tell me time is passing. The birds ceased their dawn chorus a while ago. A neighbour who always leaves at eight thirty for her food shopping has driven away. At nine o'clock I hear the clack of horses' hooves on the road as the kiddie's riding school leaves for the first trek of the day across Winterfold Heath. I've never known Rose to sleep in this long. Is she ill?

I creep upstairs and accidentally hit the creaky step. I freeze. All I want to do is check she's okay. There's no sound from Rose, so I keep going. There are two bedrooms and a bathroom. The door to what was her Aunt Kay's room is closed. I think it makes Rose sad to go in there and she loved her aunt so much she can't bear to change a thing. I've only ever ventured into that room once. I'll admit the dolls with their glassy eyes and curled eyelashes freaked me a little but otherwise it would be cosy and inviting, if it wasn't for the faint but pervasive smell of illness.

The other bedroom door is open. I find Rose curled up in a ball with the duvet tucked under her chin and her hair strewn over the pillow, mouth open, snoring like a piglet. Her clothes are strewn over the carpet and the room smells of wine.

I put my nose close to her face. My breath makes the fine hair around her temples flutter. I sniff deeply but quietly, getting the smells up into the back of my nose where the magic happens. The alcohol almost drowns out her usual scent, and the strength of it makes me stagger a little. I also get stale cigarettes, wood smoke, lingering hints of Big Man Joe, Malcolm the vet, and several other people I don't recognise, but there's nothing else out of the ordinary there. I step back and let out my breath slowly.

Then I hear Dante's distinctive dodgy-lawn-mower screech coming from the back garden. I zip down the stairs, run outside and find him marching up and down one of the oak's lower branches. He spies me and stands to attention.

'Get over here right now. I don't have all day,' he orders.

I sit on the grass and peer up at Dante, back straight as if I'm at a military academy.

'What did you find out?' I almost say 'sir' and only just stop myself.

'I completed several fly-overs of Clapper Farm last night. I can report the following. There are many dogs on the property, probably hunting hounds. I saw only one guard dog. Tank may be big and fangy but he's not very bright. I landed several times inside the perimeter and he didn't even notice.'

I suspect birds fly over the farm all the time, so I'm not surprised that Tank didn't notice Dante. 'That's good to know. What else?'

'One visitor, probably his son, left shortly after I arrived.'

'I didn't know John had a son. What did he look like?'

'I would hazard a guess he's no more than twenty, but hooman ages are hard to discern. He had tattoos on his hands. Wore one of those items of clothing hoomans call hoodies. He wasn't happy, I can tell you. Shouted at John as he left, slammed his car door.'

'Did you hear what he said?'

'By the time I was close enough, he had driven away.'

'Can you describe the car?'

'It was dark, Monty. All I can tell you is that it was very noisy, like a racing car, even though it was about the size of Rose's vehicle.'

'Were you able to look inside the house?'

'I'm glad you asked me that.' Dante preens his wings before he continues. 'I had no problem gaining entry. John left his bedroom window open just enough for me to slip through. Furniture was a bit tired. Stylish though. Loads of fox hunting paintings on the walls. And this might interest you. There's a framed photograph of John shaking hands with the Police Commissioner, and another one of him shaking hands with the Mayor.'

'So?'

'So John is well connected, dummy. If Rose starts investigating him without her boss's permission, she could land herself in serious hot water.'

I don't like the sound of that.

'Any evidence of Anna?'

'Not that I could see.'

I scratch my ear. 'I don't understand. There must be. He definitely knew her.'

'Hoomans are fallible, just like the rest of us. Perhaps Rose was mistaken. I suggest you consider other suspects.'

I'm still scratching my ear, racking my memory for another suspect. So far the only other person who knew Anna and lied to Rose was Kacper, and he's been questioned by the police. I can't help being disappointed. My only lead is a dead end.

'One more thing,' Dante says. 'He's in financial trouble.'

I look up. 'John? How do you know?'

'In his study, there's a letter from his bank. His mortgage payments are overdue.'

Dante may well be full of himself, but he is the cleverest creature I've ever met. The reason why Dante has never been caught stealing jewellery is because he understands how security cameras work and, like me, he can read. And while I'd never admit it to his face, Dante has a far more extensive vocabulary than me.

'Mortgage?'

Rose's bedroom window opens. I know, even though I have my back to the house, because the frame catches briefly and makes a grating sound. 'Stop making that racket. I'm trying to sleep.' Rose shuts the window.

'Oops,' I say.

Dante hops down to the ground. He lowers his voice. 'Mortgages are how hoomans buy their homes. Farms too,' says Dante. 'It's complicated. How shall I explain it?' Dante speaks to everyone as if they were an idiot, so I don't take offence. 'Their lives would be vastly easier if they built their homes themselves, like we birds do, instead of borrowing those ridiculous notes and coins.' Dante leans forward so his long, sharp beak points directly at me. 'What I'm saying is that John needs to pay the bank a lot of money or he could lose his home.'

I don't like John, but it saddens me that he might lose his home.

'I have done my bit,' says Dante. 'You now have to do yours.'

'The favour? The thing Ollie has that you want? I can't steal from the boy, Dante. It's not right.'

'He has a photo of a magpie in his room. I want it. I don't care how you get it.'

'Is it of you?'

Dante doesn't answer. He takes off and is soon little more than a speck of black in the morning sky.

From inside the house, I hear the unmistakable sound of Rose vomiting. Perhaps she is ill after all? I run through the kitchen and race up the stairs to find Rose with her head over the toilet bowl. She flushes the toilet, turns around and attempts to sit. She almost misses the seat and very nearly ends up on the floor.

'Dizzy,' she mumbles.

Her skin is white and clammy. I can see pinpricks of perspiration on her forehead. I pant in her face, hoping my concern shows in my eyes.

'Not doggie breath,' she says, gagging.

Rose grasps a basin tap with one hand and pulls herself to her feet. She then throws cold water over her face and dries it with a towel.

'Why did I do it?' she says.

Do what? Vomit?

Gripping the banister rail, she descends the stairs slowly, then shuffles like an old lady into the kitchen.

We have a morning routine. While the kettle boils, Rose feeds me, then makes herself a strong cup of tea with a dash of milk. This morning, she pours milk into the kettle. When she turns it on, the smell of hot milk fills the kitchen.

'Oh no.' She switches it off and pours the milk down the sink.

Rose is unable to open her eyes properly and mutters about the brightness. She takes her sunglasses from her handbag and puts them on. The kettle is washed out, refilled with water and set to boil again. Rose slumps into a kitchen chair, with a tea bag on a string dangling from a limp hand.

'Oh Monty, I feel like crap.'

Rose is definitely unwell. First the vomiting. Now she can't remember how to make tea. Maybe I should take her to the vet? I'm sure Malcolm could make her better. The tea bag slips through her fingers and lands on the floor. When the kettle boils she leans down to pick up the teabag, emitting a soft groan as she does. Her second attempt at making tea is more successful. She takes a big sip.

'That's better.'

Rose grabs a frying pan, then peers into an almost empty fridge. 'Please tell me we have bacon.' Sighing, she shuts the fridge door. 'I really must go food shopping.' She squints at me. 'I guess it's a bacon butty from Mama Jo's. And two pain killers.'

Mama Jo's happens to be my second favourite place after the McDonald's Drive Thru. I take this as a sign that Rose does not need to be rushed to the vet.

Rose shuffles upstairs to shower. A few minutes later I hear the sound of running water and a scream. I guess she forgot there's no hot water. I stare at my empty food bowl. My stomach rumbles. I hope Rose means to buy two bacon butties.

A vibrating noise comes from Rose's handbag. I nudge the bag with my nose and her mobile phone slides out enough for me to see the caller ID: *Mum*. Eventually it stops buzzing.

Rose appears in the kitchen in a sweatshirt that she has on inside out. She shoves her mobile phone back into her bag and grabs her car keys. She sways. 'Maybe I shouldn't drive.' She drops her car keys on the table. 'Come on Monty, looks like it's the village shop. I'll do a fry up. Best cure for a hangover there is.'

27

Rose sat on a fallen tree trunk and watched Monty bound across Winterfold Heath, jumping heather, diving through bracken, and slaloming between fir trees. The fry up had quelled the nausea, but she still felt dizzy if she moved too quickly. What a fool she'd been to polish off that bottle of wine!

In the light of day, she wasn't even sure why she had been so upset with Malcolm last night. He was right: she was probably closer to Monty than she was to anyone else. He made her smile. He simply accepted her for who she was. His company was an unerring antidote to her anxiety or when she wondered what the point of it all was. And to make matters worse, she'd left in a strop like some kind of prima donna. Poor Malcolm. She owed him an apology, but it would have to wait until she could string a coherent sentence together, because right now her brain had been replaced with pea soup.

A pheasant burst into the air with a clattering call. Monty barked as though he was sounding a cavalry charge and bounded through the heather after the bird, clearly having the best time. Her phone rang. It was Jenny. Perhaps she wanted to meet up over the weekend? That would be nice.

'This isn't a social call, I'm afraid,' Jenny began. 'I've got Anna's parents coming in to identify their daughter.' Rose's stomach churned. Watching parents say goodbye to their dead child tore her up. She couldn't imagine how dreadful it must be for them. 'Zofia's here already. She's going to translate. But she just said something odd. I don't know if it's significant and I can't get hold of Leach or Pearl. Maybe it's nothing.'

'What did she say?'

'She said she was going to stay with Anna's parents at their motel. I assumed it was to comfort them. But she said it was because she wanted to stay away from Mila.'

'Her housemate?'

'Yes.'

'Why?'

'Wouldn't say. But she's definitely on edge.'

Rose had suspected all along that Zofia knew more about Anna's death than she had let on. 'When are the parents arriving?'

'In thirty minutes. A PC is picking them up from the airport. Pearl was meant to be meeting them but there's been a mix up. He's won't get here for at least an hour.'

Much as Rose wanted to find out why Zofia wanted to stay away from Mila, she knew that if she trod on Pearl's toes he would go straight to Leach. 'Tell Pearl when he arrives.'

'I will but she's already said she doesn't want Pearl here. She's afraid he'll upset Zofia's parents.'

'I wish I could help, but Pearl has to be the one to talk to her. Or Varma.'

'Okay,' Jenny said, 'but expect a call. You seem to be the only copper she trusts.'

Jenny's call had cleared her head. Murders were usually committed by people close to the victim. Mila might be involved somehow. 'Monty! Come!'

Way off in the distance, she spotted his golden tail and head poking out of the bracken. He broke free of the foliage and bounded towards her.

'Time to go home.' She needed a very, very strong cup of coffee.

Forty minutes later, Rose was seated on a purple chair in the mortuary's reception. On the wall behind Rose's head was a corkboard and pinned to it were cards of thanks for the kind words and compassionate treatment the bereaved had received.

Zofia had refused to talk to Pearl about Mila – she would only talk to Rose – which was why Rose was there. Pearl had of course made it clear it was under sufferance.

The sound of Mrs Czubinska sobbing reached her, despite the doors and walls separating them. Rose stared at her hands, finding the woman's wails of grief distressing. Unable to bear it anymore, she stood up and read the thank you cards on the wall.

Jenny pushed open the double doors and ushered the Czubinskis through, followed by Zofia, who carried an overnight bag, and Pearl. Jenny thanked the parents and hurried away.

Mrs Czubinska had a round face and short grey hair with a distinctive gap in her lower front teeth. She clung to Mr Czubinski's navy blue jumper and sobbed into it. His cheeks and moustache were also wet with tears as he said something to his wife in Polish. It was all Rose could do not to cry herself.

'Zofia, please tell them how very sorry I am for their loss,' Rose said.

Zofia nodded and translated. The mother was so enveloped by grief she didn't hear Zofia speak, but her husband looked at Rose and said thank you in English. Beneath dark, bushy eyebrows his eyes were those of a broken man.

'This police officer will drop you at your motel,' Pearl said to the parents. Then, 'Zofia, can we have a little chat?'

'I should be with them,' she protested.

'I'll drive you to the motel when we're done,' Pearl said.

Zofia clutched Rose's hand. 'You will stay with me?'

'Of course. Come and sit next to me,' Rose said. 'We just have a few questions. It won't take long.'

When the Czubinskis had left, Pearl dragged one of the purple chairs over and positioned himself opposite Zofia. Rose could feel Pearl's animosity towards her presence. She shut her eyes for a second to try and gain some composure.

'Tell me the real reason why you're staying at the motel,' Rose said.

'I am the only person they know here. They need a translator.'

'You told the Forensic Pathologist that you wanted to stay away from Mila. Why is that?' Rose asked.

Zofia shrugged. 'She is difficult to live with.?'

Rose tilted her head to one side. 'What's the real reason?' Zofia was silent. Rose persisted. 'Do you suspect Mila had something to do with Anna's death?'

'She is jealous woman. Mila wanted Kacper to herself.'

Pearl cut in. 'Was Anna dating Kacper Kowalski?'

'No. Kacper is a bully. Anna did not like him. But Kacper, he was obsessed with Anna. Don't you see? Mila thought Kacper would never love her as long as he loved Anna.' The girl chewed her lip. 'I can't go to my house. If she knows I speak to Policja, she will be very angry with me.'

'Are you afraid of Mila?' Rose asked.

Zofia nodded. 'Mila boasted she was going to make Kacper hate Anna.'

'How?' Rose asked.

'She told Kacper about Anna's boyfriend.'

'He didn't know?'

'Nobody knew. Just me and Mila.'

'How did Kacper react?'

'Mila told me Kacper was so angry he punched a hole in the wall.'

Rose and Pearl looked at each other. Both Mila and Kacper had motive.

Zofia shook her head. 'Now Mila has Kacper all to herself.'

28

Zofia left the mortuary and got into the back of Pearl's car. She stared listlessly out of the side window, looking as though all the life had been drained from her.

Pearl yelled at Rose, 'Oy! Follow me!' He sped off.

Monty was patiently waiting for Rose in her car. She followed Pearl to the motel, where he dropped off Zofia, and then on to Dorset Street. A light was on upstairs at number twenty-four. Rose told Monty to be a good boy and that she wouldn't be long. The dog seemed to understand. He lay down in the back and closed his eyes.

Pearl rang the doorbell. 'I'll do the talking,' he said to Rose.

Mila yanked the front door open. 'Yes?'

'DI Pearl. You know Rose Sidebottom. I have some questions. Can we come inside?'

'No. Ask me now.' She folded her arms and scowled at him.

'What is your relationship with Kacper Kowalski?'

Mila rolled her eyes. 'That blonde bimbo, she knows nothing.'

'Answer the question, Miss De Vries. How well do you know Kacper Kowalski?'

She shrugged. 'He is friend of Anna.'

'Why did you tell Kacper that Anna had a boyfriend?'

'Why do you say this?'

'Answer the question.'

'I do not have to answer your questions. I know my rights.'

'Then you're coming down the station with me,' Pearl said.

Mila held up her hands. 'Okay, okay. I tell you. Anna, she treated Kacper like shit. She thought she was beautiful. She flirted with men all the time. She toyed with him.'

'So you wanted Anna out of the way so you could have a relationship with Kacper. That's motive.'

Mila's stroppy attitude melted faster than butter in a frying pan. 'No, I didn't kill her. I tell the truth.'

Rose didn't experience one little tingle.

'If you didn't kill her, who did?' Pearl said.

'I don't know.'

Rose felt a sting, as if she'd trodden on a sharp rock with bare feet. That was a lie.

'You do know, and if you don't tell us, you could be charged as an accessory to Anna's murder,' Rose said.

She received an angry glance from Pearl. 'You stoked Kacper's anger, didn't you?' Pearl said.

'You cannot prove this.'

'Kacper won't lie for you. He won't go to jail for you.'

Mila picked at a fingernail. 'Maybe I told him Anna had a lover. And about the gifts. Kacper was angry, yes, but he's not a killer.'

'You're coming down the station,' Pearl said.

'You don't understand. You waste your time with wrong man. You should find the man who threatened Anna the day before she died.'

'Why didn't you mention this before? Who threatened Anna?' Pearl asked.

'I do not know. He pushed his way into the house. I hear him shouting. I lock my bedroom door. I was afraid. He told Anna to keep her mouth shut.'

'Can you describe him?'

Mila pursed her lips. 'I see him briefly from bedroom window. Young. Maybe twenty. He moved his hand across his mouth.' She demonstrated.

'As if telling her to zip it?' Rose said.

'Yes. On his knuckles were tattoos. Words.'

'What did they say?'

'I could not see. But Anna tell me. On right hand it say THUG. On left hand it say LIFE. She was scared.'

Rose sat in her car in Dorset Street and dialled the vet hospital. She asked if Malcolm was working today. She was told he was. Rose headed straight there.

In the waiting room, Rose opened a copy of *Dogs Monthly* and flicked through the pages. There was an article on an eight-year-old boy raising money for a local dog rescue charity through his paintings, but her mind kept drifting. Rose hadn't worked out what she was going to say to Malcolm.

An elderly woman arrived, wheezing loudly, as did her portly Pug. Rose recognised Mr Squishy and his talkative owner. Rose lifted the magazine so that it hid her face, keen to avoid a long-winded conversation with the Pug's owner. Fortunately, the old lady sat across the room from Rose and began reading the *Geldeford Gazette* which, it soon became clear, she couldn't do in silence.

'That's outrageous…gone soft if you ask me…ooh, twenty percent off, I like the sound of that.'

She proceeded to tear out a corner of the newspaper and slip the torn-off piece into her over-sized handbag. Monty showed no interest in Mr Squishy or his owner. He steadfastly peered down the length of the corridor at the kitchen. He let rip with a single bark. The talkative old lady looked up too. Before Rose could admonish Monty, a Cavalier King Charles puppy ran down the corridor towards them. It was B, Malcolm's adopted pup, her tail wagging frenetically, followed by Malcolm, who was in the middle of putting on his waxed coat. Around his neck dangled B's lead.

'Hi, I'm taking B around the block. Would you…' He appeared to be having trouble getting an arm into the sleeve of his coat.

'It's inside out,' Rose said. 'Let me help.' She pulled the sleeve through to the right side. After a moment's struggle, Malcolm's hand appeared through the coat cuff. 'Um…okay, good. Would you like to join us?'

He strode ahead and out the door before Rose could answer. Was he pissed off with her or embarrassed at his coat fumbling?

She followed him, Monty walking beside her. How should she broach the subject? The sooner she apologised the better, but he dashed across the car park at such a rate it was hard to catch up. Oh dear, he must be upset with her. Monty gave a deep bark and B responded with a *yip yip*. B stopped walking, forcing Malcolm to come to a sudden halt. This was Rose's chance.

'Malcolm–' she began.

'Rose–'

'I'm so–'

'Sorry–' Malcolm said.

'No, I'm sorry–'

Before either could say another word, B's lead slid from Malcolm's hand and she bolted back inside the vet hospital.

To Rose's surprise, Monty did the same. He never bolted when he was on a lead. By the time Rose and Malcolm had reached the reception area, Mr Squishy had ripped the local paper from his owner's grasp and dragged it over to where B and Monty were barking like crazy. Anyone would think there was a fire and they were sounding the alarm.

Then they did the weirdest thing Rose had ever seen. Monty gently took the newspaper from the Pug, who willingly released it, then he lay it on the floor so the front and back pages were visible. All three dogs sat around it.

'What on earth…?' said Malcolm.

'My Squishy,' shrieked the old lady, using her walking stick to get up from her chair, 'give me back my paper!'

Rose watched Monty carefully. He dropped his snout to the front page. There were three main stories, but the banner headline was about the theft of a six-month-old Airedale Terrier from St Martha's village and a recent spate of dog thefts around Geldeford. He was trying to communicate; she was sure of it. But she didn't say anything because Malcolm had already made it clear he thought her relationship with Monty was weird. She shook her head. *Pull yourself together, Rose*, she told herself. *Dogs can't read.*

Monty dropped his snout once again and placed his black nose over the article. Rose had seen him do this before when he wanted her to notice something. But how could she tell a vet that her dog wanted them to take notice of story in the newspaper? He'd think she had totally lost her marbles. And if word got back to her boss, or Dr Doom, she'd never get her job back.

Malcolm kneeled down. 'What's got into you, B?'

B tapped a front paw on the newspaper.

'Oh my God!' Rose exclaimed, unable to stop herself. 'They both think…' Rose squeezed her lips shut. *Don't sound like a crazy person*, she told herself.

'Think what?' Malcolm asked.

'Nothing.' Rose took hold of Monty's lead. 'I think it's best we leave. I don't know what's got into him.'

Monty locked his front legs out in front of him and lowered his head, refusing to budge. It took a piece of liver treat to get him moving. Rose glanced back. Mr Squishy had placed himself on top of the newspaper and his owner was furiously tugging at one end of it, telling her Pug to get off. The paper tore in half.

Malcolm ran after Rose, with B in his arms. 'Wait!' He caught up. 'I'm sorry. I was a fool last night. I get nervous, you see, and words tumble out.'

'I overreacted. I'm sorry, too.'

There was an awkward silence as they faced each other in the car park.

'Joe says you've identified the murdered girl. Well done, you.'

Rose blushed. 'Well, yes, um, I suppose I did. It's nice to know I still have what it takes.' Rose shuffled from foot to foot.

'Of course you do.'

Rose was taken aback by his faith in her. 'I just wish my boss thought the same.' The words slipped out. Had she said that out loud?

'You don't need his validation, surely? If you're not appreciated, you should set up your own business. You know, as a PI. At least then, you are your own boss.'

Rose stared wide-eyed. 'But I love what I do.'

It was Malcolm's turn to shuffle from foot to foot. 'I'm just saying that…oh, it doesn't matter, I'm probably talking rubbish again. What I mean is you could do very well running your own detective agency.' He looked down at the ground, then back up at her. 'Got time to come for a walk?'

'Not right now, but thanks for asking.'

As Rose drove away, she thought about Malcolm's suggestion. She had never even considered being a private investigator. Wasn't it the kind of thing retired detectives did? She was only twenty-one. She should have a few more years' experience under her belt before she considered setting up on her own. Nevertheless, it was nice to feel she had options.

29

I always know we are nearly home because the woodland either side of the road is ripe with the scent of fox and owl and badger, and the soil has a salty smell to it with a touch of honey from the heather. I thought I was on to a winner when B and Mr Squishy volunteered to help me warn Rose and Malcolm about the threat to the vet hospital. At one point I even thought Rose understood. But she hasn't said a thing on our way home, so I guess I was mistaken. I only hope she can forgive me for being such a bad dog.

I give her a sniff behind the ear. Rose laughs.

'That tickles.'

With one hand on the steering wheel she gives me a quick scratch under the chin. Oh yeah, that's the spot! When she stops, I rest my muzzle on her shoulder. She doesn't push me away, so I suppose that's a good sign.

As we pull into the rutted driveway, I detect a hooman scent that doesn't belong. Rose honks her horn at a squirrel directly in our path that looks like Nigel but he jumps away so fast I can't be certain. I poke my nose out of the open window and inhale the hooman smell of juniper berries and alcohol, the tang of burnt sage and a perfume that reminds me of jasmine flowers. I inhale again, detecting something else, something more subtle. It's the fresh smell of the sea.

'Oh!' exclaims Rose, hitting the brakes sharply when she spots a woman sitting on the front doorstep with a huge suitcase at her feet. Rose turns off the engine and throws open the car door.

'Mum!'

The woman raises a hand and waves, her bangles jangling discordantly. 'Darling!' She envelops Rose in an embrace. 'Now none of this *mum* business, remember? Call me Liz. We don't want people thinking I'm older than I look, now do we?! By the way,' she points to the gap between her eyebrows, 'look! No lines. Or here.' She points to the side of her mouth. 'Botox. Takes ten years off me, don't you think?'

'You definitely look younger, yes, but I can't call you Liz. You're my mum.'

'It's okay when we're alone darling, but in public, it's Liz.'

'All right. What's brought on the Botox?'

'Who doesn't want to keep looking young?'

'Okay. It's just that…Anyway, the house is a bit of a mess. I'd have tidied up if I'd known.'

'I left several messages, although I suppose you're too busy fitting up suspects and trampling people's rights to notice.'

'Don't start. Please.' Rose tenses.

I watch everything through the car window. My mum told me when I was very young that I would grow up to look just like my dad, but I never met him. Rose must resemble her dad because she looks nothing like her mother. Liz is tall with short curly hair that's dark grey at the roots. The rest of her hair is black. Her lips are glossy red and her belted raincoat is a vivid pattern of sliced watermelons, which makes me hungry just looking at it. Rose has a small build and straight, auburn hair

'Can we go inside? I'm freezing. Kay used to keep a spare key under the flowerpot but I couldn't find it.'

'No point. Front door's jammed. The back door's open, though. I don't bother locking it.'

'How was I supposed to know that?' Liz throws her hands up to the sky and then sets off down the side of the house without so much as a glance behind her. Rose lets me out of the car, rolls her eyes at me and then proceeds to drag the gigantic, wheeled suitcase behind her.

It's covered in multi-coloured stickers saying things like *Rescue The Rain Forest, Unite Against Racism,* and *Stop Police Brutality.* I don't understand the last one. Rose's job is to stop brutality and put away killers. Seeking clarification, I sniff the bag's wheels as they bounce over the gravel, but I'm none the wiser.

'I see what you mean,' says Liz, hand on hip, looking around the kitchen at the plates and cutlery piled up in the sink and the hamper full of dirty laundry next to the washing machine.

It's time I welcomed our guest. I amble up to her mother, giving her my best panty-dog-smile.

'Good God! What is that thing? Get it away from me.'

I turn around and growl, ready to accost "that thing", whatever it is. But there's nothing but Rose and the monster suitcase.

'That's Monty. I told you about him. His previous owner was murdered.'

'Oh darling, why do you always collect the waifs and strays? You should be out socialising. Meeting eligible young men.' She looks me up and down. 'Looks like a biter to me.'

'Only if you're a bad guy,' Rose grins.

I try to grin too. Liz is clearly in need of reassurance.

'Got a drink? It's been a hell of a journey. Five hours on that ghastly train, then the Uber driver was a complete fool. Had no idea where he was going. I almost clobbered him. Even with a sat nav, he couldn't find Farley Green. I had to ask a cyclist for directions!' She pulls open the fridge door and peers inside. 'Where do you keep your wine?'

'Um, I drank it.'

'It? You only have one bottle?' She shakes her head. 'What about gin? Vodka?'

'I think I've got gin somewhere. Isn't it a bit early? It's only lunch time.'

'It's never too early for a G&T.'

Rose pokes her head into the larder and pulls out a bottle of Gordon's Gin and a bottle of red wine. 'I'd forgotten about that.' She holds both up. 'Which would you like?'

'I'll start with the gin.'

'I don't have any tonic, but I do have bitter lemon.'

'That'll do. It's like an ice box in here,' Liz moans. 'Don't the pigs pay you enough to afford heating?'

There she goes with that pig thing. Rose doesn't work for pigs, although I will admit that Leach's bald pink head and stocky body is a bit pig-like.

'Please don't use that word. It's insulting.' Rose opens the boiler cupboard's door. 'Oh, bums. I forgot, boiler doesn't work.' She grimaces. 'Sorry, Mum, no hot water or heating, but I can get a log fire going in the sitting room.'

Her mother throws her arms up. 'I despair. My sister left you a shit box.'

'It's fine, Mum,' says Rose through gritted teeth. I can feel the tension rising. It prickles like static electricity. 'Make yourself comfy in the lounge. I'll bring through your drink in a minute.'

Her mother gives an exaggerated sigh and departs. Rose prepares a gin and bitter lemon and pours herself a lemon squash. She swallows a painkiller. Then she carries the drinks through to the sitting room. Her mum isn't there.

'Ahem.' Liz stands in the study doorway holding up a letter from Dr Doom. 'When were you going to tell me the pigs had dumped you?'

'Mum! I can't believe you snooped through my stuff!'

'Says here you're suffering from PTSD. When were you going to tell me? I mean, I have a right to know.'

I follow Rose into the sitting room. She takes the armchair and Liz takes the sofa.

'Well?' Liz says.

'Because you'd blame them, just like you're doing now. I've had one or two panic attacks and sleeping difficulties, that's all.'

'Darling, you're seeing a psychiatrist. They must think there's something wrong.'

'I guess they must.'

Rose looks into the depths of her lemon squash. Liz takes a big gulp of her gin and bitter lemon.

'It was always going to end badly,' Liz says. 'You're just not cut out for the brutality. Why don't you put this wreck of a house on the market and get yourself a good lawyer to negotiate a disability pension. Then you can have any career you want.'

'I know you mean well, but I love being a police officer. And if it means I have to see the psychiatrist, then that's what I'll do.'

'My poor baby, broken and battered.'

'Mum, you're not helping.'

'Fine. Waste your life working for fascists, if you must. But you simply can't stay in this dump. Look, I've done my share of roughing it. The Greenham Common Peace Camp wasn't exactly comfortable, or sanitary for that matter. I know you feel you have to keep the place because it belonged to Kay, but I'm sure she'd understand if you sold up and found yourself a nice little flat with all the mod cons.'

'I like it here. It's quiet. It has ducks and a beautiful heath on my doorstep.'

'But daaaarling. You're so isolated. And the house is simply falling down around your ears. Why don't you sell this... burden, and move into town? You can meet new people. People your age. Maybe even find a nice boyfriend.'

I rest my head in Rose's lap. She strokes my furry ears.

'Mum, please stop. I'm not interested in boyfriends.'

Loneliness has a smell and that smell is coming off Rose. That's one of the things we dogs know that the hoomans don't – everything has a scent. Love, grief, anxiety, joy, anger, contentment. Loneliness is like the old-fashioned moth balls my previous owner used to keep in his wardrobe. I hate to admit it, because Rose is my world, but maybe Liz is right. Rose might be happier if she had a hooman companion.

I glance at Liz. There's a twinkle in her eye like the one Betty gets when she's hatching a plan. The smile on her face says she has no intention of letting the subject drop.

30

I'm salivating at the meaty smells in Rose's kitchen. I lie under the table, waiting for titbits. Liz, a shawl over her shoulders, has hardly touched her rump steak, although she's managed to down two gins and bitter lemon and three glasses of red wine.

'Too rare for me,' Liz says, putting down her knife and fork.

It looks leathery to me, but I'll eat it any way that it comes.

'Sorry, Mum, I thought I'd cooked it enough.'

Rose takes the plates to the sink. The tall pedal bin, almost a place of worship for Betty, is positioned between the sink and the fridge. I follow and give Rose my most intense, big-eyed, pleading look.

Please give it to me. Please!

Rose cuts up Liz's leftovers, tells me to sit and then drops the pieces into my open mouth. I gobble them and then lick my lips, several times actually, just in case I've missed any of the meaty juices. *Yum!*

'Do you want dessert, Mum?' Rose asks as she pops the plates in the sink.

'Need to watch my figure, darling. You might consider doing the same. You've put on a little weight.'

Ouch! Even I know that isn't very nice.

Rose peers down at the waistband of her jeans where a little roll of skin pokes over the top, causing the hem of the woolly jumper to bulge a bit. 'I'm working on getting a muffin top,' she says, grinning.

She helps herself to a slice of cheesecake from the fridge, then resumes her seat opposite her mum. Liz pours herself another glass of wine. Rose hasn't had any of it; she's sticking to water tonight. 'So what has Dad done this time?'

Liz looks sheepish as she sips from her glass. 'Can't I visit my daughter without you assuming we've had a row?'

'Mum, this is the first time you have ever come to stay. Something must be wrong.'

Liz picks up the wine bottle and studies the label. 'I needed a break, that's all,' she says.

'So, everything's fine between you and Dad?'

'Not exactly.' Liz takes a big gulp of wine.

Rose puts down her spoon. 'You normally go and stay with Margie or Gina when you're fed up. What's different this time?'

'Ah, well, I might have overstayed my welcome.' Liz preens her curly hair.

'They're your best friends.'

'I thought so too. Let's not go there.'

'Mum, it's lovely to see you but I get the feeling you've fallen out with Dad.'

'Maybe.'

'What's he done?'

'It's not something he's done. It's more what he *isn't* doing.'

'You mean he's not pulling his weight?' Rose asks, taking another mouthful of cheesecake.

'He's always been a lazy so-and-so, granted. But no, that's not it. What I mean is he's not satisfying me...sexually.'

'Ew!' exclaims Rose, screwing up her face. 'Too much information.'

'Come, come, darling. I never took you for a prude. Your father and I have always had a good sex life. Up until a few weeks ago, when he did his back in.'

'Mum! You can't blame him for that!'

'Well, if he'd listened to me and been more careful when he went up on the roof, we wouldn't be having these problems and our sex life wouldn't be non-existent.'

'But you sent him up on the roof.'

'That's irrelevant, Rose. The problem is I have needs.'

'Mum, please.' Rose shuffles in her chair.

'I have to talk about it. You see, your father may call you, and it's best if you hear it from me first.'

Rose blanches. 'What do you mean? You're not…I mean, you're not separating?'

'Well, not exactly. Not yet.' Rose's spoon has stopped its passage to her lips as if frozen in time. Liz continues, 'I've taken a lover and your father doesn't like it.'

The spoon falls to the table with a clunk.

'A lover?' Rose repeats, agog. 'Oh my God! Who?'

Liz bats away the question with a hand. 'Oh you don't know him. And it doesn't matter. Your dad took it rather badly when I told him. We agreed I needed time away to think about what I want. It was your father's idea.'

'Poor Dad.'

'He's *not* poor. *I'm* the aggrieved party. I thought you'd be on my side.'

'I'm not going to take sides, Mum.' Rose shakes her head. 'I thought you two were happy. I can't believe it.'

'We'll work something out, I'm sure. No need to look so upset.'

Rose carries her dessert plate to the sink. 'I…look, I'm sorry. I'm really tired. We can talk more in the morning. The spare bed is made up. I'll get you some towels. Help yourself to whatever you want.'

'But darrrrling! I need cheering up.'

Rose's mobile phone rings. 'I have to take this.'

'What could possibly be more important than your mother?' Liz says, pouting.

'Sorry, Mum.'

I follow Rose into the study that smells of musty books, candle wax and dried flowers. She shuts the study door.

'Malcolm?' Rose says, as she plonks down into a wheelie chair.

'I'm sorry to call you this late. I need your help.' Malcolm's voice is higher pitched than normal. He sounds distressed.

The fur down my spine rises. I think I know what he's about to say. I should have tried harder to warn him.

'No problem,' says Rose, relieved to have a distraction from Liz. 'How can I help?'

'There's been a break-in at the vet hospital.'

Oh no! I find myself whining.

'That's terrible,' Rose says. 'Have you called the police?'

'Yes. But they won't understand.'

'Understand what?'

'They've taken B.' Malcolm's voice is shaky. Rose gasps. 'Can you come over? Please?'

'I'm coming now,' says Rose. She dashes into the kitchen. 'Mum, I have to go out. There's an emergency.'

Liz emits a squeal, then jumps onto her chair. She points. 'Rat!'

I turn my head. Betty races along the skirting board and dives into her hole. The back half of her gets momentarily stuck. With a wriggle, she disappears behind the wall.

'You can't leave me alone with that thing! It's enormous!'

31

Rose leaves her mum at the cottage armed with a broom, having promised to deal with the rat in the morning. I can only hope that Betty knows to stay hidden.

By the time we reach the vet practice, I'm as jumpy as a Jack Russell. Blue light from a parked police car swirls and bounces off the building's glass doors. A female uniformed officer is talking to Malcolm in the reception area, which looks like a bomb has hit it. The dogs staying overnight at the hospital howl and yelp and yip, rending the night. I want to howl, too, in solidarity. It's my fault B was taken. I should have done more to warn Malcolm.

The PC notices us and dashes outside to head us off.

'Ma'am, you can't come in here,' she says, although it's difficult to hear her above the baying and howling.

Rose smiles at the officer. 'Barika, isn't it? It's Rose Sidebottom. Malcolm asked me to come. As a friend.'

PC Barika Zaid is a nice lady. Lives with three rescued dogs, four children and one husband who builds houses.

'I should warn you,' Zaid says. 'Malcolm was struck on the head. He keeps saying he's all right but there's an ambulance on its way.'

I can't keep my paws still. I want to go to him. Comfort him.

'What happened?' Rose says.

'He said there were two of them. Stole three dogs. When he tried to stop them, one of them clobbered him.'

'Security cameras?'

'Afraid not. He saw a white van. Didn't catch the number plate, though, so it's not much to go on.'

'Can I go inside?'

Zaid screws up one edge of her mouth. 'Can't, sorry. You know the drill.'

Rose nods. 'Is cash kept on the premises?'

'Very little. It goes into a safe at night and they didn't touch the safe.'

'Can you let Malcolm know we're here?'

'We?'

'Monty and me.'

Zaid looks at me, and I look back at her. She holds my gaze for a few seconds and then turns back to Rose. 'Between you and me, I think those poor dogs are lost forever. There's been a spate of dog thefts over the last few months and we haven't managed to find any of them.'

My stomach churns. This can't be happening. Not to Malcolm. Not to B. Or the other dogs. I have to find them.

Zaid heads inside. We wait near the entrance. Rose gnaws a fingernail. I sit, get up, sit, get up. I just want to get going. I sniff the ground around me. There are so many scents of dogs and hoomans, there's no way of telling if one of them is the dognapper. I need to sniff the cages where the stolen dogs were kept.

Malcolm is talking into his phone. Is he breaking the news to Dr Rochester, the other vet? His white shirt has blood spots down the back and across the shoulder. Packets of medication and flea treatments litter the floor. Cupboard doors have been flung open and their contents thrown out. Down the corridor, I can see that the back door is wide open. That must be how the dognappers broke in.

A tall figure in uniform enters the back door. It's Big Man Joe. I bark a hello. He peers down the length of the corridor, through the glass doors, sees me and Rose standing outside and beckons us to come in. We head straight for Malcolm.

'Thank God you're here,' Malcolm says. He sways.

Rose takes his arm. 'Come and sit down. You're in shock.'

'I can't sit. I have to find the dogs. Why would anybody do this?'

'I don't know. Joe and Barika will do everything they can.'

'I know they will. But what if it's not enough? Help me find B.'

I look up at Rose. *Say yes. I can find them. I know I can.*

'I shouldn't interfere.'

'Please. I was so stupid. They tried to warn me, don't you see? The time they sat on the newspaper story about dogs disappearing, remember? Monty even pointed his nose at it. He knew the thieves were coming. God only knows how.'

Rose's eyes widened. 'You know, I think he tried to warn me, too. At home. He kept showing me your vet bill.'

'If Monty knew they were going to steal my dogs, then maybe he can find them.'

Come on, Rose, I think. *You know he's right.*

I sidle up to Malcolm and rub my ear against his knee. *I'll help you.*

He kneels down and hugs me, burying his face in my fur. 'You'll find her, won't you, boy?'

I bark once. *Yes I will!*

'All right,' says Rose, no doubt thinking of how the Leach would react if he knew what she was doing. 'We'll help find her. But you have to keep this just between us.'

'Of course.' Malcolm stops hugging me and stands. 'Where do we start?'

'How did they get in?' Rose asks.

'Crowbarred the back door. Come and take a look.'

The car park continues around to the back of the building, where the vets and nurses usually park. There's a cattery in a separate building and from the volume of their mewling and yowling, I'd say the cats are just as freaked as the dogs. There's just one car there – Malcolm's Vauxhall Crossland X. A movement-sensitive exterior light flicks on. There are black tyre marks on the tarmac.

'Looks like they left in a hurry,' Rose said.

'I tried to stop them. One of them had B in a cage. The other one hit me from behind.' He runs his fingers across the back of his head. 'I must have passed out for a moment.'

'Careful where you walk,' Rose says, staying well clear of the tyre marks. She examines the door frame and the lock. So do I. I detect a new scent on the door jamb. 'Why was B in the vet hospital on a Saturday night?'

'I live in the flat upstairs. I like to check on the animals at night.' He glances at Rose, clearly embarrassed. He's a softie, that's for sure. 'These last two nights, B has refused to leave the hospital. I'd come down in the night and find her wandering about the place.'

Zaid finds us and asks if Malcolm can do anything to calm the remaining dogs and the cats.

At last there is something I can do. I take a deep breath and bellow an almighty series of barks. 'You're safe now. The thieves have gone. Stop barking so the police can do their job.'

The howling from the cages stops immediately. Zaid, Rose and Malcolm stare at me.

'Did he just tell them to shut up?' Zaid asks.

'Of course not,' Rose says, but she looks at me quizzically out of the corner of her eye, 'Can I take a look at the cages?'

Zaid sighs. 'Oh all right then, but hurry. There are more officers on the way.'

Outside the Recovery Area, B's scent is very strong. This must have been where she sat on guard tonight. I imagine how terrified she must have been when two hoomans broke down the door.

Malcolm leads us into a room filled with cages of various sizes. Seven fearful pairs of eyes watch us. Each dog sports stitches or bandages. But they all have one thing in common. They all cower, heads lowered, tails tucked under their bellies. I make a point of sniffing each and every one of them.

'Chanel, a Standard Poodle, was here.' Malcolm points at a corner cage. On the floor of the cage is a crumpled blanket and an overturned water bowl. 'And that's where Gizmo the French Bulldog was.' The cage doors hang wide open. 'They took a carry box, which is how they captured B.' There's a muddy footprint on the floor. I lower my head and pulse my nostrils, sucking in every smell I can detect. That's when it hits me. Just a whiff, but its effect on me hurtles me back to my puppyhood. I jump backwards and bash my backside on an empty cage.

'Why just three dogs?' Rose asks. 'Why not the others?'

I feel sick to the stomach and, after two spasming retches, I vomit onto the floor, narrowly missing Malcolm's shoes.

'I'll clear that up,' Rose says, pulling a poo bag from her pocket.

'It's okay, I'll do it.' Malcolm kneels next to me and strokes my back. 'Not your fault, Monty. We're all distressed.'

I'm trembling from snout to paw.

'Something's wrong with him,' says Rose. She leans over me. 'Monty, what's happened?'

'He probably senses how stressed everybody is. He hasn't eaten anything he shouldn't, has he?' Malcolm asks.

'No, I don't think so. I'll take him outside.'

But I dig my paws in. I try not to allow memories to distract me. I have to find those poor dogs before it's too late.

'Looks like he wants to stay,' Malcolm says, scooping up the vomit.

'Where were you when the thieves broke in?' Rose asks.

'At a mate's birthday bash, but I left early. I wasn't in the mood.'

'Perhaps you surprised them.'

While Rose continues to ask Malcolm questions, I ask my own.

The cage next door to Chanel's empty one is occupied by Benji, a black and tan Dachshund with a bandaged leg. 'Get me out of here!' he pants.

'Who took Chanel?' I bark softly.

Benji's eyes look as if they are about to pop out of his skull. 'I can't. I can't. He'll come for me,' Benji bays, then scarpers to the back of his cage and hides his head under a blanket.

Next to him is an elderly black Labrador. The sign on the door says Max. He appears to live up to name: his mid-section is shaped like a barrel. His spine sags with the weight of his belly.

'Tell me who did this, Max,' I say.

'It was him,' his voice wobbles.

'Who?'

'He who shall not be named. He took the females. He always takes the females.' Exhausted from stress, Max collapses onto the concrete floor.

My stomach makes weird noises but there's nothing left for me to spew.

An Irish Wolfhound wearing a cone of shame around her neck says mournfully, 'There's nothing you can do to save them.' The Wolfhound, named Deidre, has stitches on her belly.

'Why didn't they take you, Deidre?' I ask.

'Nobody wants Wolfhounds these days. We're too big. Hoomans want a pet that fits into a tiny flat and happily pees on a piece of plastic. The world's gone mad,' she exclaims with a dramatic shake of her scruffy grey head.

'Who stole Chanel, Gizmo and B?'

A Jack Russell crossbreed named Mash scratches his neck frantically with nerves. 'You know his scent as well as I do, Monty.'

It can't be him. Not after all this time. Why is he back?

I sniff Gizmo's empty cage and get another sudden hit of the scent of the man who stole her. It explodes inside my head like fireworks. It starts with a chemical smell overlaid with meaty bones, dry straw and that sweet scent of pig shit. I jump back as if a cat has tried to slash my face.

'Hey, boy,' Rose says. 'This is B's special toy. Can you sniff it for me?' She holds a tiny plush cuddly toy that looks like an angry green cactus wearing a pink hat. A very odd creature. But there again, I've never met a Cavalier King Charles pup who think she's a guard dog, so I guess it's perfectly understandable that B would have an equally spiky toy.

I inhale the toy's smell. It carries Malcolm's scent of Imperial Leather soap and also B's aroma which is like Magic Marker pens.

'Find her. Go on Monty, find B.'

Nose to the ground, I follow B's smell out of the Recovery Area and into the rear car park. B must have sprayed some wee through her cage because I detect her message on the wall.

I yelp.

'Monty?' Rose asks, kneeling beside me.

I back away, the whites of my eyes as bright and round as snooker balls.

32

All the way home I pace in the back of the car. At my feet is Lady B's angry cactus toy. Rose wanted me to keep it, to remind me of B's scent. When we reach Duckdown Cottage, I smell smoke, but it's not wood smoke. There is an earthy, herbal quality to it that I don't recognise. I bark a warning.

Rose hastens into the house. The kitchen is an opaque fug.

'I don't believe it,' Rose mutters and heads straight for the sitting room.

Smoke spirals up from the sofa. We find Liz lying with her head on a cushion. In one hand is Rose's telephone. In the other is a homemade cigarette where the odour is coming from. Liz is oblivious to our presence. She giggles like a little girl.

'Oh, he's *very* good at that,' says Liz. 'It's such a relief to talk to you. I knew you'd understand. After all, you're on your fourth husband. Plenty of practice, hey?'

'Mum!' Rose coughs. 'I'm going to pretend I can't smell marijuana. Please put it out.'

Through heavy eyelids Liz gives her daughter a floppy-handed wave. 'Whatever you say, darling.' She turns back to the conversation as if Rose isn't there. 'That's my daughter, Rose,' she says into the phone. 'Remember her? Yes,' Liz sighs, 'She's a cop. Humiliating, but what can I do?'

'Mum, can you please put that out.'

'Oops!' Liz giggles. 'I'm in trouble. Bad mummy is having a joint.'

'Oh for goodness' sake.' Rose tries to take the cigarette and Liz slaps at her hand. In the kerfuffle, Liz drops it onto a sofa cushion, where it smoulders on the chintz fabric, giving an acrid edge to the smoke.

Rose dives on the offending item and stabs it out in a ceramic ashtray decorated with little ducks. Kay was a smoker. It must be her ashtray.

'What are you doing?' squeals Liz. 'Don't waste it!'

She reaches for the coffee table, loses her balance, and falls to the floor. 'Whoopsy!' She drops the phone with a clunk. Liz bursts out laughing and wags a finger at her daughter. 'You're so funny!'

'Time for bed, Mum,' Rose says, 'Up you get.'

Liz slaps Rose's proffered hand. 'Go away. I'm talking to Cheryl.' Liz peers blearily around her. 'Where did she go? Coo-ee! Cheryl! Where are you?' She pats the carpet trying to find the phone.

'Cheryl? You mean your friend Cheryl who moved to Australia?'

'Of course. Who else would it be?' Liz continues to call out Cheryl's name, but each time with less strength, as though her voice is draining away like water in a sink.

A muffled voice responds. Rose finds the phone beneath the sofa and notices the call length. 'Two hours and six minutes? You've been using my landline to call Australia for two hours and six minutes? Why didn't you use WhatsApp? It's free.'

'Oh stop your fussing.' She yawns. 'I'll just rest my head for a moment. Feel sleepy.' Rose manages to pop a cushion under her mother's head. 'Mmm, this is comfy.'

Within seconds, Liz is asleep. Rose tells Cheryl that Liz is suddenly very tired and politely ends the call. She then covers her mum with a blanket and takes herself upstairs to bed.

It's not long before I hear the slow rhythmic breathing that tells me Rose is asleep. Liz has barely moved a muscle since Rose went upstairs. I pad softly to the kitchen and put my nose half in a hole in the skirting board. 'Betty!' I say in a low whimper. 'Are you there?'

I hear the patter of tiny claws behind me and spin around.

'What's up?' Betty asks.

Skewered onto one claw is a piece of chipolata pork sausage. She takes a bite and chews slowly, savouring it. She must have gone rummaging in the neighbours' bins because Rose hasn't eaten sausages for weeks. If I wasn't so agitated, I'd be drooling.

'It's him!' I say, wide-eyed, licking my lips repeatedly even though I haven't eaten in ages. My mouth is dry.

'Him? Who ya talkin' about?'

'I daren't say his name.'

Betty takes another bite. 'You're kidding me. You're the bravest dog I know. Come on, Mr Monty, spit it out,' A piece of sausage the size of a pinhead shoots through the air.

'The Bo...Ray...' I whisper. The words stick in my throat.

'Can't hear ya, mate,' says Betty, her squeak loud enough to wake Liz in the sitting room.

'I don't want to say it out loud.'

'That's all well and good, my friend, but I can't bleedin' well hear ya.'

'I said, The...Bone...Ranger.'

Betty is about to snatch another bite of sausage. She pauses, jaw wide. 'Who's he, when he's at home?'

'A nightmare. A ghost.'

Betty nods knowingly, 'That weed's gone to your head, my friend. Imagining ghosts and ghouls.' Betty raises her nose and twitches her whiskers. 'Strong stuff, too.' She takes a deep sniff. 'I'd say it's Northern Lights. Sold locally by a dealer named Franky. Not that that's his name, mind you, but he's...how shall I put this, very frank with anyone who owes him money. He makes it very clear what he's going to do if any of his clients are daft enough to default on payment. Which is mighty generous of him, in my opinion.'

I'm momentarily distracted from my terror by Betty's comment. Does she really think Franky is a good man to warn people before he hurts them? Betty doesn't talk much about her time living in the Eurotunnel, but from what little she has said, it sounds like a tough life. Sometimes brutal. And she does only have half a tail.

'You don't understand,' I say. 'This hooman preys on dogs.'

I chase my tail and for a minute I forget everything except the need to catch it in my mouth, which is kind of the point. I know I look like a furry doughnut, but there's something soothing about the circular trance-like shuffle I go into once I nab my elusive appendage. It's like when hoomans hug themselves. It makes me feel less distressed.

'Stop, Mr Monty! I believe you. You're makin' me dizzy.'

Betty shoves the remaining piece of sausage inside the hole in the skirting board. She then plonks down in front of me. 'Okay, I get this is serious. Tell me more.'

Reluctantly, I let go of the tip of my tail and lie down so I can look into Betty's eyes. 'Every culture has a boogeyman,' I begin. 'A ghost-like creature that comes at night to get you. There's got to be one in your world too, Betty.'

'Yeah we got one of those. I used to use it to scare the bejeezus out of my pups when they ran off down the tunnel or strayed too near the powerlines. We call him Sack Man, because he steals the little 'uns at night and throws them in a sack, never to be seen again. Word is Sack Man eats the baby rats for his tea.'

'You told your pups that story?' I'm horrified.

'Sure did. Worked every time. That's why my babies survived. Cause they stayed near mama. Miss 'em all. I wonder if they miss me.'

Betty's ball-bearing-like eyes glaze over and I know I've lost her. I wave my paw at her. 'Betty?'

'You what? Oh yes, where were we? Ghosts.'

'But this one is real,' I say and explain how I found his scent tonight at the vet hospital.

Betty scratches under her chin. 'Hold on a sec. How do you know what this Bone Ranger smells like?'

I whimper. 'He took my mum away.'

'Your mum!' Betty scuttles over and strokes my paw. 'You poor dear. Tell me all about it.'

'My mother was called Summer. She had long golden fur and kind eyes and a soft jaw when she picked us up in her mouth. I was one of a litter of six, all destined to be Guide Dogs, if we made the grade, of course. Anyway, we were the "M" litter, which meant we all received names beginning with M. You already know mine. There was also Max, Marley, Missy, Maggie and Midge. Summer taught us to respect the Dog Commandments and to love our masters. I remember the way her ear twitched when she warned us about the Bone Ranger. Us pups cowered in a huddle because we felt our mother's fear. Run, she told us. If he comes for you, run. Never take the bones he offers. It will be the death of you if you do. Then, one night, when I was five weeks old, the Bone Ranger broke into the Guide Dogs' kennels. He stole two breeding bitches and a couple of my sisters. Summer defended us, snarling and gnashing. But he put a noose on a pole around her neck and dragged her away with him. I'll never forget the terror and sorrow in her eyes as she called out her goodbye.'

Betty lies across my paw, sobbing. 'That's so sad. Poor Summer. To be taken, forcibly like, from her pups.' Betty sniffs. She shakes herself out to dispel the melancholy like mud from her fur, and then sits up, straddling my paw. 'This Bone Ranger is rotten through and through. And,' she taps her nose, 'what happened to you as a pup explains a lot.'

'Does it?' I consider this. 'What exactly?'

'Oh you know, you needing a mother-figure like *moi*.' She points a claw at her furry chest. 'And it just so happens you found the best mother in the country. I'd do anything for my pups, and that includes you, although I have to say you are a bloody big pup. You want me to go sort this Bone Ranger fellow out?'

'No!' I bark, forgetting the slumbering household. 'He's dangerous.'

'All right, then. But we have to find him. He's got B and the other pups. What is his scent?'

'First up, there's the smell of lamb bones.'

Betty licks her mouth. 'Go on.'

'He lures dogs into his van with them.'

'Okay. Anything else?'

'And straw. And his van reeks of dog wee riddled with the vinegary bite of fear. And pig shit. And also a bitter chemical that he uses to subdue his victims. My mum warned me about it. It has a funny name. Sounds like Pento-Barbie.'

'Okay, so let me get this straight. A man who goes around stealing dogs smells of wee and straw and pig shit and bones and Barbie dolls?'

'Near enough.'

'That's really weird. Any idea where he lives?'

'No. What do we do now?'

'Let me see,' Betty says. 'Them dogs could be miles away by now. Does every dog know what the Bone Ranger smells like?'

'Oh yes.'

'Then we need to spread word fast. Wee-mails are too slow. We need something more immediate.' Betty grins. 'You're going to have a night of howling, my friend.'

'If I howl, I'll wake Rose.'

'You probably will. But, my friend, there are times when you just have to break the rules.'

33

Betty and I steal down to the far end of the garden to put as much distance between us and the cottage as possible. But what I am about to do is almost certainly going to wake Rose *and* the entire village. I must start the howl-a-thon from here so that every dog knows to send the information back to me at Duckdown Cottage.

We creep past sleeping ducks and geese, their bills turned astern and resting on their feathers. Cyril the pigeon sits in their midst. He opens one eye and watches us pass, then closes it again. Once I begin howling there's going to be hell to pay. But it can't be helped. I have to find B and the others.

'Are you ready?' Betty asks.

I stand with my legs wide and take a few deep breaths. I face the hedge on the perimeter. Beyond it is the railway line and beyond that is Winterfold Heath. To the north is Geldeford. To the east is Milford. To the west is Abinger Hammer. There must be hundreds of villages around Geldeford, and each village has its population of pooches. This network of howling hounds will spread my message the length and breadth of the country. Think of us as a canine cellular network. Millions of hoomans will have a bad night's sleep and I will be the reason for it. That burden weighs heavily on me, but my fear for the fate of those poor pups drives me onward.

I tilt my head back and look at the stars. A tingle runs down the length of my spine. I take a big breath and then let rip with the loudest howl I can muster. Betty covers her ears. The ducks wake and flap their wings, but to my surprise they observe silently. Perhaps they can hear the desperation in my voice.

'Beware The Bone Ranger!' I begin. 'Help me find B and Chanel and Gizmo, stolen from Geldeford Vet Hospital tonight. White van. Two hoomans. All information to Monty at Duckdown Cottage.'

It's a long message and I run out of breath. Before I can suck in some more air, the dogs of Farley Green, big and small, young and old, relay the message. Some bay from inside houses, others from their kennels. Three houses away Bear, a German Shepherd, howls in his bass voice. His owner yells at him to shut up, but he keeps going.

The dogs of Milford join in the howl-a-thon, as do those from Abinger Hammer and beyond.

More and more howling voices join my cries as I repeat my message. Farm dogs, city dogs, dogs at the pound, stray dogs, lap dogs, guard dogs join the chorus, some deep and resonating, others high-pitched and warbling. It melds into a repeating chorus that has its own special harmony.

'Monty!' shouts Rose. I glance over my shoulder. Her head pokes out of her bedroom window; her hair hangs loose. 'Stop that!' She closes the window and draws the curtains.

'Keep going!' yells Betty through a megaphone she has made out of a rolled-up leaf.

I howl my message three more times, then sit in silence, listening to dogs far and wide take up the call. The howl-a-thon has its own momentum now. We all fear The Bone Ranger. We have a common mission. There's not a dog in the land who won't take up the call.

'Wow!' says Betty, dropping her leafy megaphone. 'Sends shivers down my spine.'

Gradually, the howling fades into the distance, with faint echoes drifting back to us occasionally on the night breeze. The local villages have gone quiet, except for the hoomans complaining about the disturbance.

'What manner of creature is making that dreadful noise?' Dante demands as he swoops down on us. He lands in the oak tree behind us.

'Here comes trouble,' Betty grumbles.

We turn to face the magpie.

'Monty, what the devil are you doing?' Dante demands.

He doesn't wear a string of pearls around his neck tonight. He must have left them in his nest.

I look up at Rose's window. 'Can you tell him, Betty?' Her squeak won't be heard from inside the house.

Betty explains about The Bone Ranger and the break-in at the vet's.

'You realise there is no such thing as the Bone Ranger,' Dante says with a weary condescension. 'It's a myth. Like Big Foot and the Tooth Fairy.'

'Take it from me,' I say. 'He does exist. Will you help us, Dante? Can you search for a white van, two hoomans, three dogs? We need eyes in the sky.'

'I most certainly will not. You haven't yet paid your debt from last time.'

'Oy!' says Betty, paws on her hips. 'Can't you just do somethin' nice, you selfish bird!'

Dante drops his head and screeches at Betty, 'Shut up, you stupid rat!'

'Stop this!' I say in the doggie equivalent of a whisper. I wait for Dante to lift his head and for Betty to calm down. 'I told you, Dante. I can't steal from Ollie. It's wrong.'

'Then I won't help,' Dante says.

'Selfish prick!' Betty mutters.

'I heard that, harridan!'

There's a sharp tapping of claws on bark, but it's not Dante: his claws aren't moving. I tip-toe over to the oak, where Nigel is clinging to the trunk, head facing the ground, tail skyward. Squirrels are the only mammals that can do this. They can rotate their back ankles and turn their paws all the way around so they don't lose their grip in a vertical position. He bangs his four protruding front teeth on the bark. *Tap, tap, tap.*

'Now listen here, Monty, you young pup,' says Nigel. 'All this howling has to stop.'

'It has stopped,' Betty says, rolling her eyes.

Nigel's eyes almost pop from their sockets. 'No it hasn't, Miss Blabble. Dogs everywhere are howling.'

I want to keep the peace. 'Sorry, Nigel,' I say. 'It's an emergency.'

He scampers down the trunk and sits up on his hind legs in the grass. He shakes a claw at me. 'No more excuses. This is a breach of rule 5(a) of the Animal Neighbourhood Watch Regulations. Namely, a breach the peace.'

There's an ear-splitting screech and Dante drops from the tree's higher branches, claws out, and tries to grab Nigel.

Nigel scampers underneath me and cowers there. 'Save me!'

Dante struts towards us, his sharp beak glinting in the moonlight. 'Dante, you can't eat Nigel,' I say.

'Whyever not?'

I've already had to insist that he not eat Betty. There are only so many times I can persuade such a cantankerous bird to turn away from his prey. I come up with an answer that I may live to regret but it's all I can think of. 'He's part of the team.'

'I am?' Nigel says.

'He is?' asks Dante, coming to a stop. 'Since when?'

'Since we discovered his many skills.'

'What skills?' Dante scoffs.

I rack my brain. What are squirrels good at? 'Digging. He's a great digger.'

'That's it? He's on the team because he can dig!' Dante laughs. It sounds like rapid gunfire.

Nigel pokes his head out. 'I'll have you know I can dig as fast as any dog.'

'So what?' Dante says.

'And...' There has to be another reason. 'And he has the sharpest teeth. He can chew through power lines.'

Nigel looks up at me. 'You really want my help?'

'I do.'

His bushy tail vibrates with what appears to be delight. 'I can cut through power lines, that's true. Not that I would. I'm a law-abiding citizen.'

I add, '*And* he can cover vast distances very fast.'

'Wow! Nobody's ever been nice to me before.' Nigel sniffs, a tear in his eye.

Dante stares at me, incredulous. 'You're not serious?'

'I am serious. Nigel is the kind of public-spirited fellow who would gladly help his fellow creatures track down The Bone Ranger,' I say.

'How perfectly ridiculous.' Dante shakes his black head, opens his wings wide, and leaps into the sky, chuckling derisively as he ascends into the blackness.

Nigel's jaw drops, his mouth wide enough to swallow an acorn. 'Not The Bone Ranger!'

Finally, a creature who knows what I mean. 'Yes. Tonight he stole three dogs. We have to locate him and free the dogs.'

'Hmm. So that's what the howl-a-thon was about?'

I nod. I tell him about the white van.

'I'll see what I can do.' Nigel salutes me as if he's in the military. 'Do we…do we get a badge or something, you know, to show who we are, like the police?'

'We haven't got around to that yet, Nigel,' I say, having never considered the need for badges. 'Let's find the pups first.'

Nigel's furry chest swells with pride. 'I won't let you down, Mr Monty. Did I tell you I'm a distant relative of the prairie dog? All squirrels are, actually.' He gives me a toothy grin. 'Us dogs must stick together.'

34

On Sunday morning, Rose, Monty and Malcolm were door-knocking in Woodbridge Road where the white van had been seen racing away.

The vet hospital's back door and recovery area had been dusted for fingerprints. CCTV was checked, but the thieves had been smart enough to avoid roads with cameras. Unfortunately for Malcolm, an hour after attending the incident, Barika and Joe had been called to a bar brawl in town. Malcolm had made an appeal on local BBC radio, which had resulted in some crank calls but nothing of any use. As the morning passed, Malcolm became more and more dejected. Joe joined them at eleven. It was his day off, but he was happy to help his mate search for B.

Rose had just had a door slammed in her face.

'Bugger off,' said the man. 'Bloody Jehovah's Witnesses.'

Rose's phone rang. Oliver's home number showed on the screen, but the caller wasn't Oliver. It was Brenda, his mother.

'Somebody's given my poor boy a walloping. Punched him in the eye. You have to help him.'

'Have you reported it to the police?'

'No, what's the point? He's a juvenile offender. Cops aren't interested.'

'He's been assaulted, Brenda. I promise you it'll be investigated.'

'He won't talk to coppers but I reckon he'll talk to you. He loves your dog, see. If you bring the dog, he'll talk. I'm sure of it. Please.'

Rose stared across the street at Malcolm, who was talking to a friendly young couple. She didn't want to abandon him. She knew how devastated she would be if the same thing had happened to Monty. But Ollie had been assaulted and his mother had begged for her help. If she could persuade Ollie to report the assault, she could be back with Malcolm and Joe within an hour.

She explained the situation to Malcolm and promised to be back as soon as she could. At least Malcolm had Joe with him.

When Rose and Monty arrived at Brenda's flat, angry, grinding guitar music was crashing through the door to Ollie's room like a storm surge. Brenda stood with Rose and Monty in the hallway. She knocked on the door, calling for her son to open it. There was no response. She beat on the door with the heel of her fist, calling his name loudly. Linkin Park's *One Step Closer* fell silent and Ollie opened his door.

'Mum! What did you call her for?'

The skin around Ollie's right eye was swollen and already turning violet. His glasses sat crookedly on his face. One lens was fractured into three pieces. Black electrical tape held the frame together at the bridge of the nose.

'I'm at my wits' end, Ollie,' said Brenda. 'Tell Rose what's going on or I'm calling the cops, whether you like it or not.'

'No, Mum, don't. Seriously. Don't.'

'Talk to Rose then. I've got to go to work. See you about five. And for God's sake, stay out of trouble.'

'I'm not a kid,' he said sulkily.

Brenda rolled her eyes and turned back down the hallway.

'Your mum works hard,' Rose said to Ollie.

'Suppose.'

'Have you got a bag of peas for that eye?'

'Yeah, done all that.'

'Can I sit?'

'Suppose.'

Rose sat on the desk chair. 'Mind if I let Monty off the lead?'

'Nah.'

Rose was beginning to understand the phrase *monosyllabic teenager*.

As soon as Monty was free of his leash, he went up to Ollie, tail wagging. The teenager stroked Monty's head. 'Hello, boy.'

The front door clicked shut. They were alone in the flat. 'Has this got anything to do with the gang you stole the car for?'

'Nah.' The pins and needles were very sharp.

'Are they trying to force you to do another job for them?'

Ollie stared down at Monty. He scratched him on the chest. 'I can't say nothin'.'

Rose suspected that whoever had talked Ollie into stealing a car was now pressuring him to do something else illegal. Theft perhaps. Maybe drugs. Once a kid like Ollie got in with a gang like The Blockers there was no walking away. Not unless Ollie moved out of the area or the gang went down, neither of which seemed likely anytime soon. And Ollie was clearly too scared to inform on them. Rose looked around the cramped bedroom. 'Done any more work on your inventions?'

His swollen face brightened. 'Yeah. Tested my drone. It flies really high and can go five miles. I'll show you how it works.'

Ollie switched on his drone and, using the remote control, it levitated off the shelf and hovered above the bed. It buzzed like a hornet on steroids. Monty barked, snapping his jaws at it, then clambered onto the bed, trying to bite it, but Ollie easily kept it beyond Monty's reach.

'He thinks it's a giant fly or something,' Ollie laughed.

'Off the bed, Monty.'

Monty got down from the bed and Ollie piloted the drone back to the shelf above his bed. The buzzing sound stopped. Suddenly, Monty leapt up on the bed again, his nose pointed up at the shelves. Rose followed his line of sight and realised he wasn't looking at the drone. He was focused on the shelf above, which had half a dozen printed photos on it, some framed, others simply propped against the wall.

'What's up with him?' Ollie asked.

Rose peered at the photos. 'Tell me about these.'

'Why?'

'Humour me. Something about them has got Monty excited.' She pointed at the first photo of a large, black rat. 'Is this Cody?'

'Yeah.'

Brenda had told Rose that a boy called Nathan killed Ollie's pet rat.

'What happened to him?'

'Died.'

Rose found it interesting that he didn't tell her about Nathan. Was he Ollie's assailant?

'What's this one? A magpie?'

Monty stopped barking and pricked up his ears. Why would Monty be interested in a photo of a magpie?

'Yeah. She was beautiful. I found her at the side of the road. I think she'd been bumped by a car or something. I carried her home tucked inside my jacket and trained her to take seed from my hand.'

'What happened to her?'

It was as if Ollie hadn't heard her. 'Did you see that?'

Rose did a double take. The photo of the magpie moved. On its own. A pointed nose and whiskers poked out from behind it.

'Is that a—' Rose began.

'Rat. Where did it come from?' The rat ducked back behind the photo as if it were hiding. 'I'll get some cheese.'

Ollie raced to the kitchen. When he returned, he carried a packet of cheese slices. Monty immediately started sniffing the packaging. 'Sorry mate,' Ollie said, 'this is for your little friend.'

Ollie stood on the bed and placed a piece of cheese the size of a one pence coin on the shelf a few centimetres from where the rat was hiding.

'It won't be able to resist,' he said.

Sure enough, the rat poked its head out from behind the photo, whiskers quivering as it sniffed the cheese, then made a dash for the morsel. It grabbed the piece of cheese and took cover behind the photo again.

'She's female,' Ollie said. 'Bet she was caught in a trap once. Half her tail's gone.'

Ollie repeated the exercise, although this time he placed the piece of cheese in the palm of his hand. He then laid the back of his hand on the shelf close to the rat. The little creature tentatively crept onto his hand to grab the cheese. Ollie stroked her back. 'Aren't you a beauty?'

'Where did she come from?' Rose asked, recovering from her shock.

'Way too fat to be a street rat. I'd say she's a pet that's legged it.'

Monty barked at the rat in Ollie's palm, or perhaps it was at the cheese, Rose wasn't sure. What the creature did next stunned her. The rat tore off a chunk of cheese and dropped it on the floor for Monty. Monty snaffled the tiny piece of cheese in the blink of an eye.

'Did she just–?'

'Yeah,' Ollie said. 'Can't believe it. She's a clever one. Hope Mum will let me keep her.'

The rat sat on her haunches, twitched her whiskers, then scampered up his arm, down his T-shirt, over his belt and down his jeans to the carpet. She walked with a rolling gait, her round stomach almost on the carpet. She then sat contentedly between Monty's two front legs.

'Dogs don't normally like rats, do they?' said Rose.

'Not normally, but this one likes Monty. It's like they know each other.'

Rose kneeled down and studied the rat. 'I wonder if you're the one my mum has been going on about. You're a big one, aren't you?'

The rat got on all fours, her back arched, and hissed.

'She didn't like that,' Ollie said, laughing. 'It's like she knew what you said.'

'Is this your rat, Monty?'

Monty hadn't moved since the rodent positioned itself between his front paws. He lowered his face so his muzzle almost touched the rat's head. The rat didn't run.

'I'm speechless,' Rose said.

'Monty,' Ollie said, 'can I play with your friend?'

Monty stepped back so the rat was out in the open. Ollie carefully picked her up, stroking her. She even lay on her back so he could tickle her belly, which made the rodent wriggle. Ollie laughed. Rose was happy to watch for a while, then her eyes wandered back to the shelves. There was a framed photograph of four boys of about fourteen years old. Ollie was easy to pick out, with the same wild curly hair and chiselled face. Different glasses, though. 'That's you, isn't it?'

Ollie glanced up briefly. 'Yeah.'

'Who are the others?'

He shrugged. 'Dunno.'

The pins and needles in her limbs confirmed what she already knew:

Ollie was lying. 'You have a framed photo of you with three boys and you don't know who they are?'

'It's not important.' He placed the rat in his lap and continued to stroke her with a finger.

'Is that the Ten Pin Bowling Alley in the background?'

'Yeah.'

'So they're your mates?'

'Were.' That was the truth. No tingling.

One boy was definitely older than the rest. His hair was shaved at the side but longer on top and a long fringe obscured his eyes. He held up a bowling ball like he was going to throw it at the camera. He had a word tattooed between his knuckles and the first joint of his fingers. She removed the photo from the shelf and studied it.

The tattoo said THUG LIFE.

Thug Life? Wasn't that the tattoo Mila saw on the hands of the man who threatened Anna?

Rose pointed at the eldest boy. 'Is this Nathan, the one who killed Cody?'

'How do you know–? Ah, Mum told you, didn't she? Shit! That's all I need.'

'He's young to have a tattoo,' Rose said, tapping the glass of the photo frame. 'He was already a member of the Blockers, wasn't he?'

'Don't know.' Another lie.

'He gave you the black eye. Why?'

'I don't want to talk about it.'

'Was he trying to shut you up?'

Ollie lifted the rat off his lap and passed her to Rose, who put the photo on the desk so she could cup her hands together. 'You look after her. I gotta go.'

'Wait, Ollie!'

He gently pushed Monty aside, took his coat from a hook on the back of the door, and hurried into the corridor.

'Wait, please.' Rose followed him down the hall, still holding the rat in her hands. 'Ollie, this is important. A girl's been murdered. Anna Czubinska. Not much older than you. She was threatened by a guy with a THUG LIFE tattoo on his hands, just like the boy in the photo. Did Nathan have anything to do with her murder?'

Ollie was trembling. Behind his broken glasses, his eyes darted about like those of a hunted animal.

'Please, Ollie,' Rose continued. 'Tell me where Nathan lives.'

She thought he wasn't going to say anything. Then he blurted out, 'Block B, flat 37.'

'Surname?'

'Hill.' Ollie sunk down to the floor and hugged his knees to his chest. Monty sat next to him and licked the back of his hand. 'I was walking home after that day I did chores for you. I passed Nat, with his mates, an' he was boasting how he'd scared the shit out of some girl. Threatened to strangle her if she talked.'

Anna had been strangled to death. A shiver ran up her spine. 'What girl?'

'Don't know.'

'Does Nathan know you heard him?'

'Oh yeah. I went to the shops yesterday. He jumped me on the way back. Gave me this.' Ollie pointed at his swollen, bruised face. 'Said if I grassed him up, I'd end up dead.' Ollie peered up at Rose, his lip quivering. 'Like the girl in the woods.'

35

Rose knew Major Crime would be hard at work on the murder case, regardless of it being a Sunday. She had left Monty with Ollie, who was clearly terrified of Nathan Hill. Monty excelled at providing comfort, but he was a perfectly capable guard dog too. Rose planned to pick him up once she'd updated Leach on what she knew. But first, she phoned Ollie's mother. At seventeen, Ollie was a child in the eyes of the law.

'Why didn't he tell me? The silly sod,' said Brenda.

'I don't know. But he's scared and I need to tell you it might get worse before it gets better. Once Nathan gets hauled in for questioning, Ollie could become a target.'

'Leave my boy out of it, then.'

'He'll be a confidential source. But Nathan might guess where we got our intel from.'

'No, you can't do this. Please don't drag him into it.'

'Brenda, a girl not much older than your son was murdered. Nathan may have valuable information. I can't just sit on this. But I've got a suggestion. Ollie can stay with me for a few days. Nobody will think of looking for him at my place. What do you say?'

'But you're a cop. Why would you do that?'

Rose thought about the question. She was pretty much providing protective custody to a juvenile. And yet she wasn't formally on the case because she was on sick leave. Having a thieving teenager wanted by a street gang at her house was a really bad idea. Probably one of her worst. And her mom definitely wouldn't be happy about it. Yet, Ollie had grown on her. He had a good heart and she didn't want anything bad to happen to him.

'I like Ollie, he's a good lad. And Monty loves him.'

'Yeah, animals always love Ollie.' Brenda sighed. 'What does Ollie say?'

'I haven't told him yet. I wanted to clear it with you first.'

There was a beep and a click of Brenda remotely unlocking her car. 'I'll talk to him and let you know, okay?'

'Okay.'

Rose then phoned Leach. 'Don't come to my office. Buzz me when you're in the foyer,' Leach said.

Leach was deliberately keeping Rose out of the investigation room. Nevertheless, she drove to Geldeford Police HQ and waited in the foyer as instructed. On a noticeboard was a poster: *Rat on a rat, drug dealers ruin lives.* This got Rose wondering about Nathan. She knew the Blockers dealt drugs. Was Anna involved? Was that the connection?

'Well, well. Look who it is,' said Leach as he barrelled down upon her. 'Missing us, hey?'

Rose was relieved to find Leach in a good mood. He must be making progress with Kacper and Mila. With a shiver of trepidation, she wondered how he would react when she threw him the curve ball that was Nathan Hill.

He led her into an airless meeting room on the ground floor. He gestured to the seat across the table, which she took. 'Is this about Kowalski?' he asked.

'No, sir.' She cleared her throat. 'A new suspect.'

The smile left his face. 'We're this close to squeezing a confession out of Kowalski.' He held up his thumb and first finger so that their tips almost touched, then shook his head. 'Who's your suspect?'

'Nathan Hill. He was overheard boasting that he threatened to strangle Anna the day before she was murdered. He's with the Blockers.'

'I know him. Almost nicked him a couple of times but he's managed to get off. He's trouble, sure. But what makes you believe he threatened Anna?'

'A confidential source. Both my source and Mila identified the man who threatened Anna by the tattoos on his hands. "Thug life" is pretty distinctive.'

The chair groaned as Leach leaned back and folded his arms. 'I thought she made that up to deflect us from Kacper.'

'What if she didn't, sir?'

'This is a high profile case. There's a ton of pressure on me to close it fast. I have the likely killer in custody. A new suspect could bollocks that up.'

'Maybe Kowalski is a stalker but not a killer.'

'No way.' Leach counted off each point on his stumpy fingers. 'One. He had Anna's phone on him. Two. Forensics found the same soil on the sole of Kowalski's shoes as we found on Anna's boots. Three. His alibi is lame – some love-sick seventeen-year-old he shags every now and again, who's dumb enough to lie for him. Four. He has scratches on his hands and we're checking to see if his skin is under Anna's fingernails. Five. When I get the paternity test result back, it's going to prove he was the father of Anna's baby. And finally, six, he has a history of stalking – a protection order was filed against him ten months ago.'

The evidence was certainly stacked against Kowalski, but much of it was circumstantial. His alibi placed him nowhere near the crime scene at the time of Anna's death. The soil on both Anna's and Kacper's footwear was interesting, though, because it was only found in the chalky hills behind Geldeford, which included Hinchley Wood.

'Does Kowalski own a car?' Rose asked.

'You're not working this case, Rose. How many times do I have to tell you to leave it?' Leach stood up. Their meeting was over. 'Thanks for the intel on Nathan Hill. We'll interview him, but unless your source is ready to testify, I doubt it will lead anywhere.'

'My source is afraid of him.'

'And he should be. Hill is guilty of at least two assaults but we couldn't get enough to charge him. His dad's serving time for drug trafficking and GBH. His aunt got busted for running a brothel. I hear she's now running a pet shop, but leopards don't change their spots.'

Pet shop? Rose thought of the woman in Pawfect Pets and the sad puppy.

'What's her name?'

'Who?'

'Nathan's aunt.'

'Janet Hill, why?'

'Just curious. Don't fancy buying dog food from her, that's all.' Rose stood up. 'Thanks for hearing me out, sir.'

As she left the police station, her phone rang.

'He wants to stay with you,' Brenda said. 'Can you pick him up?'

Rose said she could. Immediately afterwards Malcolm called.

'We're taking a break,' he said. Rose blushed with embarrassment. She had completely forgotten about her promise to return to door knocking after she'd dropped in on Ollie. 'We're meeting Sarah. She's bringing Daniel.' Joe's wife and son. 'We're going to the Bull and Spectacles for lunch.'

In the background she heard Joe whisper, 'Spit it out.'

Malcolm continued, 'Do...you want to come?'

Rose was hungry and the idea of a nice cosy pub and a Sunday roast was incredibly tempting. 'Sounds lovely, but I have to swing by my place and collect Mum and I'll have a friend with me. It'll probably take me three quarters of an hour or so. Will you still be there?'

'Yes, of course. We'll wait,' Malcolm said.

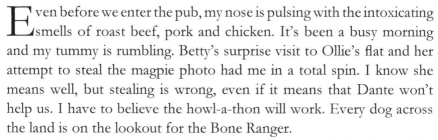

36

Even before we enter the pub, my nose is pulsing with the intoxicating smells of roast beef, pork and chicken. It's been a busy morning and my tummy is rumbling. Betty's surprise visit to Ollie's flat and her attempt to steal the magpie photo had me in a total spin. I know she means well, but stealing is wrong, even if it means that Dante won't help us. I have to believe the howl-a-thon will work. Every dog across the land is on the lookout for the Bone Ranger.

Ollie has Betty stowed in his inside coat pocket. Only I know this. He's given her a bread crust to keep her occupied, but that won't last long. What happens then?

We pile out of the car. Through the windows, Rose spots Malcolm, Big Man Joe and a pretty woman cradling a baby. Rose waves at them.

'Oh, do leave him in the car, Rose,' Liz says. 'He'll be a pain.'

Ollie and I glance at each other. We're clearly both wondering which one of us she's talking about.

'No, he won't, Mum. And anyway, this is a dog-friendly pub.'

Ah, it's me Liz is objecting to. Ollie shrugs at me apologetically. I wag my tail so he knows I don't blame him for Liz's slight upon my doghood.

Malcolm has secured a large table that seats six. They've been nibbling on garlic bread while they waited. He stands up and shakes Liz's hand, but his eyes are on Rose, who is busy kissing the pretty woman on the cheek.

'I've kept this seat for–' Malcolm begins to say to Rose.

'Lovely!' says Liz, taking the proffered seat.

Poor Malcolm will be assaulted by nonstop chatter the whole time we are here. He stares pleadingly at Rose, who fails to notice. At least she sits opposite him. Big Man Joe greets Ollie, introduces his wife, Sarah, and their one-year-old, Daniel.

'Looks like you've been through the wars, mate,' says Joe to Ollie. 'There's a chair here.' He points to one at the head of the table, next to him.

I give the sleeping baby strapped to Sarah's chest a little sniff just to check he's okay and then I lie down under the table next to Rose's feet. I snaffle a couple of crisps that lie discarded on the floor. Salty and crunchy. I lick my muzzle. So far so good. Next, the roast!

Above me, the hoomans chat. The heel of Malcolm's left shoe bounces up and down like it's on a spring. His sock has a repeating pattern of little sausage dogs. Liz, in high-heel, knee-length boots, shuffles her chair closer to him. A few moments later, he shifts his chair away by about the same distance.

Have I mentioned Liz is dressed like a leopard today? At least, her dress has a leopard skin pattern. Having watched David Attenborough's documentary on leopards with Rose, I can't help but notice there's a distinctly predatory feel about her today.

One of the bar staff takes the food and drinks order. The smells are driving me nuts. It's not just the roasts, you see. It's a cornucopia. Gravy. Fish and chips. Cheese. Sausages. I could go on, but I need to take my mind off it, so I distract myself by sniffing everyone's shoes. Big Man Joe is wearing big man police boots that lace up above the ankles and smell of the pavements he's been walking. Sarah's smell of talcum powder and baby puke. Malcolm's, not surprisingly, smell of the vet hospital. Ollie's scuffed trainers have a musty smell, but I'm not so interested in his shoes as I am in his jacket's inside pocket, which is now hanging on the back of his chair. Betty is in the pocket. Except there's no bulge anymore. Does he even know Betty has gone? I swallow down a gulp of alarm. A rat in a pub is a recipe for disaster. I swing my head from side to side, sniffing. I can't see her and I can't smell her. And I can't go looking for her either.

'Are you married?' I hear Liz ask Malcolm. Her perfume is pungent. I think she must have taken a bath in it.

'N-no, I…'

'Girlfriend?'

'I, um…'

Rose kicks her mother in the shin. More like a nudge really. This is interesting. Never seen Rose do that before.

'Ouch!' says Liz.

Rose speaks hurriedly, 'So, Malcolm, how did you go this morning? Any sightings?'

'Nothing. But I won't give up. Somebody must have seen something. I'm going back to it after lunch. There's so much ground to cover.'

Rose suddenly sits up as straight as a Doberman on guard duty. 'I've got an idea. Hey, Ollie!' she says, loud enough for the boy to hear from the other end of the table. Ollie stares at her. 'You left your drone at my house, didn't you?'

'Yeah. I wanna test it on Winterfold Heath.'

'How far did you say it flew?'

'Five miles. Why?'

'Does it have audio or just video?'

'I can switch on audio, although it's tough to hear anything on the ground unless it's loud.'

'What about this for an idea. Malcolm's dog was stolen last night, along with two others. The thieves drove a white van. It's a long shot, but your drone could help us locate the van. Maybe if we then hear barking, we could investigate.'

Ollie grins. 'Cool. I'm in.'

'Hold on a sec,' says Joe. 'It's a good plan but if you find anything you have to let the police know.'

'Of course,' Rose says, with a tinge of disappointment.

Malcolm's leg has stopped bouncing. 'What a great idea, Rose. We can set up at the vet hospital and then work a five-mile radius from there.'

'And Ollie loves animals,' Rose says. 'Maybe you can show him around the vet hospital, too?'

'Sure.'

'Cool,' says Ollie.

Liz taps a long, painted fingernail on her thigh. 'That's all well and good, but what am I supposed to do? I'm not spending the afternoon at a vet's.'

'How about the shopping centre?' Rose suggests. 'There are some great clothes shops, even designer labels.'

Liz pouts. 'That's no fun on my own. Come with me. Let the boys play with their gadgets.'

Malcolm's leg starts bouncing again. 'I…um, it would be good to have Rose's expertise–'

Liz screams. My natural instinct is to get up, ready to defend my hooman. I forget I'm under the table and my head smacks into the underside of the tabletop. Luckily, I have a thick skull. Liz leaps to her feet, her chair falling backwards with a thwack. 'Look!' she squeals.

Liz's glimmering red fingernail is pointing at Betty, who is chowing down on the garlic bread on Liz's side plate, oblivious to the horrified stares encircling her.

This is bad. Very bad.

'Oh my God!' says a woman at the next-door table. 'A rat!'

I place my front paws on the tabletop and crane my neck to reach Betty. Liz screams again – I do wish she would stop doing that. Betty finally drops the garlic bread as I close my teeth around her. I'm careful not to hurt her, which is a neat trick us soft-mouthed Golden Retrievers can do. She wriggles and calls me all sorts of things in language that would make a wharfie blush. Before she gives my tongue a nip, I race for the conservatory door. Rose runs after me, throws open the door and I charge across the car park to Rose's car. Hidden from the gawking diners crowding the window to watch the doggie kill the rat – which, of course, is the last thing I'm going to do – I open my mouth and Betty plops to the ground, her whiskers and face slick with my saliva.

'What the hell do you think you're doing?' Betty demands.

'Saving your life! You can't steal food in broad daylight. Didn't you hear the panic in there? The pub could get closed down.'

'Spoilsport!'

37

Huddled behind a computer screen at Geldeford Vet Hospital, Malcolm and Rose watch sky-high images of a giant hornet-like-creature they call a drone. Ollie controls it from a box in his hand. I've always wondered what a bird sees from the sky and now I know. After a while, though, my eyelids droop as my attention wanders. Betty is curled up asleep in Ollie's jacket pocket. She's promised she'll stay there until we reach home. Thankfully, Liz is shopping for clothes and doesn't know Ollie has become Betty's hooman protector. When she discovers this, I imagine she'll start screaming again.

I open one eye. On the screen is a village I recognise. The church is on one side of the road and the Jolly Farmer is on the other. Far below, a couple of old men leave the pub and wander up the main street.

'This is as far as the drone'll go,' says Ollie. 'I'll have to bring it back.'

'Abinger Hammer,' Rose muses under her breath. 'Can we go just a little further? Two doors down from the pub is Pawfect Pets. I want to take a look at it.'

'Have to be quick,' Ollie replies. 'Battery's low.'

'Why the pet shop?' Malcolm asks.

'I have a bad feeling about the owner.'

'Janet Hill? She can be a bit prickly but she's all right.'

Rose and I both stare at Malcolm. 'How do you know her?' Rose asks.

'She's the sales rep for Basil's Pet Foods. Comes in every now and again trying to get me to stock it. Saw her Friday, actually.'

'I ain't going anywhere near that bitch,' says Ollie.

Malcolm's eyes move from Rose to Ollie to me. 'What do you all know that I don't?'

'She's done time,' says Rose. 'And her nephew is a nasty piece of work. He gave Ollie that black eye.'

'Prison? Really?'

'Yes,' Rose says.

Ollie taps the computer screen. 'Shop looks closed. I'll take a look at the back.'

The drone passes over the Pawfect Pets' tiled roof and the chimney stack. In the rear, a sleek red car and a white van are parked against a brick wall.

White van! I bark in alarm.

'Yes, Monty, we've seen it,' says Rose. 'Let's go.'

The fur down my spine is up and my tail is held high. Instinct tells me this is the Bone Ranger's van. I can't work out what Walnut Face, otherwise known as Janet Hill, has got to do with the dognappings, but I do know she has no love for animals.

'I'll come with you,' Malcolm says, reaching for his coat.

'Count me out,' Ollie says. 'I'm staying here.'

'Malcolm, why don't you keep going with your door knocking? Take Ollie with you?' Rose says to Malcolm.

'I don't need baby-sitting,' Ollie says.

'No, but Malcolm needs your help.' Rose replies.

Ollie lapses into silence. I think Rose wants to keep Ollie safe.

'I'd rather come with you,' Malcolm says. 'The dog thieves are violent.'

'I promise I'll call the police if I find anything.'

'All right, if you're sure,' Malcolm says. 'The red BMW is Janet's. It always causes a bit of a stir when she shows up in it.'

'Did she ask about the dogs convalescing overnight?'

'Come to think of it, yes she did. I thought she was just making conversation.'

'Did she meet B?'

He looks suddenly sad. 'Yes. How could I have been so naïve?'

In two shakes of a lamb's tail, we're in Abinger Hammer. Between the pet shop and the greengrocer next door is a narrow, crushed-stone driveway that leads to four parking spaces at the back of Pawfect Pets. It's late afternoon and being mid-winter, it's getting dark. A security light flicks on as Rose parks next to the red sports car. She turns in her seat to look at me.

'Stay here, Monty. If they are dog thieves, I don't want anything happening to you. And stay quiet, okay?'

I don't like this plan at all. If I'm in the car, how can I defend Rose? Walnut Face is a nasty hooman and the Bone Ranger is vicious. Through the gap in the rear window, I smell his stench hanging in the air. His van is parked on the other side of the sports car but even from here the smell of the lamb bones he uses as bait and the vinegary stink of terror makes me want to gag. I am afraid, but I can't let Rose face them alone. I claw at the side door. *I want to come with you!*

'Stay!' she whispers and closes the door softly.

She circles the white van. The rear windows are tinted almost black. She peeks through the driver's window. She tries the door but it's locked. She photographs the number plate with her phone, taps out a message and sends it. Then she creeps to the shop's back door.

I want to bark. *No! Don't go in there!* But I've been told not to make a noise. Rose opens the door a fraction. Light pours through the gap. There's a rumble of hooman voices. One male. One female – she sounds like Walnut Face.

Rose eases the door open and steps inside.

I jump up and frantically paw at the window. *Come back!*

Rose slowly pushes the door to, not fully closing it, leaving a halo of light around the door jamb.

I pause and listen. The sky has turned indigo and birds are heralding night's arrival. In the woods behind the car park wall is a badger set. They make little snorting sounds and smell like peanut butter. I can't hear Rose, just the man and woman talking.

Inside the shop are raised voices. Walnut Face is shouting, 'Get out of my shop!' There's a chime as the shop's front doorbell rings then a rapid and regular crunch of shoes on the driveway. The rear security light blazes to life, dazzling my eyes. A silhouette runs past Rose's car. My tail tucks right under my belly. My mouth goes dry.

I remember my mother's terrified face as the Bone Ranger used a noose on a pole to catch her. 'Run,' she said, 'Run like the wind!'

I grab the car's door handle with my mouth and pull. Can I get out before he notices me?

The Bone Ranger stops and turns. I duck down and make my body as flat as I can. His shadow blots out the glare from the security light as it envelops the car and me. *Don't whimper. Not a sound*, I tell myself.

He peers in the rear window. I dare to look into his frigid, blue eyes. Grey beard, round face.

'I can see you, puppy dog,' he says tauntingly. 'Aren't you a stunning specimen?'

I rear up, bare my teeth and snarl, so loudly that birds screech and fly away. The Bone Ranger rears back.

'I know exactly what to do with bad dogs like you.'

He throws open the car door. I lunge at him. He rears back and I miss my mark.

Rose bursts out of the back door. I'm snarling and barking like a rabid beast.

'You're under arrest! Back away from the car!'

The Bone Ranger runs to his van, shoving Rose out of the way. The engine screeches to life and he speeds off, narrowly missing Rose, who pulls out her phone.

38

The police have the white van's number plate and Rose has made a statement. Unfortunately, the number plate doesn't belong to anybody, or so Big Man Joe says. Walnut Face also made a statement; she lied through her teeth, claiming that she had no idea who the owner of the white van was. When Rose has told Malcolm and Ollie what happened, bought some groceries for tonight, and picked up Liz, we are all exhausted and long for home. The rear car seats have to be put back into position so Ollie can squeeze in, and I sit on the back seat next to him. One big happy family!

As soon as we walk into the kitchen, Liz drops her clothes-shopping bags on the floor and makes a beeline for the boiler cupboard.

'I have something to show you,' says Liz, opening the cupboard door. 'Watch this.'

She uses the same sweeping hand gestures of a magician I once saw on TV who made a woman disappear. She clicks the switch that somehow heats up the radiators and turns cold water hot. There's a puffing sound as the flame inside the boiler ignites.

'Ta da!'

'My God!' Rose says, looking delighted. 'It's working. How did you do that?'

The old pipes that run under the floors, up walls, and into radiators, clank and gurgle. This is a good sign. The old house is coming to life again.

'A very nice man called Albert fixed it,' Liz says, eyes twinkling. 'While you were out this morning chasing lost dogs, I got the boiler working.'

'That's brilliant, thanks Mum. Did he charge extra for a Sunday call-out?'

'Just for the parts. No labour. No call-out fee.'

'That's very nice of him. Why would he do that?'

'Well, darling, a little bit of charm can go a long way.' Liz takes a bottle of pink wine from one of her shopping bags. She pours two glasses and hands one to Rose. 'Here's to a hot shower.'

Ollie stands awkwardly near the back door, a canvas overnight bag in one hand and an open box in the other that has his drone and Rat Cam equipment in it. His glasses have slid down his nose and are balancing on the tip, but his hands are full and he can't shunt them back up again.

'What would you like to drink, Ollie?' Rose asks.

'A beer, thanks.' He lowers the box and his overnight bag onto the table.

'I don't have beer, and it's probably not a good idea. I have juice, Coke, milk.'

'I'm old enough,' he says, pushing his glasses up his nose a little defiantly.

'Your mum didn't want you to, I'm sorry. How about Coke?'

Ollie takes the proffered can, then Rose shows him into the sitting room.

'You're sleeping on the sofa. I'll get the bedding later,' I hear Rose say.

She shuts the door, leaving Ollie watching TV, and starts to unpack the groceries.

Liz is still looking at the sitting room door, as though her disapproval can bore through it. I wander over to my dog bed and lie down. She's about to start complaining again. I can sense it.

'He's a yob!' Liz says.

'Mum!' says Rose, putting a packet of pasta on the counter near the hob. 'He'll hear you.'

'That boy will steal anything he can get his hands on,' Liz says. 'Mark my words.'

'He's staying. He made one mistake and he was bullied into it. He's a good lad. It wouldn't go amiss if you were to show some compassion.'

I wag my tail. It's good to see Rose standing up to her mother. Is her confidence returning?

Liz flares her nostrils. 'Well really! I am the epitome of compassion. But I must insist you get rid of the rat.'

'Ah,' Rose says, looking sheepish. 'About that. Turns out the rat is domesticated, and Ollie wants to keep her as a pet.'

'You can't be serious!'

'The vet checked her over so she's not going to spread the plague or anything.'

'Ha, ha, very funny,' says Liz, and gulps down the contents of her glass.

'Ollie needs something positive in his life right now and he's very fond of her. I can't take her away from him.'

Liz rolls her eyes. 'What about me? What about *my* feelings? To think you used to be such a sweet girl. Since you joined the police, you've become cold. Heartless. I'm sure it's part of the brainwashing.'

'Mum, please don't start. Can we just have a nice quiet evening?'

'I'm not the problem here.' Liz stares pointedly down the hall to the sitting room.

I can hear Ollie talking softly to Betty. He's trying to persuade her to wear the Rat Cam.

Liz throws her arms up in the air. 'I give up. I'm going upstairs to have a *hot* shower, then I'm trying on my new frocks.' She picks up her shopping bags.

Once her mother has gone, Rose sits down like a hot air balloon that's lost its lift. I'm with Rose. A nice snoozy night is what we all need, but I guess with Liz around that's not likely to happen. I get up from my bed to stand close to Rose. She strokes my back.

'I'm sorry we didn't find the missing dogs,' she says. 'I won't give up, I promise.'

Nor will I.

'Shame the number plate came to nothing. Fake plates.' She tuts. 'He had to be the dog thief.'

I bark an affirmative.

She gets up. 'Guess I better put this stuff away and make dinner.'

A dog howls. A long plaintive cry, far, far away. So far, I can't make out the message. Rose doesn't notice it. The door is ajar, so I head outside and look up at the sky, ears pricked. The next howl is from a dog nearer to Farley Green, probably in Milford. Then Star, a Staffordshire Bull Terrier who lives with a young family at the other end of our village, lets rip. She repeats the message.

The Bone Ranger is at Clapper Farm. Tell Monty from Duckdown Cottage.

I howl back my thanks and ask the dogs to let me know if The Bone Ranger moves location. Star acknowledges my thanks and passes my message to the next dog, who passes it to the next, and the next.

I sit and consider this news. Clapper Farm! John Clapper lied when he said he didn't know Anna Czubinska. But why would the Bone Ranger be at his farm? Does John now have the stolen pups? Maybe there's a connection between Anna's murder and the dognapping, but for the life of me, I have no idea what it might be.

What I do know is that time is of the essence. What if he takes the pups somewhere else? I have to get to Clapper Farm tonight. But how? It would take me all night to walk there and back, and I can't rescue a load of puppies on my own. I need Rose. But she's settled in for the night. I grab my tail in my mouth and go around in circles for a while as I ponder this problem. As the howling fades, I hear Rose's voice from inside the house.

'Hi Jenny, how are you?' she says.

Ah, the nice lady who likes dead bodies and is trying to work out who killed Anna. I release my tail and trot into the kitchen. The grocery bags are empty and folded at one end of the table. Rose has Jenny on loudspeaker as she pours boiling water into a pan with salt in it.

'I really shouldn't tell you this, but the paternity test came back negative. Kowalski isn't the father of Anna's baby.'

'Any idea who is?' Rose asks, opening the bag of pasta shaped like little shells.

'Not so far.' There's the sound of a drawer shutting on noisy runners.

'Are you still at the mortuary?'

'Been here all day.' She lowers her voice. 'Anyway, they've let Kowalski go. Everything we have on him is circumstantial and this hot-shot lawyer turned up and demanded his release.'

I bet the Prancing Pony and the Leach are furious. They were convinced he was Anna's killer.

'Who's the lawyer?'

'Andrew Clapper of Drayton & Clapper. God only knows how Kowalski can afford him.'

'Clapper?' Rose says. 'Any relation to John Clapper?'

'Yes, his son. You do know John plays golf with the Police Commissioner. They go back a long way.'

'No, actually, I didn't. Thanks for the update, Jen.'

Rose switches off the gas burner and leaves the bag of pasta on the counter. She stares, unseeing, at the tiles on the wall. By now I'm hyped, my paws doing that dance they do. *Yes, John Clapper. We have to go to his farm right now!*

'John's son,' Rose says to herself. 'That can't be a coincidence.' She looks down at me.

I bark once. I agree. But Rose doesn't budge. I rush to the rack where she keeps her red Wellington boots. I pick up a boot and carry it to Rose.

'No walk tonight, Monty.'

That's not what I mean. I drop the boot at her feet, but she's not paying me any attention. She's staring at her phone.

'Their fees are astronomical. Maybe Kowalski's parents are wealthy?' She searches his Facebook profile. 'Okay, that must be his father. Let's take a look…engineer. No, he'd have to be paid *really* well to afford those hourly rates.'

I am so frustrated I take the hem of Rose's jumper in my mouth and tug.

'Stop it. You'll rip the wool.'

Okay, this isn't working. I run out the back door, down the side passage and wait at the car. At some point Rose will notice I'm not in the house and come looking for me. Sure enough, here she comes. I claw at a car door.

'You want to go to Clapper Farm, don't you?'

One bark for yes.

She chews her lip. 'You have a bad feeling about John, too. Don't you?' She looks at her watch. 'We'll go in the morning.'

I bark raucously, over and over.

She tries to quieten me, but it doesn't work. 'Okay, okay, we'll take a quick look.' I immediately go quiet.

Rose goes back to the house, leaves a handwritten note for her mum, then tells Ollie she's forgotten an ingredient for dinner and won't be long. I think that's called a little white lie. I catch a glimpse of Betty wearing the Rat Cam and Ollie whooping with delight at the images he's receiving on his phone, and I wish Betty was coming with us. Rose closes the sitting room door firmly behind her, presumably to keep Betty away from Liz. She throws on her coat and clips the lead to my collar.

As we drive away from Farley Green, I'm wondering which of us is in the most danger: Rose and I, on our way to a farm that belongs to a nasty man with an equally nasty dog, or Ollie and Betty, who will have to cope with rat-hating Liz.

At a red light, Rose dials Malcolm. 'Do you by any chance know John Clapper?'

'Yes, I look after his sheep. And Tank.'

'Good. Can I swing by and pick you up? I have some questions for John and I have a feeling he won't want to talk. But he might talk to you.'

'You've lost me. You think John has something to do with the theft of my dogs?'

'Actually, it's about a murder.'

39

Malcolm sits in the passenger seat of Rose's car. One of his knees is bouncing up and down. He radiates nervousness.

'I'm not sure this is a good idea,' he says as the car hurtles towards Clapper Farm. The hedgerows lining the single-track road swallow the car's headlights, so it feels as though we're in a dark tunnel. 'Shouldn't one of the detectives working the case question John?'

'They did question him,' Rose says. 'But I get the feeling John is untouchable. He's good mates with the Police Commissioner, which might explain why my DCI was reluctant to investigate the gunshots that almost killed Monty.' Rose glances at Malcolm. 'If you're worried about upsetting a client, I can drop you back home.'

'No, you've bent over backwards to help me find B, so it's the least I can do.'

I rest my chin on his shoulder and he pats my head. Slowly his knee stops bouncing.

'Is Tank the only guard dog?' Rose asks.

'Yes. There used to be two, but he gave the other Rottweiler away some months ago.' Malcolm glances at Rose. 'Tank is an unregistered dog, by the way. He's breaking the law.'

'That's good to know. Are you sure it's just one dog? He told me he had a couple and I swear I heard another dog barking the last time I was there.'

'Not that I know of.'

I recognise Clapper Farm by the sheep poo smell. John and Tank give me the shivers but the possibility of coming face to face with the Bone Ranger again has me gulping with fear. Of course, Rose doesn't know what I know. I'm expecting to see the Bone Ranger's white van. The car jolts as a tyre hits a pothole then the headlights illuminate the unwelcoming mechanised wooden gate at the entrance to the farm.

A rear window is open just enough for me to get my nose out. It barely takes a moment for me to pick up the scent of the Bone Ranger. But he didn't go through the gate. He took the unmade track that follows the farm's perimeter. I bark and point my nose at the muddy track.

'What's up, Monty?' Rose says. 'What's over there?'

Leaving the engine running, she gets out and opens my door. I jump to the ground and sniff the tyre tracks in the mud. This is definitely the way he went. Rose peers down the dark track.

'Any idea where this track leads?' she asks Malcolm, who has joined us.

'It leads to Foxden Lane and Foxden Woods. There are a couple of farms up that way.'

She crouches. 'The tracks look fresh. Can we get back to Geldeford this way?' She straightens.

'It's a bit circuitous, but yes, we can.'

'Okay, but first, we chat to John.'

Rose turns her back on me and walks to the intercom beside the portcullis-like gates. I stand rigidly pointing down the dark track, but it's not working. Why are we wasting time questioning a man we know is a liar? I'm more convinced than ever the stolen pups are on Clapper's land somewhere and this track might lead us to them. I whimper.

'Get back in the car, Monty,' Rose says.

What do I do? Do I break rule two of the Ten Dog Commandments and disobey my master? And if I do that, I'm also breaking rule five, which is to not appear cleverer than my master.

A gust of wind blows in my face. New smells fill my nostrils. Dogs. Lots of them. Many different breeds. And with it, the breeze carries their cries. Cries of fear, anxiety and bewilderment. But they're so faint, and the wind whisks their voices away again as though it's toying with me. I look behind me at Rose, who is about to place her finger on the intercom button. She clearly hasn't heard them. I bark twice. Rose looks around at me.

I run.

'Monty, stop!'

I know I'll be in trouble for this. But the call of the terrified pups is one I cannot ignore. The muddy track is pitch black. I can make out the looming hedgerows and the occasional glint of mice and hedgehog eyes regarding me with puzzlement from the undergrowth. I rely on scent. I know my nose won't fail me. Rose calls my name again, then her car engine revs and tyres crunch on gravel. I hope she's following me. I stumble through a puddle that's deeper than I realise and the muddy water splashes my chest and belly. It's icy cold and makes me gasp for breath. The distant barking has stopped and I wonder if I imagined it. Behind me, Rose's Honda Jazz has caught up. The car's headlights help me to see the track ahead.

The brick wall that fronts Clapper Farm gives way to wire mesh fencing.

Just inside the fence, a line of fast-growing poplars have been planted as a visual barrier. Because I am low to the ground I can see between the trunks much the same way I could see what was going on under the table in the pub. Hidden behind the trees are three grey buildings with corrugated roofs that arch like a horseshoe. They remind me of sheds where chickens are kept but I don't smell any cluckers. A little further on is a metal gate as tall as the fence.

Beyond the row of poplars, an exterior light carves through the darkness. I can now hear more loudly the pitiful yelps and whines of many dogs. The smell of their faeces and urine along with the sour stink of infection hits me like an explosion. And throughout it all is the stench of terror. Then just as quickly, the light goes off and the barking stops. Rose pulls up just behind me and kills the engine. She must have seen the light and heard the barking too.

From the other side of the fence comes the roar of a car engine. The vehicle does a U-turn, the headlights momentarily blinding me. I duck down low. It heads back towards the house.

My heart is pounding, my breath comes fast. Is this my moment of reckoning? Is the Bone Ranger in one of those sheds? Rose and Malcolm catch up with me and crouch down to my level so they can see what I can see. They switch off their torches.

'Who was that?' Rose asks.

'From the boxy shape of it, I'd say that was John's old Land Rover,' Malcolm says.

'There are dogs in there, Malcolm,' Rose says. 'I heard them.'

'Me too,' Malcolm says. 'Sounded like twenty or more.' He shakes his head. 'John's never said anything about having that many dogs. The poor creatures sound like they're in terrible distress.'

'The sheds must have super thick walls. Can't see any windows, but they must have roof vents. I'm guessing we can only hear them when the door is open. That's why the sound comes and goes so suddenly.' She gives me a hug. 'Good boy, Monty.'

'This has all the signs of a puppy mill.'

'Puppy mill?' Rose asked.

'Puppy mill, puppy factory. Same thing. Bitches are kept in cages like battery hens. Their pups are sold through dodgy outfits.' He pulls out his phone. 'I'm calling the RSPCA.'

'Do they come out at night?'

'Not normally, but I know the local inspector.'

'Wait a sec. We should take a look inside. We'll need proof they're in there, otherwise Clapper will just deny everything,' Rose says.

I'm with Rose on this one. I lock onto the Bone Ranger's scent and follow it to the metal gate. I can't see his white van, but the trail is very strong. I search for a way in. Rose and Malcolm follow.

'We can't go in there,' Malcolm says. 'That's trespassing. I'll ring Bill Slater. He'll know what to do.'

There's a rustling in a beech tree on the other side of the track, then a flash of bright squirrel eyes. Nigel darts down the trunk and peers at the three of us. He's panting heavily.

'Ah, there you are, Mr Monty!'

Pant.

'I was told you were heading this way.'

Pant.

'I have good news.'

Pant.

'I've found the stolen dogs.'

Pant.

He raises a front paw in the direction of the sheds and points.

Unfortunately, because he has lifted one paw off the trunk, he loses his grip and tumbles to the ground. But he's a nimble little fellow and does a forward roll which turns into a jump that lands him onto all fours.

'Oh my God!' Rose says. 'It's that crazy squirrel again.'

Nigel pays no attention to Rose's gawping. 'Over there.' He grins toothily.

I don't have the heart to tell him I already know this. I just bark a thank you.

'Monty, quiet!' Rose says.

Okay, communication with Nigel is going to be difficult. We listen as Malcolm leaves a message for Bill. 'We've stumbled on a puppy mill at Clapper Farm. I think my dog's in there…'

Nigel's grin evaporates. 'Oh, I get it, you knew already.' He smacks his forehead. 'Drrr! Otherwise why would you be here.' His twitching tail droops. 'No matter how hard I try, I never seem to get things right. And to think that's the fastest I've ever run.'

Pant.

'Probably a world record. Twenty-one miles per hour,' Nigel says.

Pant.

'What are you going to do now?' he continues.

'Get under the fence. Can you help me?' I ask.

Nigel stops at a section of fencing where an animal has dug beneath it. Definitely a fox. Foxes are like a moody, weird cousin who never shows up to family gatherings and always stays out way too late. Their smell is utterly unmistakable. Its constant visits have pushed up the wire too. But the hole isn't big enough for me to squeeze through. I'm going to have to make it bigger. I start digging, as fast as I can, damp dirt flying behind me. Rose grips my collar. 'No Monty, you can't. That Rottweiler will kill you.'

Malcolm catches up with us. 'Bill's not picking up. I left a message.'

I keep digging. More frantically.

'Leave this to the professionals,' Nigel chitters to me. 'We squirrels know how to dig.'

He lines up next to me, then gets stuck in. His long claws rip through the mushy soil.

Rose gasps. 'Oh my…what's it doing?'

Nigel sends lumps of grit and mud flying, until soon the mound of soil behind him is bigger than he is.

Rose tries to pull me back by my collar. 'Stop, Monty. We'll come back in the morning.'

No, by then it could be too late. I heard dogs crying for help. I can't abandon them. The trench might just be deep enough now. I duck under the fence and use my front paws to pull forward. Rose loses her grip on my collar. I manage to get my shoulders through, but my name tag snags on the wire.

'Oh God,' Rose says. 'Malcolm, help me lift the wire.'

I hear a growl. An exterior light above the first shed's entrance switches on. 'Look what we have here. Monty-the-pretty-boy.' A four-legged shadow precedes the muscular bulk of Tank, teeth bared in a ferocious snarl. 'Caught like a rabbit in a snare.'

40

Tank's lips are peeled back, his teeth and gums bared all the way, his head jutted forward. He means to kill me. I struggle to free myself from the jagged wire fence. My leg muscles burn as I try to reverse through the muddy trench.

'Stay away!' yells Rose, her voice shrill. 'Leave my dog alone!' She fumbles with my collar, trying to unclip it. Her hands are trembling. 'Malcolm, help me!'

'I'll distract him,' says Malcolm. He shakes the fence, his fingers gripping the wire mesh. 'Hey, Tank, you know me. Come here, boy.'

Tank doesn't even so much as look at Malcolm. His eyes are glassy with rage. 'How dare you trespass on *my* territory!' he snarls.

There is no more than a car's length between me and Tank. He stalks closer. If I can't go backwards, then do I go forwards? I'm a sitting duck right now. I have to do something.

I'm no coward, but I'm no match for a Rottweiler. He's a trained guard dog. He outweighs me by fifteen kilos. If he gets hold of me, there's no way Rose or Malcolm will be able to prise his jaws open.

'Tank,' I say, 'those dogs are suffering. They're stolen. Let us help them.'

Our barking prompts the dogs in the sheds to howl and yelp and bay. It's muted by the walls, but I can hear them clearly. Paws and bodies slam into metal cages that clank and rattle.

'Help us!'

'Free us!'

'Save our puppies!'

Tank inches closer. In a few more steps, he'll have my neck in his jaws. 'Finally I can prove I'm not weak like my brother.'

My collar falls away. Rose has undone it.

'Back you come,' she says.

Malcolm grabs my haunches and tries to haul me backwards through the trench. At the same time, Tank lunges forward. But before he reaches me, Tank suddenly rears up, yelping. He twists his head, jaws snapping.

Nigel is on the Rottweiler's back, his sharp claws dug into the dog's flesh, his front teeth sunk deep into his shoulder. Blood glistens on the big dog's jet black coat. Tank shakes himself maniacally, and the squirrel leaps clear like a martial arts master. He darts for the fence, but Tank takes one stride for every twenty of Nigel's. With surprising speed he lunges for the squirrel, catching his fluffy tail. Nigel squeals.

I can't let him die like this.

Malcolm is distracted by the commotion. His fingers loosen. Instead of crawling backwards, I claw my way forwards until I'm through and on the other side. One bite from Tank and Nigel will lose his head, literally.

'Monty!' screams Rose. 'Come back!'

The fence clinks. Malcolm starts to climb over it. 'I'm coming, Monty!' he shouts.

Tank will rip him to shreds.

'Tank, your beef is with me,' I say. 'Let the squirrel go and face me like a real guard dog.'

Tank drops Nigel, who scampers up the fence to safety. Tank spits out squirrel fur. He circles me, saliva coating his jowls with foam, his teeth bared. I brace myself, my legs wide, and lower my chest, the better to survive the impact. He charges and the impact is like being hit by a locomotive. I end up my back, which, as any dog knows, leaves me totally vulnerable. He goes for my neck, biting down hard. I yowl at the pain.

But Golden Retrievers have rolls of lose skin and thick fur around our necks. Tank tears at my skin but doesn't get my throat. I catch sight of Malcolm raising his Maglite torch. He brings it down between Tank's shoulders. Tank opens his huge jaws as he yowls and swivels to face Malcolm. Tank wobbles a bit. He must be in pain. I scramble up. All Malcolm has to protect himself is a torch. It's not enough.

I sink my teeth into Tank's back leg. I feel something snap. Tank's leg gives way. He collapses, yelping. I back away, the taste of blood in my mouth.

'I can't walk,' Tank yowls. He peers around at his back leg. Tries licking it. Yelps again. 'Don't leave me. He'll shoot me.'

What have I done? I've broken another dog's leg. My stomach heaves and I vomit.

'What happened?' Rose cries from the other side of the fence.

'I think Tank's cruciate ligament's snapped,' Malcolm says.

I grip Malcolm's coat and tug, whimpering. 'Help him. Help Tank.'

'It's okay Monty,' Malcolm says. 'I'll help him. Let go.'

The vet tentatively kneels near Tank's injured leg. 'It's all right,' he says soothingly to the injured dog, 'I can fix this. I'll need to take you with me.'

Malcolm's shoe dislodges a piece of metal in the grass. A keyring with one key. The pendant looks like a smiling Dachshund with a big black nose and a body studded with tiny pieces of twinkling crystal. The sparkling pendant isn't what draws me to it. It's the smell: Anna's unique scent. How did a murdered girl's keyring end up here?

I scoop it up in my mouth.

At that moment, car headlights top a ridge and the vehicle barrels down the hill towards us. A green Land Rover skids to a halt throwing poplar needles and leaf debris into the air. John Clapper throws open the driver's door and gets out. In his hand is a shotgun.

'What the hell do you think you're doing?' he shouts.

41

Rose was in the office of Drayton and Clapper on Monday morning, waiting for Malcolm. She had been summoned by the senior partner of Geldeford's most prestigious law firm, who just happened to be the son of the plaintiff, John Clapper.

Andrew Clapper had phoned Rose at 9 a.m. on the dot, informing her of his father's intention to press civil charges against Rose and Malcolm for trespassing and damage to property. He had insisted they come to his office. Sitting alone in a cavernous foyer that oozed wealth and success from every marble tile, huge floral display, and bespoke sculpture of a man with a spear, Rose found it hard to contain her anxiety. She was responsible for getting Malcolm into this mess and now he was paying the price. And if she couldn't persuade John to drop the charges, Leach wouldn't have her back in Major Crime. Her heart was beating too fast, and her chest wouldn't expand enough for her to get enough oxygen.

Breathe calming breaths, she told herself.

She stared out through the swathe of glass that had the law firm's name embossed on it, her fingers locked together in her lap. Malcolm entered the middle of three revolving doors, accompanied by a portly man in a suit that had seen better days.

'This is my solicitor, Robin Robinson,' Malcolm said.

Robinson shook Rose's hand. His were clammy. 'My mother's idea,' he chuckled. 'She said nobody would be able to forget my name.' Robin dabbed his forehead with a cotton handkerchief.

Malcolm wore a fawn corduroy jacket and trousers and whatever magic he'd worked, it had been sufficient to tame his usually wild hair. The look suited him.

'Any news from the RSPCA?' Rose asked.

'Bill's on his way to Clapper Farm now, with another inspector,' said Malcolm. 'My video should be enough for him to gain access to the sheds. If we can prove we were trying to rescue dogs from a puppy farm, the trespassing charges should go away.'

Malcolm looked at Robin for confirmation. Robin nodded. His double chin wobbled.

'Thank goodness you had your wits about you enough to leave the video running,' Rose said.

Robinson dabbed the handkerchief across his upper lip. 'It could also work against you. You see, it does prove you were trespassing. We're now reliant on the RSPCA to prove you had just cause.'

A young woman with a black bob and pointed nose showed them into a meeting room that seated fourteen. A tall man in a navy chalk stripe suit with a circular balding patch on the back of his pink head had his back to them as they entered. In his hand was a white cup and saucer. He drank from the cup as he stared out at the fountain featuring three leaping dolphins within a circular pool. He turned to face them and gestured to the leather and chrome Eames office chairs.

'Please take a seat.' Andrew Clapper had his father's reddish complexion. 'Robin,' he said, with a curt nod at Malcolm's solicitor. Andrew then sat at the head of the table.

'Andrew,' replied Robin, his face sweaty.

Malcolm sat next to Robin and Rose took a seat opposite. The pointy-nosed woman closed the door as she left.

Andrew placed his cup and saucer on the table. He didn't offer them a drink. 'Why don't we cut to the chase? Rose Sidebottom and Malcolm Kerr, you were caught trespassing on Clapper Farm at 8.25pm yesterday by John Clapper, my father. You caused damage to property, namely the fence and the guard dog. I have advised my client to demand punitive damages in the order of fifty thousand pounds. From each of you.'

Rose couldn't believe it. She didn't have fifty thousand pounds. She didn't even have one thousand pounds. Malcolm might be able to re-mortgage the vet hospital, but the only way Rose could pay out that kind of money was to sell Duckdown Cottage. The thought made her teary.

'My clients had just cause to believe there were stolen dogs in sheds on Clapper Farm and that John Clapper was running a puppy factory,' said Robinson. 'They heard cries of distress. Dr Kerr is a vet. He deemed it necessary to climb the fence. He believed the dogs were in danger.'

Andrew crossed his long legs. The hem of his trousers rode up to reveal blue and white candy stripe socks and Oxford shoes. 'Poppycock. The sheds are used for storage. There is no puppy farm.'

'You're questioning the word of a police officer and a respected vet?' said Rose.

'A police officer with PTSD who hasn't worked for months. Not exactly what I'd call a reliable witness.'

Rose felt like she'd been punched in the gut.

'I heard them barking,' said Malcolm. 'There had to be twenty, thirty dogs.'

'Did you actually see any dogs, apart from Tank?' Andrew asked.

'No, I...no. But I–'

Andrew picked up his tea and sipped. He was a smug bastard. Rose wanted to knock the cup out of his hands. By all accounts, father and son were close. He had to know his father ran a puppy farm. How could he turn a blind eye to such cruelty? Rose felt the anger rising in her chest. She had to clench her fists to control it.

'What we did,' said Rose, her voice squeaky with indignation, 'was the right thing. Any human being with an ounce of compassion would do the same. John is guilty of animal cruelty.'

'One more word, Ms Sidebottom, and I'll advise my client to add a claim for defamation to the list.'

'It's all true.' Rose couldn't stop herself. 'And we'll prove it. RSPCA inspectors are searching the farm right now. You might want to pay some attention to defending your father against charges of animal cruelty.' She rose from her chair. 'I'm leaving.'

'There won't be any charges. Because there are no dogs.' He took another sip of his tea.

What did he know? A chill of foreboding made her shiver. As soon as she and Malcolm were out on the footpath, she dialled Bill Slater's mobile.

'Please tell me you've found the dogs.'

'Afraid not,' Bill said. 'Someone's cleared the lot out.'

42

It looked so different in daylight. Not terrifying at all. Just a normal farm. But it wasn't normal. Rose knew that.

But knowing something and proving it was a whole other matter. In the milky morning light, Rose saw that the sheds were in a dip in the land and were so well hidden by the surrounding trees that she could have driven past them every day and not noticed their existence.

The rear gates to Clapper Farm were wide open. An RSPCA van was parked on the grass verge. Bill Slater beckoned to Rose and Malcolm, who had driven there straight after leaving Drayton and Clapper. The shed doors also hung open and the stench flooding out was enough to make Rose gag. Apart from a few crows bickering and the squelch of mud beneath their boots, the farm was quiet. Not a bark or a yelp or yip to be heard.

Rose was incredulous. 'How's it possible to shift all those dogs so fast?'

Bill had the buzz cut and rigid stance of a military guy. He spoke abruptly but his eyes were kind. Rose imagined he must have seen some harrowing acts of cruelty and would have to have a coping mechanism, just as the police and firefighters did.

'They took them under cover of darkness,' Bill said. 'The track is all churned up. Looks like they used a couple of vans.'

'And Tank?'

'No sign of him.'

Rose hoped Tank was getting the care he needed. 'John must have had help shifting the dogs.'

'He must have done.'

'Any idea where they took them?' Malcolm asked.

'Another farm, probably.' Bill pointed at the sheds. 'They're full of cages. Lord knows how many breeding bitches and pups they had per cage. At a guess I'd say at least thirty adult dogs, so there aren't many places you can hide that many dogs. We have to hope somebody complains about a sudden influx of barking dogs.' He glanced at Malcolm. 'Mate, I don't know how to break it to you, but they could decide to get rid of them. Keep the puppies, sell them into pet shops and other outlets, but the adults are a liability.'

Rose was horrified. 'You mean kill them?'

Bill nodded. 'Seen it done before. Poison.'

'Oh my God.'

'B will be okay,' Malcolm said, trying to convince himself. 'She's young. They won't hurt her.'

'We'll keep looking, Malcolm,' Rose said. 'We'll find her. But does this mean you can't build a case against John Clapper?' Rose asked Bill.

'There's no doubt in my mind this is a puppy farm and the animals were distressed and filthy and in need of medical attention. I'll talk to our lawyers, but we can only afford to pursue cases we've got a good chance of winning and the current laws aren't on our side. I'm very sorry.'

Their defence had just weakened. And they hadn't saved the poor dogs either. She had to believe they were still alive and that they could find B.

Monty had been traumatised by the night's events. Tank had ripped Monty's flesh but hadn't done any lasting damage. Malcolm had sedated Monty to clean and stitch his wounds, but Rose suspected Monty was more distressed by the injury he had caused Tank and his fear for the Rottweiler's life. He had gone berserk when Clapper refused to allow Malcolm to take Tank to the vet hospital. Malcolm had offered to do the surgery for free, but it made no difference. The police had been called, questions asked, and all the time Tank lay whimpering in pain. This morning Rose had left Monty at home, still drowsy from a sedative.

'Can I take a look around?' Rose asked.

'You best be quick,' Bill said. 'John could turn up at any moment. He's at the house waiting for his solicitor.' He led them to the nearest shed. 'You might want to cover your mouth and nose.'

Rose pulled a long woollen scarf from her pocket, scrunched it into a ball and held it over her nose and mouth.

'I can't help wondering if these were World War Two bunkers,' Bill said. 'The walls are really thick and they're down in a dell, hidden by the poplars. No wonder nobody heard anything.'

Rose and Malcolm followed Bill into the first shed. Rose gagged. The smell of dog faeces and urine was like hitting a wall. Bare lightbulbs hung at regular intervals from the A-frame roof. The only natural light came from the open doors. Laid out on both sides of the shed were cages of various sizes. All were dirty. Some were rusted. Others were bent out of shape. The cage floors were filthy straw on concrete. No toys, no blankets or beds, just rusting water bowls. A cockroach floated on its back in one bowl.

'I suspect some of these dogs have spent their lives in these cages,' said Bill. 'No exercise. No daylight. They'll be weak and unhealthy.'

Bile rose up Rose's throat. She couldn't stop it. She bent forward and retched. Her eyes watered, her nose stung and her mouth tasted foul. She used a tissue to wipe her mouth.

'Rose,' said Malcolm. 'Do you need to get some air?'

'I'm okay.' She steeled herself to look around.

Stuck in the wire of the cages were tufts of dog hair, some dark, some tan, some white. The deeper they went into the shed, the denser and heavier the smell became. Piled in a far corner were dozens of fifteen-kilo bags of dry dog food and some bales of straw.

'John claimed he likes to stock-pile dog food for his Rottweiler,' Bill said, snorting with disgust.

'Basil's Pet Food again,' Rose said, noting the branding on the food bags. 'Mind if I take a look?' She moved some of the bags to one side. 'Maybe there's a receipt or something with a name on it.'

'I'll help.' Malcolm said, grabbed one of the bags and shifted it aside, then paused. 'What's that?' He pulled more bags out of the way, then climbed over the rest of the pile. 'It's a dog.'

Slumped between the straw bales and the bags of food was a black dog, eyes shut, body limp. It was Tank. The straw around him was sticky with dried blood.

'Is he dead?' Rose asked.

'He's been shot,' said Malcolm. He pressed two fingers on the dog's inner thigh. 'There's a pulse. Very faint. I need to get him into surgery right away.'

'John did this? To his own dog!'

43

'Shit!' Rose slapped the steering wheel.

She was late for her session with the psychiatrist and she couldn't find a parking spot.

Dr Doom was one of four medical practitioners who worked from a shared medical practice on the outskirts of Geldeford. In front of the house were four parking spaces reserved for clients. All were taken. Rose had no choice but to park on-street, which had a thirty-minute limit unless you had a residential parking permit, which she didn't. She'd have to move her car part-way through the hour-long session.

As she hurriedly locked her car, the sunlight streaming in the back drew her attention to the blood-stained towels where Monty had lain last night as she'd rushed him to the vet hospital. Something glinted on the towels. It was a metal pendant shaped like a Dachshund, no more than an inch and a half long. The Dachshund was covered in little sparkling gems that looked like faux diamonds. Attached to the ring was a large house key.

That's odd.

Jogging up the wheel-chair accessible ramp to Dr Doom's office, Rose arrived panting and muddled. There was too much going on: a murdered girl, a puppy farm, a civil case against her, the possible break up of her parents' marriage, and her job on the line. Her hand shook as she knocked and entered.

Dr Doom was seated with her legs daintily crossed at the ankles. Rose couldn't help but stare at her shiny teal-coloured stilettos, which had the highest, pointiest heels she'd ever seen. 'Ah there you are, Rose. Please take a seat.' The psychiatrist smiled.

'Sorry I'm late, Doctor.'

'Call me Doris, please.' Her golden hair hung neatly around her shoulders and she peered at Rose over the top of narrow, rectangular glasses. On the lap of her matching teal dress was a notepad.

Rose took the beige sofa that was positioned at right angles to the psychiatrist. Opposite Rose was an unrendered brick wall painted off-white and a framed picture of birds in a blue sky.

'It's good to see you, Rose. How are you doing?' Dr Doom leaned back in her modern armchair, upholstered in the same beige fabric as the sofa.

Rose hadn't eaten dinner or breakfast and she felt light-headed and anxious. Her hands were trembling in her lap. She was probably becoming hypoglycaemic. 'It's been a bad morning and I haven't eaten.' She held up her shaking hands. 'Have you some biscuits?'

'Of course, come with me.'

With surprising steadiness, given her six-inch heel stilettos, Doom led Rose to a shared kitchen that was spotless and very white. She handed Rose some mini tongs and a glass jar filled with shortbread fingers, Jammy Dodgers, custard creams and chocolate digestives. 'Take as many as you want. How about a tea? Sugar?'

Rose didn't usually have sugar in her tea, but right now she needed it. She sat unsteadily on a stool. 'Yes please, milk, two sugars.'

The sun poured into the kitchen through a large window. Rose used the tongs to pull out four biscuits and attacked them with the kind of zeal that Oliver Twist would take to his bowl of porridge. As the tea brewed, Dr Doom studied her. 'Do you want to tell me what happened this morning?'

Rose had prepared set answers to questions she imagined the psychiatrist would ask. Her aim had been to convince the doctor she was ready to return to work, even if it meant fudging the truth. Right now, however, Rose didn't feel prepared. In truth, she felt vulnerable.

'How much of what we discuss goes back to my boss?' she asked.

'None of it. The only thing he receives from me is my opinion on whether you are ready to return to your job which, we both know, is a highly stressful one.'

Rose swallowed the last piece of her fourth biscuit. On the window ledge, a robin landed and pecked at the wood for scraps. The bird's feathers were puffed out, which made it appear like a ball with tail feathers and a beak. 'The way things are going, my DCI isn't going to let me back, whatever you recommend.'

Dr Doom took milk from the fridge, poured, stirred and handed the mug to Rose. 'Why do you think that?'

Rose sipped the hot tea and relished its sweetness. Should she trust this woman? Hell, what did she have to lose?

'Because I suffer from anxiety and because this morning I was accused of trespassing and causing property damage after I tried to rescue dogs from a puppy farm.'

The psychiatrist's poker face dropped for a minute as she blinked rapidly over the top of her reading glasses. This was the first time Rose had admitted to having anxiety, even though she took the medication.

'Thank you for your honesty, Rose. Tell me about the puppy farm and these charges.'

Rose sipped her tea. Oh well, in for a penny, in for a pound. She told Dr Doom everything: how desperately she wanted to solve the Anna Czubinska murder and how her actions had irritated Leach and Pearl. She told her about the break-in at the vet's and their discovery of the puppy farm at Clapper Farm and how the dogs had been moved during the night so she had no proof. And that she was facing a civil case which would likely prove the death of her policing career. 'On top of that, my mum washed up on my doorstep a few days ago because she and my dad are having marriage issues and my dog nearly died last night.'

'Oh my. That's an extraordinary amount of pressure. Rose, you should applaud yourself for handling it all so well.'

'You think so?'

'Yes I do. What you've been through is enough to make most people feel overwhelmed. Who do you turn to when you need support?'

'I, um, don't know. I talk to Joe about some stuff, but he's a guy so there are some things we can't really talk about.'

'Friend, boyfriend?'

'I don't have a boyfriend.' Rose blushed. 'Joe's a friend. He's married. We went to Police College together.'

'Anyone else? Family? Someone you feel comfortable with?'

Rose hated to admit that she was a loner or that she found her parents difficult to talk to. Malcolm popped into her head. Over the last few days, she had got to know him better. She had felt comfortable chatting to him, but was that because they were both so focused on finding the stolen puppies?

'I don't like to share personal things.'

'Okay. What do you do to look after yourself?'

'How do you mean?'

'I mean, apart from your medication, what is your coping mechanism when you're upset or stressed?'

'I don't really have one.'

'What calms you?'

'My dog, Monty. Stroking him. Talking to him.' Rose scrutinised Dr Doom's face for signs that she thought her mad.

If she did, she gave nothing away. 'Yes, dogs can be very calming. That's why therapy dogs work so well. They cheer people up in hospitals and nursing homes and also soothe those prone to fear or panic.'

Monty was more than that, Rose thought. They had a special connection.

The doctor continued, 'Can you diarise time with Monty to relax or walk together, just the two of you?'

'It's a bit difficult at the moment. Mum's staying and so is a teenager who's been having a rough time. Mum and the boy hate each other, and Mum doesn't like Monty either.'

Dr Doom nodded slowly, taking time to absorb the complications of Rose's home life. 'I'd like to return to my office and maybe we can brainstorm ways you can get some quiet space back. Friction at home is only adding to the stress you're feeling.'

Rose finished the last of her tea and followed the doctor. Rose would love to spend more time with Monty and the poor boy needed time to convalesce. He'd been incredibly brave last night. She had been terrified she might have lost him forever.

A thought popped into her head. The keyring. How had it got there?

A diamante dog pendant wasn't the kind of accessory Malcolm would have. And nobody else had been in the back of the car. Except Ollie, but she couldn't see him having a keyring like that either. Monty must have put it there.

'Oh my God!' Rose said, startling Dr Doom. 'You've been amazing. Thank you. But I have to go.'

44

I come out of a deep sleep. Eyes still shut, I stretch out my front legs and splay my paws. Ah, that feels good. I do the same with my back legs and paws.

Now for a big yawn.

Fully awake now, I lift my head off my bed and look around the kitchen. Big mistake! My throat feels like it's on fire and the stitches pull when I twist my neck to look around. Oh boy! That really stings.

I smell Malcolm on my fur. Last night comes flooding back. Getting caught on the wire under the fence. Tank ripping at me, trying to kill me. Biting his back leg, and his yowls of pain. Leaving Tank behind because John Clapper wouldn't let Malcolm help him. Malcolm carrying me into the vet hospital. Then…nothing.

I gingerly peer out of the window. The sun is above the oak tree, which means it must be lunch time. Why didn't Rose wake me? Where is she? From the sitting room, the television is blaring.

'Will you please turn that down?!' Liz bellows from the hall. 'I have a headache.'

'All right, Mrs Sidebottom. There's no need to shout,' Ollie says, lowering the volume.

Liz saunters into the kitchen wearing a denim apron over the tubular dress she'd brought home from Top Shop. She takes two lamb shanks from the fridge that have my nostrils pulsing and my mind wandering. I get up slowly: every muscle aches. I try to lick my stitches to soothe the stinging, but even my long tongue can't reach them. The lamb shanks are the perfect distraction. I sniff the counter.

'Shoo!' She flicks a hand at me. 'Stay away.' She picks up a wooden spoon and threatens me with it.

I get the message. And anyway, I want to find Rose. She wouldn't go out without me, would she? While Liz is busy in the kitchen I creep upstairs. Rose isn't there. Back downstairs I check in with Ollie, who is all alone. Well not quite. He's lying on the sofa with his feet up. Sitting on his chest eating a crust of bread is Betty.

'Hey there, Mr Monty,' Betty squeaks. 'Good to see you up and about. Sleeping like a baby, you was.'

'Hello, champion!' says Ollie. He pushes his glasses up his nose and stares at the stitches in my neck. 'You take it easy. Rose will be back soon.' He cups a hand around Betty so she doesn't fall off his chest.

I head out the back door for a pee. A crow *caw caws* from atop the willow. He's laughing at the ducks doing yoga under Henrietta's direction.

'Cobra pose,' Henrietta says.

The ducks and Cyril the pigeon lie on their bellies with their feet behind them and stretch their necks up to the sky. Tufty, who performs her Cobra perfectly, sees me coming. She clacks her beak together in laughter. 'Look at your shaved fur, you ugly dog!'

Don't take the bait, I say to myself. Words to live by. I hold my head high. At least I'm not pretending to be a snake. Nasty rubbery things, snakes. I head for the tumble-down shed and relieve myself on a rotting door post.

'That Liz really has to go,' Betty says, catching up with me. She breathes heavily as she leans against a flowerpot. 'She don't like dogs. She don't like rats. She don't like the boy. She don't like much from what I can tell. Except men. Blimey!' Betty rolls her eyes. 'She sure does like to flirt with men.'

'Who do you mean? Malcolm?'

'No, silly! Albert, the boiler man. Never seen a performance like it.

She'd win an Oscar for it. Got on the blower and talked the guy into fixing the boiler for free. Well, not quite free. She's got a date with him. Today. I'll lay you any money Rose doesn't know about it.' Betty taps the side of her pointy nose and gives me a wink.

'I think Rose is worried about her mum and dad staying together.'

'If you ask me, she's got a wandering eye, that one.' Betty leans against a spade covered in cobwebs before realising what she's done. 'Them spiders really do make a bleedin' mess.' She gets rid of the sticky strands by rubbing her back and face against a roll of netting used for covering the gooseberry bushes. 'Sorry to hear about them poor pups.' She drops her nose and looks solemn. 'Anything I can do, just ask, okay?'

I hear Rose's car coming up Shophouse Lane. I race to the front of the house to greet her, tail wagging. She gets out and gives me a gentle hug. 'How are you, boy?' She kneels and inspects my stitches. 'Looking good.' Then she whispers, 'Went to see my psychiatrist and turns out, she was really supportive.'

Rose carries the scent of new people. The most recent is someone who wears perfume that smells like cinnamon and jasmine and who likes to feed birds with birdseed. I'm guessing that's the psychiatrist. The other hooman smells of asphalt footpaths, sandalwood and whisky. There is a hint of something threatening about his scent and I pull back.

In the kitchen, Rose asks Liz if she has fed me.

'The lazy thing's just got up,' Liz says.

'He's recovering from surgery, Mum.'

Rose doesn't remark on the lamb shanks in the baking dish which Liz puts in the oven quick-smart or the peeled potatoes on the drainer. Rose feeds me. I snaffle it and lick my bowl until it shines.

'Tell me how you went with the nasty lawyer,' Rose's mum says, pouring herself a glass of red wine.

Rose gulps down a glass of water from the tap. 'I'm in a fair bit of trouble, Mum.'

She describes the meeting with Andrew Clapper, John's son. I wonder if it's Andrew's smell on Rose that I find threatening. It certainly fits with the way Rose describes him. I don't think I'm going to like him. I know she's also been to Clapper Farm this morning: I can smell it on her shoes, but she doesn't go into that. She also doesn't mention the psychiatrist.

'Then I had an epiphany,' Rose says with a newfound energy that makes her eyes shine. 'Not only was Clapper running a puppy farm. He's also got something to do with the murdered girl, I'm sure of it. I think Monty holds the key.'

Liz rolls her eyes. 'Not the bloody dog again. Seriously, Rose, you give that animal way too much credit. It's just a dog.'

Rose kneels on the floor and calls me over. In a gloved hand she holds a glittery ornament. I sniff it.

I'd forgotten about the keyring. I was dazed and in a lot of pain after the fight with Tank. I give it a tentative sniff. That jogs my memory. I had it in my mouth when Malcolm carried me to the car. I must have dozed because I don't remember dropping it. The metal Dachshund covered in sparkly gems and the big key smelt of the dead girl.

'Did you find this at the vet's?' Rose asks.

Two barks from me. A definite no.

'Good boy. Did you find it at the farm last night?'

I sit, head high. One bark. Oh yes!

'Rose, listen to yourself, will you? The dog doesn't understand a word you're saying,' Liz chastises.

'Mum, please! I know what I'm doing.'

Yes, you do!

Liz huffs out a breath and then turns her back on us to start putting crosses on the bottom of Brussels sprouts with a knife.

'Did you find this at Clapper Farm?' Rose repeats. She's testing me.

Again, I give her a firm yes.

'I can't see John having a cutesy keyring like this,' Rose says, watching it dangle in her gloved hand. 'Maybe it belongs to someone who worked for him.' She gasps. 'Someone whose boots had dog fur and dog poo on them.' Rose holds the keyring close to my nose. I wait for the question that I'm silently urging her to ask. 'Is it Anna's keyring?'

One loud bark. A big fat yes.

'Oh my God!' Rose stares at it for a moment longer, then pops it in a zip-lock bag and seals it. 'Good boy.'

'Rose, darling,' says Liz, turning around. 'I have a guest coming to lunch and you're in the way. Can you be a love and take that boy and the dog with you on a nice long walk?'

'What? Oh, um, sure.'

I don't think Rose is listening properly.

'I need to eat before I pass out,' Rose says. 'I can't think if I haven't eaten.

'I'll make you scrambled eggs on toast if you promise to bugger off in thirty minutes,' Liz offers.

Rose gets off the floor. 'What's the rush, Mum?'

Liz sighs. 'I already told you. I have a guest coming for lunch and I'd like the place to myself.'

At last Rose realises her mother is up to something. 'Who's coming?'

'Never you mind. Do you want scrambled eggs or not?'

'Can't I have whatever you've got in the oven?'

'No, there isn't enough for three.' She opens the fridge and brings out a carton of eggs. 'It'll be ready in a jiffy.'

'Thanks, Mum.'

Rose wanders into the lounge room and drops into an armchair, oblivious to the TV, to Ollie or Betty, who is lying, once again, on his chest, eating bread and getting a tummy tickle. Betty really is shameless. I stay close to Rose. She looks at me. 'If I take this to Leach, he'll want to know how I got hold of it.' Ollie glances at her, curious, then turns his attention back to the TV. 'He's going to find out about the civil case sooner or later, so I guess there's no point trying to hide it.' She chews her lip. 'What if I'm wrong and this keyring has nothing to do with Anna? I'll look like a fool.'

Ollie switches off the TV and sits up, cupping Betty in his hands. Betty continues to gnaw on what remains of the crust.

'She hoovers up everything,' Ollie says. 'I've decided to call her Hoover.'

Betty's squeak is high-pitched with disapproval. 'I'm Betty Blabble! Always have been. Always will be.'

The boy doesn't know her name, of course. How could he?

'Don't let mum see you with her,' Rose says. 'Maybe we should get her a cage? It could be a nice cosy home for her.'

Betty's squeak is even more high-pitched. 'Not bloody likely!'

Rose laughs. 'I don't think she likes that idea.'

'I've been training her to wear my Rat Cam,' Ollie says. 'I'll show ya.'

He hands Betty to Rose. Betty sits calmly in Rose's cupped hands, whiskers twitching. However, her eyes stay on Ollie, who picks up his

Rat Cam. He positions the tiny video camera so it sits on the top of her back and points forward, then he does up the Velcro straps. Betty doesn't put up any resistance. In fact, I think she's loving the attention.

'Fits you perfectly,' Ollie says. He fiddles with his phone. 'Reception is perfect.' Then to Rose, 'Put her on the floor, nice and gentle.'

'Won't she run away?' Rose asks.

'Nah.'

Rose releases Betty onto the carpet. Betty takes a few steps forward, as if unsure of the load she's carrying,

'Look.' Ollie says, turning his phone to face Rose so she can see it. 'Live images. How cool is that?'

'That's amazing.'

I bark in agreement.

Ollie takes a solitary pellet of my dry dog food from his pocket. My ears prick up. That's *my* food!

'Here!' he says, holding the pellet level with the carpet.

Betty scurries under the coffee table and wraps her front paws around her prize. It disappears into her mouth.

'That's incredible,' Rose says.

Ollie glows with pride. 'She could be a spy, Rose. Go places we can't. Watch this.'

Betty has already swallowed the pellet. I am drooling, wishing I could join in.

Ollie picks up Betty. 'Go back to Rose,' he says to her, then places her on the carpet.

Betty stays put and cleans her whiskers.

'How can she understand a command like that?' Rose asks.

'I don't know, but she does.' Ollie frowns. 'She did it before. Why isn't she doing it now?'

All of a sudden, Betty sets off across the carpet, under the coffee table and comes to a halt at Rose's feet. Rose picks her up.

'I don't believe it!' she says. 'What a clever rat.'

Ollie hands Rose a pellet of my dry dog food, which Rose gives Betty as a reward. By now there is a pool of drool at my feet. 'Can Monty have one?' Ollie asks.

'Ask him to come, then he can have one.'

Ollie calls me over. I'm there in a flash and I get my reward.

'Can you take back your rat?' Rose says. 'I need to wipe the carpet.'

Oops!

I follow Rose to the kitchen, where she wets the floor cloth. The keyring in her pocket clanks against the stainless-steel sink. Rose taps her pocket.

'Zofia!' she exclaims.

Zofia? Where? I turn a full circle but can't see her.

'Jeez!' says Liz, who is scooping scrambled egg onto two pieces of buttered toast. 'Can you stop doing that? I almost dropped the pan.'

Rose fishes out her phone and dials Zofia.

'Did Anna lose a key by any chance?' she asks.

'Yes,' I hear Zofia reply. 'Her house key. It was lucky I had a spare one. Please don't tell the landlord. He will change all the locks and then make us pay.'

'I won't. Was the key on a keyring?'

'Yes, a sausage dog in diamante.'

'I'm going to send you a photo right now. I need you to confirm this is Anna's.' Rose photographs the contents of the transparent bag and sends the image. She then takes a bite of her scrambled egg. Not long after, Zofia responds.

'Yes, it is Anna's. Where did you find it?'

Rose gives me a huge smile.

45

Craig Leach was having a fag in the Geldeford Police car park when Rose showed up with Monty on a lead. Ollie had wandered down the road to the KFC, having promised Rose he would keep his head down. She could have sworn she saw something wriggle in the boy's jacket pocket as she watched him go, but decided it was best not to ask.

Unfortunately for her, Dave Pearl was having a smoke with the DCI. When he spotted Rose he was in the middle of telling a funny story. His smile evaporated.

'You really know how to pick your enemies,' Pearl said, shaking his head.

They knew about last night, which wasn't surprising. Clapper had probably complained to the Commissioner about her. Leach would have got a bollocking as a result. She tried and failed to read his expression. He blew smoke at the sky, then stubbed the end of his cigarette against the wall.

'Dave's right. What in God's name were you thinking?' Leach said.

'John Clapper was running an illegal puppy farm, sir, and we believed the animals were in danger.'

Leach dropped the stub into a bin. 'You're making it very difficult for me to even think of reinstating you.'

'I know it looks bad, but Clapper is a liar and I can prove it.'

'You might want to keep your voice down, Rose,' said Leach.

'Can we talk in private? I appreciate this is sensitive, sir.'

'I'm working a murder case, Rose. I don't have time for–'

'It relates to Anna's murder.'

'Oh for God's sake,' Pearl complained, raising his voice.

She felt Monty stiffen. He didn't take his eyes off Pearl.

Leach raised his hand to hush his DI. 'You have two minutes, Rose. Shoot.'

Rose pulled from her pocket the zip-lock bag with the glistening key ring and key in it. 'I found Anna's front door key.'

'Dare I ask where?' said Leach.

'In my car. It's a long story.'

Leach's eyes hardened. 'Make it short.'

Rose's mouth had gone dry. It was coming out wrong. 'Last night, my dog found it outside one of three sheds on Clapper's land. He carried it to my car.'

Leach looked down at Monty, then back up at Rose. 'Did you see it on Clapper's property before the dog removed it?'

'No, sir, but there's nowhere else it could have come from and Zofia has confirmed it's Anna's key.'

Leach's face and bare scalp turned blotchy red. 'You spoke to a witness before consulting with me?'

'I wanted to be certain–'

'It's inadmissible. It's useless!'

'It proves John is lying. He claimed he didn't recognise Anna.'

'How the bloody hell do you know that?'

She cleared her raspy throat. 'Because I asked him.'

'You what?' said Pearl.

It was all or nothing now. 'Why would John lie about knowing Anna, unless he had something to hide? I think she worked for him, perhaps cash-in-hand. I think she worked in the puppy farm, which explains the dog fur and poo on her boots. I think he should be questioned again.'

'Oh you do, do you?' Pearl's sarcasm stung her. Monty stepped between them protectively.

Rose touched Monty's head to calm him.

'Christ!' Leach rubbed his eyes with his knuckles. Rose waited. 'This could get very awkward.'

'You're not going to take this—' Pearl began.

'Dave, get Jenny onto this right away. I want to know whose prints are on there.'

'We don't have John Clapper's prints on file, sir.'

'He was done for drink driving two years ago,' Rose said. 'His prints were taken.'

'How do you…oh never mind,' said Leach.

Pearl snatched the zip-lock bag from Rose and went inside.

'If there are prints,' said Leach to Rose, 'and it's a big *if*, you'll need to make a statement.'

As Rose left Police HQ, she rang Malcolm's mobile. He answered, groggy.

'Did I wake you?' Rose asked, feeling guilty.

'Sort of. Was up most of the night operating on Tank.'

'How is he?'

'Alive. For now. I'm not sure if he's going to make it, though.'

'I'm sure you've done all you can.' She heard the gurgling of an espresso machine. He was making coffee. 'Can I drop by? I need to ask you something?'

'Sure. Just give me a chance to shower. Fifteen minutes?'

When Rose arrived, Malcolm had dark bags under his eyes and his shirt, although clean, was generously wrinkled.

'Come through,' he said, showing Rose, Ollie and Monty into the recovery room to get away from prying eyes. 'Please don't touch any of the dogs. Some of them are very ill.'

There were eight dogs in all. At the far end, Dr Rochester, Malcolm's partner, was checking on a drowsy English Springer Spaniel he'd neutered that day. Rochester was in his forties, but his hair was a striking white. Rose said hello.

'I'll leave you to it,' Rochester said. As he left the recovery room, he placed a hand briefly on Malcolm's shoulder. 'Go home and rest, there's a good fellow. I can handle your appointments.'

'I'm fine. Really. Just need some more coffee,' Malcolm replied.

Tank lay in the largest cage. He was very still, the fur on his chest shaved. There were six white dressings on his skin and a drip attached to his leg. Monty pressed his nose into the cage and sniffed, then whimpered.

'I got all the shot out,' said Malcolm. 'But the injuries were worse than I'd thought.' He sounded desperately tired. 'If we'd found him earlier, maybe I could have...'

'You've done everything you can,' Rose said. 'He's young and strong. We just have to hope he pulls through.'

Ollie bent down to look in Tank's cage. The boy looked stricken at the sight of the injured dog.

'Heard anything from John Clapper?' Rose asked.

'Nothing,' Malcolm said, sitting heavily on the nurse's chair. He ran fingers through his once again wayward hair. 'I'm never going to see B again, am I?'

'You will, because we'll find her. And the other pups too.'

Malcolm shook his head. 'I'm a vet. I make animals better. And here I am, the only dog I've ever owned is lost and I don't know what to do.'

'Don't give up, Malcolm. It's a setback, that's all.'

He gave her a rueful smile. 'How do you stay so positive?'

'I don't. I'll let you in on a secret.' She looked down at her shoes. She found it difficult to drop her front. 'I suffer from PTSD. I get anxiety attacks. I've been in denial for a long time.' She looked at him. 'But I have to get past it.' She paused. 'I saw a psychiatrist today. I've been avoiding her for weeks. And it wasn't so bad after all. She was nice.' Rose shook her head. 'What I'm trying to say is that all I can do is keep going, one day at a time.'

'I had no idea. You always seem so...I don't know...in control, so positive.'

'It's an act. If it wasn't for Monty, I don't know what I'd have done. He keeps me positive.' At the mention of his name, Monty looked at Rose, his ears pricked up. 'It's okay, boy, I'm complimenting you.' Monty walked over to her. She stroked him. 'Good boy.'

'You two do have an uncanny connection, you know,' Malcolm said. 'He'd do anything for you.'

'And I for him. My point is, Malcolm, that sometimes we all need a reminder that there's hope. I guess this time it's me reminding you.'

Malcolm smiled. 'Right then.' He sat up straighter. 'No more moping about. What do we do next?'

'You're a respected veterinarian. People will listen to you. I think you should contact the local radio and TV stations. Make a public appeal. Ask people to look out for lots of puppies, to listen out for their barking. Warn people about puppy farms.'

Her phone rang. 'Get back here now,' ordered Leach, then he was gone.

'Malcolm,' Rose said. 'We have to leave, I'm sorry. I have to get back to the nick.'

'Can I stay here?' Ollie asked. 'I could feed the animals. Help out.'

'Sure,' said Malcolm.

Ollie's eyes lit up.

46

Rose watched John Clapper through the one-way glass of interview room three. Andrew, his son and legal representative, sat next to him. Across from them were two empty chairs which John stared daggers at when he wasn't drumming his fingers on the tabletop.

'They need to let some fresh air in here,' John said, using the back of his hand to wipe sweat from his hairline.

Andrew, in contrast, was clearly unperturbed. He leaned back in his chair, his long legs stretched out under the table, as he scrolled through emails on his phone as nonchalantly as if he was sitting at a bus stop.

'That's a two-way mirror,' Andrew said, nodding at it, which gave Rose the uneasy feeling that he could see her on the other side. Which, of course, he couldn't. 'This will be recorded. If I advise you to say no comment, say no comment.'

'Okay, stop nagging me.'

John took a sip from the cup of coffee nearest him then screwed up his mouth in revulsion. 'That's disgusting. Can't they even make a decent cup of coffee?'

'Dad, please, calm down.'

John put the plastic cup down. He glanced at the door for the umpteenth time. 'Bloody cheek, keeping us waiting like this.'

Rose knew this was deliberate.

The observation room where she sat was stuffy too, and barely larger than a decent sized broom cupboard. Leach popped his oversized head around the door. 'I want to know if he's changed his story since he spoke to you. Tap into that gut instinct of yours. I want to know if he's lying and what about.'

Leach had always been dismissive of what he called her gut instinct and she called her lie detector. She felt a warm glow of pride.

'Yes, sir.'

'You tell anyone I said that, I'll have your guts for garters.' He gave her a wink, then shut the door.

She was surprised to see Leach enter the room with DS Varma. She'd expected him to pick Pearl. But then again, Leach was no fool. Opting for the diplomat rather than the bully made sense for someone as connected as Clapper. And Varma was as straight a shooter as they came. Leach clearly didn't want to put a foot wrong.

She pulled out a note pad and pen. It was good to be back. Officers had smiled and greeted her as she'd walked in. She felt useful again. She was back where she belonged. This was her chance to show Leach she could make a difference.

Varma switched on the video equipment and the necessary formalities were performed.

'Can I remind you,' Andrew began, his attention on the senior officer, 'that my father is here voluntarily. He is a law-abiding citizen. He's happy to assist your enquiries but he's a busy man, so let's keep this short, shall we?'

'It takes as long as it takes, Andrew.' Leach paused, eyeing both men, making the unspoken point that in this room, he was the boss. His stare came to rest on John. 'Mr Clapper–'

'Oh for heaven's sake, you know me. Call me John.'

Her boss knew John Clapper? *Damn it*, she thought, *this is getting more complicated by the minute.* If Leach was friendly with Clapper, it was protocol for him to excuse himself and for another officer to conduct the interview.

'John, do you know this woman?' Varma removed a photograph of the murdered girl from a manila folder and slid it across the table. 'For the video, I'm showing John Clapper a photograph of Anna Czubinska.'

John gave the photo a cursory glance, then leaned back in his plastic chair, his arms folded across his barrel chest. 'I've told you before. No, I don't.'

Rose's in-built lie detector went off. The pins and needles were so bad she had to walk up and down on the spot to alleviate the stinging. The observation room door opened and in stepped Pearl. He acted as if she wasn't even there.

Varma handed Leach a labelled evidence bag, inside which was the house key and the diamante keyring she had given them just an hour earlier. 'John, can you explain how Anna Czubinska's front door key ended up on your property?'

Rose's heart leapt. Forensics must have confirmed the key and keyring belonged to the victim.

John didn't answer. He looked at his son.

'Before my father answers your question, I want to know how you came across this item you claim was on his property?'

'That's not something I'm prepared to discuss. I would like you, John, to answer my question. How did Anna's key end up on your property, when you claim not to know her?'

'I have no idea.' John looked Leach squarely in the eye.

Pins and needles shot up Rose's legs and arms. Liar!

'Can you explain how your thumb print came to be on this key?'

'What? That's preposterous,' John blustered.

'Come now, John,' said Leach, 'help me out here. Your print and Anna's print are on the same key. And yet you tell me you don't know her.'

'It's not my print. Has to be a mistake. Seen stories about it on the news.'

Andrew said, 'I suspect this key was illegally attained by DC Sidebottom when she trespassed on my father's land. If that's the case, you know as well as I do, it's inadmissible.'

'That meddling woman probably planted it,' growled John.

Leach glanced at Varma. It was time for a change of tactic. Varma spoke, his voice quiet and cultured. Despite the seriousness of the situation, Rose noted how Andrew looked Varma up and down, his eyes drawn to the DI's tailored suit and his stylish paisley tie. The lawyer tugged on an earlobe in annoyance.

'Sir, how many mobile phones do you have?' Varma asked John.

'What?'

Varma calmly repeated the question.

John scowled. 'One, of course. How many phones does a man need?'

Rose had no physical response to this answer. She sensed this time that he was being truthful.

Varma read out a mobile phone number. 'Is this your number?'

'No.' Again, the truth.

'You see, Anna had a lover,' Varma said. 'A married man. You're married, I believe?'

'Technically. We live apart.'

Varma continued, 'The number I've just told you is for a pay-as-you-go phone. This person communicated with Anna many times over the last four months. Were you Anna Czubinska's lover?'

Rose watched John's reaction carefully. He burst out laughing. 'Me? You really are clutching at straws. I'm twice her age.'

No pins and needles and his laughter sounded genuine. Andrew chuckled politely.

'This is no laughing matter, sir,' Varma said. 'Anna was eight weeks' pregnant.'

John's laughter stopped immediately. He blinked rapidly, then looked away from Varma. 'I'm sorry to hear that.'

Andrew recovered faster than his father. 'I believe Anna Czubinska was Polish?'

'Correct.'

Andrew gave John an encouraging nod. John wiped some sweat away from his upper lip with a cotton handkerchief, then returned it to a corduroy trouser pocket.

'Look,' John said, 'I sometimes take on seasonal workers. I haven't mentioned it because it's cash-in-hand. You know, off the books.' He glanced from Leach to Varma and when they said nothing he continued. 'We have a Polish guy who's been working for me on a casual basis for a year now. Maybe he knew Anna. From what I've heard, the Polish community is pretty tight-knit. Maybe he had her key for some reason.' John shrugged.

Leach rested his elbows on the table. 'John, I'm not interested in your bloody taxes. I have a murder to solve. You should have told me this.'

'He's telling you now, inspector,' said Andrew.

'Name of this employee?' Leach asked.

'Kacper Kowalski.'

Rose hadn't seen that one coming. Regardless, it didn't explain how Anna's house key had John Clapper's thumb print on it. Clapper was using Kowalski to deflect from the mystery surrounding the key. Out of the corner of her eye, she saw Pearl grin.

Varma said, 'What kind of work does Kowalski do for you?'

'Lambing. Feeding. Mucks out the horses. In the summer, picks apples.'

'And looks after the dogs?' Leach asked.

'I used to breed dogs,' John said. 'Not any longer.'

'Would you describe yourself as a compassionate man?' Varma asked.

'I keep my animals healthy if that's what you mean.'

'But you shot your dog and left it to die a slow and painful death,' Varma said.

'Rubbish. I was aiming at a fox. The dog got in the way.' John looked down. It was meant to look like remorse, but Rose suspected it was to hide the truth in his eyes. 'I thought he was dead. If I'd known he wasn't, I'd have called the vet.'

'Anyway,' Andrew said. 'We've been over this. The RSPCA found no evidence of animal cruelty at Clapper Farm.'

Leach nodded. 'On the night of Anna's murder, you claimed, John, that you and Andrew were home all night at your farm. Is that correct?'

'Yes.' John sighed.

His biggest lie yet. Rose's feet went completely numb. She had to start walking on the spot to get feeling back into them.

Leach continued, 'We have a witness who saw a Land Rover speeding along Hinchley Lane on the night of the murder at around 1am Where were you going at that hour?'

Hinchley Lane was the single-track lane that dead-ended at Hinchley Wood. Rose hadn't known about the witness.

'Your witness is mistaken. I was asleep at home,' John said.

Andrew chimed in. 'Many farmers in the area have Land Rovers,

Craig. And I should like to clarify for the video,' he glanced at the video camera on the wall, 'that John Clapper did not leave his property the entire night in question.'

Another lie. A respected solicitor was the perfect alibi.

'Thank you for clarifying that,' said Varma. 'For routine purposes, we'd like a DNA sample.'

'No!' Andrew's response was so vehement it made Rose jump. Andrew cleared his throat, perhaps realising his reaction was excessive. 'It's unnecessary. My father has already confirmed that he is not the father of the girl's baby. This interview is over.'

The legs of his chair scraped across the floor as he stood.

'Please sit, Andrew. We haven't finished,' Leach said.

'Dad, we're leaving.' Both men left.

Leach switched off the video recorder. 'Get Kowalski back in here,' he directed Varma. 'That little shit's been lying to us.'

Rose almost collided with Leach as he left the interview room. 'John is lying,' she said. 'He knows Anna. And Andrew's alibi is a lie too.'

'Maybe that stuck-up lawyer is lying. But I can't prove it,' Leach said. 'Kowalski's the key. He knows more than he's letting on.'

'But, sir, you asked me to tell you if–'

'That'll be all, Rose. You can show yourself out.'

Leach and Pearl walked away.

'Well done finding the key,' Varma said, then followed them.

Varma was right. She had done well. She'd found Anna's missing boot. She had discovered Anna's identity. And she'd proved there was a link between John Clapper and the victim. She lifted her chin, feeling proud. 'I don't need Leach's validation,' she said to herself. 'I'm a good detective.'

This time, she wasn't saying something that she was trying to believe. For the first time in many months, she believed her own words.

She turned on her heel and made her way out of the building.

47

'Monty! How're you doing, buddy?' calls Big Man Joe from across the car park.

I now thankfully have the back of Rose's car to myself again, and I've just found a fluffy Malteser that had fallen between the seats. The crunchy centre has turned sticky and is stuck to the roof of my mouth. As a result, when I try to bark a friendly hello, I make strange sucking noises instead.

Joe squeezes his arm through the gap in the window and gives me a pat. I inhale his familiar scent – Imperial Leather soap, milk, and that curious scent of baby skin. He slides his arm a little further into the car and lifts the door handle. He opens the door and takes a look at my blue stitches.

'I heard what happened. You poor fellow.' He glances over his shoulder, then back at me. 'Rose seeing Leach, is she?'

I know he doesn't expect me to answer, but I give him a single bark, nonetheless. Yes!

'I wonder what's going on,' Joe mumbles, then shrugs. 'Nobody tells me a thing. Gotta go, buddy. Duty calls.'

Joe flicks the lock on the inside of the door and closes it, then he jogs over to a Volvo estate where another uniformed officer is waiting.

That was fun. Now what? How much longer is Rose going to be? Maybe there is another Malteser here somewhere. I drop my nose and sniff.

'Ah-hem!'

I look up.

Nigel hangs from the top edge of the open window by his front paws. His back paws slip from beneath him on the slick glass of the window.

'Pardon me for my intrusion but I have urgent news. May I enter?'

'Of course.'

Nigel wriggles through the open window and hops down onto the seat. His tail – which is shorter than it used to be, thanks to Tank's teeth – vibrates with excitement.

'What's all the noise?' Betty complains, poking her head out of the magazine pocket on the back of the seat where she's been snoozing.

'I have news,' Nigel announces.

Betty rubs her sleepy eyes. 'Go on then, what is it?'

'My fellow Musketeers…'

Betty squints up at me, 'What did he say?'

Nigel is on a roll. 'My fellow *Guardians of the Galaxy.*'

'Guardians of the what?' Betty says.

I shake my head. I have no idea where he's going with this. 'Um, Nigel, could you–?'

But Nigel will not be put off. 'My fellow Avengers–'

'All right, all right, I get the gist, Nige,' Betty says. 'Spit it out, will ya!'

'Nige?' says Nigel. 'I like that. Nige. Does that mean I can call you Bet?'

'No it bleedin' well does not.'

'Nigel,' I say, 'you have news?'

'Ah yes. I am the bearer of bad tidings.'

'Nige, you're doing it again,' Betty points out.

'Ah, apologies. I bring bad news.'

My heart sinks. Please don't tell us the dogs are gone forever. I prepare myself for the worst.

'I have found the puppies,' Nigel announces.

I wag my tail so fast I create my own breeze. 'That's great news!'

Betty jumps from the magazine pocket. clasps her front paws together and pushes them out in front of her in a circle like she's mixing a big bowl as she swings her bottom from side to side. 'We're going to save them, we're going to save them,' she sings.

'Now for the bad news,' Nigel says solemnly. 'They're on a pig farm in Lower Piddle. Well, strictly speaking, it's a mile from Lower Piddle, which could explain why nobody's heard their barking.'

I have never been to Lower Piddle, even though Rose drives past the turn-off whenever we're heading for home. There are three Piddles. Lower and Middle Piddle are hamlets. Upper Piddle is the biggest with a church, a pub and a grocer.

'Why is that bad news?' I ask.

Nigel looks glum.

'What's wrong, Nige?' I say.

'The Bone Ranger has them. It's his farm.'

The thought of confronting the Bone Ranger once again chills me to the core. That evil hooman stole my mother from me. He's stolen B. He's outwitted the RSPCA. Even outwitted Rose. My tail stops wagging and droops.

'How can a dog, a rat and a squirrel rescue so many dogs?' I say.

'We need Rose's help,' Betty says, 'and a big van.'

'How do I convince Rose the dogs are in Lower Piddle?'

'You're a clever dog, Mr Monty,' Betty says. 'You'll find a way.'

'Does the farm have a name?'

'Wiggins Farm. The hooman known as the Bone Ranger is called Harry Wiggins.'

Now I know his real name, he doesn't seem quite so scary. I feel a little more optimistic. 'Nige, mate, you are a real trooper. Not only did you try to save me from Tank, you've also found out where the dogs have been taken. High five!' I lift my front paw. Nigel slams his smaller paw into mine and grins. 'How is your tail, by the way?' I ask.

Nigel clasps his stunted tail. 'He bit off the end. It'll heal. I'm kind of proud of it actually. My battle scar.'

'You were very brave,' Betty said.

'Oh, that's very nice of you. Well, there's one more thing I should tell you. I overheard the Bone Ranger telling someone he was going to have to cull the adult dogs.'

I am so horrified I can't speak.

Betty says, in barely a whisper, 'You mean he's going to–?'

'Kill them? Yes. Tonight.'

48

Rose heads for the vet hospital to pick up Ollie. Malcolm meets us in the car park in his white coat. As soon as we see him, I can tell something is wrong. He has that pinched, tight-skinned look and frantic stare of a hooman panicking.

'I can't find him,' Malcolm says.

Rose has only just got me on a lead and out of the car. 'I'm sorry, who do you mean?'

'Oliver. He was there one minute, gone the next.'

Rose stares at him. I can see her mind working. She's thinking what I'm thinking: why would he run? 'When did you last see him?'

Malcolm beckons us inside. 'I left him with a nurse feeding the dogs and cats. I have appointments, you see.'

'And the nurse? When did she last see him?'

'She said he was in the kitchen drinking tea and staring at his phone. Can't be more than ten minutes ago. Nobody saw him leave.'

We follow Malcolm through reception and into the kitchen.

'Did he get a phone call?'

'I don't know.'

'Did he say anything about meeting someone or going somewhere?'

'I've asked the nurse. She says he didn't talk about anything but the animals.'

Rose stares at the back door. 'He must have snuck out that way.'

'I'm so sorry, Rose.'

'It's not your fault. It's mine. I promised to keep him safe and I haven't.'

'I don't get it,' Malcolm says. 'He was having a great time.'

All I can think about is how upset Betty will be, who is waiting for Ollie in the car. I sniff the floor and follow his scent to the back door. Rose opens it and I follow my nose, through the car park and onto the street.

'I have to go back,' says Malcolm, 'I have people waiting for me.'

'Of course. Don't worry, Malcolm, I'll find him.'

On the way back to the car park, Rose dials Ollie's number. It goes to voicemail and she leaves a message asking him to call. 'I just want to know you're all right,' she says.

Then she dials Brenda and explains the situation.

'I can't go lookin' for him, I'm at work,' Brenda says, sounding miffed. 'Why didn't you keep an eye on him?'

Rose apologises again, then pockets her phone.

We hop back in the car and drive to the Truscott Estate. Betty is beside herself with worry and squeaks all the way there. I'm surprised Rose doesn't hear her, but Rose is on the phone asking Big Man Joe to keep an eye out for Ollie. I am also worried about Ollie's safety, given that Nasty Nathan has got it in for him, but there are dogs in danger of being killed tonight by the Bone Ranger and the burden of that knowledge weighs on me. I can't help but wish we were on our way to Lower Piddle.

Rose pulls up next to a line of plastic bins that have been kicked over so that the rubbish bags within have spewed onto the footpath. Betty and I watch Rose through the window as she knocks on Ollie's door. There's no answer. She peers through the letterbox in the door and calls out his name several times. She gets back into the car looking dejected.

'If he's in there, he's doing a damn good job of pretending he isn't.' Rose turns the ignition and drives away. She dials Brenda again, who begrudgingly agrees to leave work early. She says she'll be home in half an hour. 'When I find the silly sod, I'll wring his neck.'

'Brenda, I have to go home. If you haven't heard from, or seen, Ollie in an hour's time, can you call me?'

'He likes the library. Can you see if he's there?'

'Sure.'

We do just that. Rose exits the library even more worried. When she gets in the car, she dials her mum. No answer. 'Oh dear,' Rose says. 'I hope she isn't pissed off with me.'

She turns the ignition. In no time at all, we're zooming along the dual carriageway heading for home. The traffic lights change to red and we stop. It is bucketing down with rain. The windscreen wipers rasp and judder because the rubbery bits are worn. Nevertheless, through the smeared glass I see the signpost: Upper Piddle, Middle Piddle, Lower Piddle. I leap up and bark hysterically, my nose pointing at the sign.

'What's up, Monty?' Rose asks, watching me in the rear mirror. 'Need a wee? We're almost home. Just hang on a bit.'

By now I am bouncing up and down on my front paws like a seesaw. I don't take my eyes off the sign.

The traffic lights turn green. Rose accelerates. I'm now yelping.

'Okay, okay, I'll pull over.'

She doesn't take the turning to the Piddles as I had hoped. She pulls into a pub car park and gets out with me. She tries to lead me to a grass verge and I try to drag her back the way we came. By now the rain has plastered her hair to her scalp and water drips off the tip of her nose.

'Okay, back in the car,' Rose says. 'I'm getting drenched.' She drags me back. I know I should obey her, but the Bone Ranger is going to kill those dogs tonight and without Rose, I don't know how I can save them. I dig my paws in, refusing to budge, but they slide in the mud. 'Get in! I'm getting cross now.'

For the rest of the journey home I am subdued. Betty, back in her hiding place in the magazine pocket, looks forlorn, which doesn't help. I rack my brain for another way to get Rose to drive to the Piddles tonight, but nothing comes to me. I try to work out how far it is to Lower Piddle. I could bolt when we get home. I'm pretty sure Rose would follow me. She'd be very angry though.

'Do it,' Betty says, seeing the indecision in my eyes. 'I'll come with ya.'

I change my mind when we pull into Rose's driveway and there's a dark grey van parked near the house belonging to Butternose Boiler Servicing.

'Oh no, don't tell me it's packed up again,' Rose mutters.

My first duty is to protect Rose, so I have to find out who Butternose is before I leave to find the stolen dogs. We run through the rain to the rear of the cottage and Rose throws open the back door. I catch a glimpse of Betty running under the fridge. The warm air is laden with the smell of cooked lamb shanks, mashed potatoes and Brussels sprouts with crosses on them. And wine too. There are dirty plates on the table, dirty dishes in the sink and dirty pans on the hob. From the sitting room I hear Liz giggling. So does Rose.

'Oh you are naughty,' Liz says.

Rose's eyes widen and she rushes from the kitchen, across the hall, and into the sitting room. I follow. Liz is on the sofa with a man of similar age, with craggy skin and a thick head of hair the colour of honey. He has Liz in an embrace and his lips are on her lips.

'Mum!' shouts Rose.

Liz and Butternose pull apart, very startled.

'Darling, this is Albert,' Liz says, standing up. She pats down her hair. 'Meet our knight in shining armour.'

Liz's lipstick is smudged which makes her look as if she'd just eaten cherries.

Butternose gets up and shakes Rose's hand. 'Don't be alarmed. The boiler's perfectly fine. Your lovely mother invited me to lunch.'

Rose glares at her mother.

'Such a charmer,' Liz says, fluttering her eyes at Butternose, oblivious to Rose's discomfort.

'What happened to your dog?' Butternose says, staring at my stitches with concern in his voice.

'He saved a friend from a dog attack.'

'Looks painful.'

'Yes, he was very brave,' says Rose. 'Mum, can I have a word?'

'I have a guest, Rose, can't it wait?'

'No, I'm sorry, it's urgent.'

'Sounds like you two ladies need to talk. I can show myself out.' He turns to Liz. 'Thank you for a wonderful lunch. See you again very soon, I hope.' He kisses Liz's hand, nods at Rose, and then leaves.

Rose looks as if steam is about to shoot out of her ears. 'I can't believe you were…you were kissing him! What about Dad?'

Liz flicks her wrist dismissively. 'He won't need to know if you don't tell him.'

'Please don't put me in that situation.' Rose tugs at the end of her ponytail. 'You can't do this to Dad.'

'Oh stop being such a prude. It was just a kiss.'

'But Mum!'

'But nothing. I won't be criticised by my own daughter.'

'Hello, again!' Butternose calls from the kitchen. 'Forgot my phone.' He comes into the sitting room and takes his phone from the coffee table. 'Use it for my appointments, see? Got one more to do. An old lady in Upper Piddle.'

Did he just say Upper Piddle? I bark like crazy. Butternose backs away, looking scared. He scarpers out of the house and down the drive. But I don't stop barking.

'That dog has a screw loose,' says Liz.

'That's the second time he's done that,' Rose muses. 'What's your beef with Upper Piddle?'

I stop barking. She has nailed it. Well, almost. My theory is that if I can get Rose to Upper Piddle, I can then steer her to Lower Piddle which is where Wiggins Farm is supposed to be.

Rose bends down. 'Do you want to go to Upper Piddle?'

I bark once. Yes.

Liz pours herself some more red wine. 'I'm telling you, that dog has to go.'

Rose ignores her. 'What's at Upper Piddle?' She scratches her head. 'Has this got something to do with the stolen dogs?'

One bark. Yes!

Rose chews her lip. Looks at Liz. 'I have to take a look around Upper Piddle. Do you want to come?'

'In this weather?! You're just as mad as the dog.'

49

The rain has finally relented, but the clouds are so dark it's as if night has come early. The road through Upper Piddle is busy with traffic and every building is lit up from within, bleaching the wet asphalt a shimmering white. Kids in rain-spattered school uniforms loiter outside the grocery store that is busy with shoppers. A Black Labrador with a gleaming wet coat is tied to a bollard, waiting for his owner to collect him.

'Okay, Monty,' Rose says, unwinding all the car windows. 'This is Upper Piddle. Take a good sniff and tell me where to go.'

I stick my muzzle out of the nearest window and soak up the village smells. Damp concrete, wet woollen coats, car exhaust, leaf litter, food smells from a rubbish bin, sugary sweets. Rose has given me Lady B's angry cactus toy again so that her scent is fresh in my mind. I prick up my ears too, but the dog voices I hear are singular and their barking is relatively happy. It's the high-pitched yowl, the desperate baying, the feverish en masse yapping that will reveal the stolen dogs' location.

Rose slows down and glances expectantly at me in the rear-view mirror. Nigel was very clear about the dogs' location: Wiggins Farm, a mile from Lower Piddle. I don't expect to pick up their smell or hear their cries in this village, but I listen for them nevertheless. I'm feeling the pressure. I can't afford to make a mistake. Lives depend on me.

'Anything?' Rose asks me as we drive past the pub that smells of heated sponge pudding, salted crisps and beer. 'Can you hear Lady B?'

I can't. I keep my head out of the window as we approach a T junction and a signpost in white wood. To the right is Middle Piddle. To the left is Lower Piddle.

'What do I do now?' Rose says.

At the junction the two vehicles ahead of us slow. The car in front turns right.

'Middle Piddle?' Rose says.

I stay quiet.

'Lower Piddle?'

I bark once. Yes! Lower Piddle.

'Looks like it's Lower Piddle,' says Rose. She turns left. 'I must be barking mad. But, what the hell!'

The lane meanders like a snake. Through the open windows, the smell of pigs and horses, manure and rich muddy earth wash over me. Lower Piddle is little more than a huddle of semidetached houses surrounded by farmland. Rose pulls over on the grass verge, her headlights illuminating bushes and fences that line the street. Rose turns around in her seat.

'Have a big sniff, Monty.' She stretches out her arm and waves B's squishy cactus toy near my nose. 'Find B.'

I inhale deeply. Nothing. I cross to the other window and inhale again.

That's when I hear it. A mournful howl. *Save me, I'm hurt. Save me.*

Then a *yip yip*, angry and challenging. It's B. I'd recognise her voice anywhere.

I howl in response. 'I'm coming! I'll free you. Keep barking.'

Just then Rose's phone rings. 'Shush, Monty, it's Brenda.'

But Rose, can't you hear them? They're just over the hill. We're so close.

'Quiet!' Rose says, and I have to stop. But I still hear their pleas carried on the breeze.

On loudspeaker, Brenda sniffs. 'They've done for him this time. He's beat up real bad. You gotta arrest that thug. I want Nathan in jail.'

'How bad are his injuries?'

'Concussion, bruises all over him, lost a tooth. A neighbour found him unconscious.'

'Did the hospital call the police?'

'I dunno. Cops don't care about us. You call them. They'll listen to you.'

'Okay and I'll meet you at the hospital. Be there in thirty minutes.'

Rose asks Brenda for the details of the ward, then calls Geldeford nick and reports the assault.

She does a U-turn.

No Rose, please. They'll die tonight if we don't rescue them. They're just over the hill.

All Rose hears is my barking.

'Wish I had the blues and twos,' she mutters as she speeds back the way we came.

I stare desperately through the rear window as B's cries recede in the distance.

 50

I've never been inside a hooman hospital before, and so far I don't like it. I hear the moans as if they are in surround sound. I can also smell the fear. It's a little overwhelming. But Rose has asked me to pretend to be a police dog because she wants me with her, and hospitals don't normally allow dogs on the wards.

'Remember,' Rose whispers, keeping me on a short leash, 'Walk to heel and no barking.'

I had imagined a hooman hospital would be much like a vet hospital. I hadn't anticipated the chaos of so many people coming and going, all of them seeming to be in a terrible hurry. As we cross the threshold of the main entrance, a number of passers-by point and gawp.

A security guard with a huge belly shuffles over as quickly as his chubby legs will allow.

'Miss! No dogs.'

Rose tenses. 'Hello Chris!' The security guard looks confused. 'You remember me. Detective Rose Sidebottom. It was a while back. The Patrick Salt case.'

'Ah, yes, of course.' He shuffles closer. 'Sorry about that, didn't have my glasses on. So what brings you here tonight?'

'Got an assault case. Name of Oliver Fernsby.'

'I won't keep you then. This here a police dog?'

'I need him to sniff the victim.'

Rose doesn't like to lie and she's generally very bad at it. Her answer is in fact truthful. I will sniff his clothes, although I think we all have a pretty good idea how Ollie ended up in the hospital.

Chris frowns at me as if assessing my credentials. I puff out my chest and lift my chin. Yup! That's me. Super crime-busting police dog.

'Looks like he's been through the wars.' He screws up his face and squints at my blue stitches.

'Just doing his job,' Rose says.

'Best of luck, then.'

As we move on, I get a waft of sugary cakes and prawn and mayonnaise sandwiches and oh no, cheeeeeeeeeeeeeeeese and ham toasties. I hear the cheese bubbling under the grill and before I know it I'm dragging Rose towards the café. She does her best to pretend that's where she wants to go, at the same time pulling back on the lead.

'Monty!' Rose hisses out of the side of her mouth. 'Behave.'

'Look, that doggie's dribbling!' a toddler shouts, pointing.

I look up at Rose, the spell broken, and she leads me back on course.

'Good boy!' she says, patting my head.

The corridor seems to go on forever and the sounds of pain – both physical and otherwise – coming through doors set my teeth on edge.

'Almost there,' she says, giving me a reassuring smile.

Rose takes the stairs up one level and then turns right, through swing doors and into the Bramshott Ward. Rose asks a nurse in a blue dress for Oliver Fernsby.

'Ah, yes, the assault,' the nurse says. 'Police said he's at risk, so we put him in a private room.'

We find Ollie with his eyes closed, a bandage around his head and a tube protruding from the back of his hand. At the other end of the tube is a bag of clear fluid that hangs from a pole. Brenda talks in hushed tones to a woman she refers to as "doctor".

'We don't allow dogs on the ward,' the doctor says.

'He's a police dog,' says Rose.

The doctor hesitates.

'Dog's going to find the bastard who beat up my boy,' Brenda says. 'I want him to stay.'

'Oliver is heavily sedated. It would be better if you came back in the morning.'

'It can't wait,' Rose says. 'I'll be as quick as I can.'

'All right,' says the doctor, 'but keep the dog quiet and it must be on the leash at all times.'

When the doctor closes the door behind her, Rose drops my lead. I wander up to the bed and sniff the bag of clothes under the bed. Just as I thought, Nathan's smell is all over them. Without his glasses on, Ollie looks younger and more vulnerable. His mouth is swollen and there's a cut in his lower lip. Beside the boy, machines beep as lines of colour zigzag across a screen. I give his hand a playful nudge with my nose. He doesn't react. At least his breathing is regular. I rest my head on his arm and listen to his pulse.

I wish I'd woken Betty from her cup-holder nest in the door and been able to bring her with us. She and Ollie have forged a special relationship and I'm sure he would have been happy to see her. On the other hand, if she'd been spotted, all hell would have broken loose, so maybe it's for the best.

I stay like this for a while, then lift my head to study his face. Nope, his eyelids are still closed. I rest my furry muzzle on his bare arm again. That's when I feel the slight tightening of the muscles in his wrist. I pick my head up and watch Ollie's hand. His middle finger lifts a fraction, then lowers. Nobody but me sees it; Brenda and Rose are deep in conversation. I nudge his hand gently. Ollie's eyelids flutter. Okay, I'm not imagining it. I trot over to Rose and nudge her hand, then return to Ollie's side. I nudge his hand one more time. Ollie moans.

'Brenda! He's coming around,' Rose says.

Ollie's eyelashes quiver like butterfly wings. Slowly the lids part. Brenda takes his hand.

'Ollie, it's Mum. You're safe, my love. You're in hospital.'

Ollie has a faraway look.

'How are you feeling, love?' Brenda says.

'I'll get the doctor,' Rose says, ducking out of the door.

Ollie's gaze focuses in on his mum. He rolls his parched lips together. 'Can I…have water?'

The doctor returns with Rose and shines a mini torch in Ollie's eyes. She asks him questions. Ones even I could get right: about what day it is, and where he is. If the doctor needs to ask, I'm not sure what she's doing being in charge.

Ollie answers as he sips water through a paper straw. The doctor then explains what concussion is and how he might feel dizzy for several days, maybe weeks, as well as his bruised ribs and hip, and lost tooth. Ollie opens his mouth and uses his tongue to locate the gap in his front teeth. He hisses at the pain of his raw gum. 'Oh great. Now I look like a right prat.'

'Your glasses got broken but I've brought your spare pair.' Brenda hands them to Ollie and he puts them on carefully, so as not to cause pain to his swollen eye from the previous beating. 'Ah, that's better. Is that Monty? Come here boy.'

Ollie reaches down and ruffles my ear. 'Good boy.' He then looks up at his mum. 'What happened?'

Brenda's joy is short-lived. 'Don't you remember?'

'I remember being punched and kicked, but nothing after that.'

'Hello, Ollie,' Rose says, stepping closer. 'Can you remember who did this to you?'

Ollie turns away from Rose and stares at me. I can smell fear starting to rise of his skin like puffs of steam when raindrops land on a hot road. I rest my head on his hand and look up at him. His eyes are watery. Oh no. I think he's about to cry. This is terrible. I take emergency action. Tensing my back leg muscles, I leap onto the bed, and settle down next to Ollie on the crisp white sheets that smell of bleach. Both Rose and Brenda gasp.

'Monty, get down!' Rose says.

'Let him stay. I like his company.' Ollie strokes my head and then my ears. He smiles. 'Soft as velvet.'

Rose glances at the door. 'He can stay for now. Please tell me who assaulted you, Ollie.' Rose asks.

Ollie doesn't respond. Rose pulls up a chair. The legs scrape on the floor. She sits. Through Ollie's hand on my ear, I feel his pulse quicken.

'PC Joe Salisbury is on his way to take a statement. If you tell him who did this, he can arrest him.'

'He'll find me.'

'You mean Nathan Hill?'

Ollie sniffs back a tear.

'Ollie, my love, Rose is right,' says Brenda. 'You and me together, we can get Nathan put away.' She pauses, searching his face for a reaction. He looks down, lips clamped. 'We can go stay with me sister for a while, so Nathan can't get to you. Give you time to recover. What do you say, love?'

'He'll find me, Mum. He'll kill me.'

'Did Nathan say that, Ollie? Did he threaten to kill you?' Rose asked.

'Yeah.' A tear rolls down his cheek. His mum hands him a tissue. He wipes his cheek, then blows his nose. 'He knows I grassed him up. I'm scared.'

'The doctor wants to keep you here tonight for observation. Monty will stay with you. He'll keep you safe. Won't you, boy?'

I *hurrumph*. I will?

Don't get me wrong, I like Ollie. But there are dogs in terrible danger tonight and only I can stop it. I can't stay here. I have to get to Lower Piddle and I need Rose with me.

In an attempt to make my point, I leap off the bed and sit staring up at Rose and bark twice. *No! I want to be at your side.*

She kneels in front of me. 'Monty, I know you want to be with me and I love you for it, but Ollie needs your protection. You can do that for me, can't you?'

How is a dog supposed to respond to that? I have to agree. Rose is my pack leader. In my head, I can hear the puppies' cries on the wind at Lower Piddle. I promised I would help them. If I'm at the hospital all night, I can't. A ball of anxiety like a nest of snakes writhes inside me.

Just then, Big Man Joe pokes his head in.

'All right, Ollie?' Joe says. 'How are you doing, my friend?'

'Not so good.'

'I can see that. You want to tell me who did it?'

Ollie looks at me, then his mum. 'Nathan Hill and his gang.'

Brenda breathes a sigh of relief.

While Ollie gives his statement, Rose takes me for a walk around the block so I can pee, then sets up a bowl of water and gives me a few dog chew treats. When Joe leaves to arrest Nasty Nathan, Rose gives me a cuddle and tells me to be a good boy. I drop my head and snuggle into her chest. I hate being separated from her.

'I'll be back at six-thirty in the morning to take you for a wee, okay? And I'll bring you a special breakfast.'

I lick her hand in gratitude, but my heart is breaking for the puppies in Lower Piddle.

51

The car felt empty without Monty. In the rear-view mirror, Rose could see the headlights of the vehicle behind her, but no furry face and no big, brown inquisitive eyes staring back at her. She wondered if she'd done the right thing leaving him at the hospital. Joe and other officers had searched the estate, but Nathan had done a runner. By now, he would know Ollie was pressing charges. If Nathan came after Ollie again, could Monty handle someone so brutal?

Yes, she told herself, yes he could. He'd tackled more dangerous criminals before. But still, he was already injured.

She turned her thoughts to her mum. Was Liz having an affair with the boiler man? Rose had always found it hard to talk honestly to her mother, but she had to try. She hadn't spent much time with her since she'd arrived. Rose rang Liz and offered to cook dinner.

'That would be lovely. Can the boy go out somewhere?'

'*The boy* is in hospital, Mum. He's been badly beaten.'

'Oh, I'm sorry to hear that. Just us girls then,' she said, chipper. 'Perfect.'

'I'll do salmon with my special dill and mustard sauce.'

'Sounds gorgeous. A Riesling will go perfectly with it. Would you mind getting a couple of bottles?'

Liz had always loved a glass of something in the evening, but she had consumed an awful lot of alcohol in the last few days. As Rose headed for the Sainsbury's seafood counter, she found herself walking down the pet food aisle. Hanging in the dog toys section was Lady B's angry cactus toy. Well, several of them. Rose immediately felt a stab of guilt. Here she was planning a relaxed dinner, when B was God-knows-where and Monty was doing guard-duty at the hospital.

Rose stopped and stared at the fluffy toy. Why had Monty so badly wanted to go to Lower Piddle? What did he know that she didn't? Had he heard the stolen dogs barking? His hearing was, after all, way better then hers. Rose stared down at the contents of her shopping basket. She had everything she needed except the salmon cutlets. It was six o'clock and dark outside and she'd promised her mum she'd spend quality time with her. She toyed with leaving the supermarket to explore Lower Piddle.

No, it would have to wait until the morning. Her mum was obviously going through a difficult time and Rose should be supportive. So she selected the fish, wine and dessert she wanted, paid and drove home.

They had eaten the salmon and polished off a bottle of Australian Riesling. Well to be honest, her mother had polished off most of it. The whole time they avoided the elephant in the room: Liz kissing Albert. Rose had just served a New York cheesecake, which she knew was one of her mother's favourites. She had been psyching herself up to broach the topic.

'Have you spoken to Dad?' Rose asked.

'Why would I? I'm having a break from him.'

Ouch! 'He's rung me a couple of times. He's missing you, Mum.'

'Good!' she said, and stabbed her fork aggressively into her slice of cheesecake. Then she looked up. 'You didn't tell him…'

'No, of course not, but if he asks me, I won't lie.' Rose put down her fork and spoon. 'Are you serious about Albert?'

Liz squeezed her daughter's hand. 'No, darling. It was nice to feel attractive and Albert made me feel special. Your father doesn't notice me.'

'He's not the most demonstrative of men, that's true. Have you told him how you feel?'

'What's the point? He won't change, and anyway, with his back problems, we don't even have sex anymore. It's like we're two strangers living in the same house.'

Oh God! Rose couldn't even get her own life in order. What chance did she have of helping her parents sort theirs? Rose tried to think of what Dr Doom would say in this situation.

But Liz hadn't finished. 'And you and I have grown apart too. I hardly ever see you these days. It's like I'm invisible.' Now was clearly not the time to remind her mother that she had refused any contact with Rose for the first two years of her policing career. 'I've been here two days and I've hardly seen you.' Liz seemed genuinely upset.

'I'm so sorry. I'll make it up to you,' Rose said.

'Don't you like me?'

At first, Rose didn't know what to say. It had never occurred to her that her mother might think that. 'Oh Mum, of course I like you. I love you.' Teary, Rose got up and hugged her mother. 'Do you think you might come to accept that I also love my job? It would mean a lot to me.'

'Well, I suppose I could try.' Liz smiled. 'Can you promise to call me more often? I like to know what you're up to.'

'I can do that.' Rose sat on a chair next to her mum. This was the most honest they had been with each other, ever. It felt good. 'You know, how about we phone Dad now and put him on speaker phone?'

Liz wriggled in her seat. 'Oh all right then. He probably won't pick up.'

'I bet he will, and I think you should tell him you're feeling neglected. He doesn't know why you upped and left so suddenly.'

Rose picked up Liz's phone and used WhatsApp to contact her dad. He picked up almost immediately.

Frank Sidebottom had a thick head of greying hair and a trimmed beard. He beamed a delighted smile as he propped up his mobile phone so he didn't have to hold it as they spoke. Both Rose and Liz could see he was in his favourite wingback armchair with a wooden tray on his lap. On the tray was a ready-meal in a plastic container that he would have warmed in the microwave. After a brief chat, Rose made an excuse to leave the conversation so her parents could talk freely, which was just as well because Rose had an incoming call from Malcolm.

Rose plonked down on the sofa.

'I've had a tip off,' Malcolm said. 'Someone contacted me because of the radio appeal.'

'What's the tip off?' Rose felt a buzz of adrenaline.

'They heard barking from lots of dogs, coming from a farm not too far from your neck of the woods. You'll never guess where?'

'Lower Piddle?'

'How did you know that?'

'I was there earlier today.' Rose rubbed her forehead. 'Monty led me there. He must have somehow known. Why didn't I listen to him?'

'I'm going there now,' Malcolm said. 'Will you come with me?'

Rose looked at her watch. It was nearly eight o'clock.

'And if we find the dogs?'

'I'm taking them. All of them.'

'How are you going to do that?'

'Horse box. It'll be cramped. We can bring them back here and I can check them over.'

'That means trespassing on private land. For the second time. And the farmer might have a gun. I just want you to realise what you are getting yourself into.'

Malcolm went quiet. While he mulled over the risks, Rose made a mental list of what to take with them, most of which were already in her car:

Warm waterproof coat and gloves? Tick

Stab jacket? She still had her police-issue stab jacket, although it wouldn't save her from a bullet. Tick.

Maglite torch? Tick. But it needed fresh batteries. She had new batteries in a kitchen drawer. Tick.

Extendable baton? Tick.

Bolt cutters? Rose was still amazed by the assortment of equipment Aunt Kay had stored in the tool shed. Tick.

Rat Cam? Ollie had left his holdall and the box of inventions on the sitting room floor. The Rat Cam lay on the top of a pile of mechanical stuff. Tick.

Rat? That was a tricky one. Rose suspected Hoover, as Ollie had christened her, lived in this house somewhere, but how on earth could she find her? Rose gave that idea a cross.

Thermos flask of hot coffee? She could make that. Tick.

Finally, Malcolm spoke. 'Rose, my whole life I've been sensible. Good old reliable Malcolm. Well, I have to try and find my puppy. There's no need for you to come if you don't want to. I don't want to mess up your career.'

'My career is already messy. It's just…' Rose sighed. 'I'd feel safer if we had Monty with us.'

'Where is he?'

Rose explained why he was guarding Ollie at the hospital. Then she said, 'I'll meet you there. I just have to explain to Mum what's happening.' In the other room, her mum was laughing. A good sign. 'Where are we going exactly?'

'Wiggins Farm. He's a nasty piece of work, by all accounts. The RSPCA has had run-ins with him before.'

'I'll see you outside the farm entrance. Give me an hour.'

Rose sat for a while, wondering how to tell her mum she was going out. Liz's laughter erupted from the kitchen. 'Oh, you are naughty!' Rose heard her say. 'What a sexy idea!'

Her mother popped her head around the door. 'I'm going upstairs, Rose. Your father and I need a bit of privacy.' Liz winked at her, then danced up the stairs.

Rose tried not to imagine what her Mum and Dad were up to, but she was happy they seemed to be mending bridges.

She nearly jumped out of her skin when a rat appeared on the arm of the sofa, right next to her hand.

'Oh my God!'

The rat sat up, squeaking at her.

'Hoover?' Rose peered closely at the rat. 'Okay, I'll assume you're Hoover and I haven't gone stark raving mad. I'm going to need you with me tonight. Monty's at the hospital, guarding Ollie. You remember Ollie, the boy who loves you?' The rat squeaked indignantly. 'Okay, good. Will you wear the Rat Cam for me? I might need to record some video tonight.'

She paused. The rat squeaked again. Rose scratched her head.

'Am I really talking to a rat?'

52

'You're so tame,' Rose said, glancing sideways at the weirdest passenger she'd ever had in her car: a rat wearing a tiny video camera that was Velcroed around her body. The little creature sat patiently in the middle of the seat as if it were something she did all the time, that is until Rose used the word *tame*. Hoover screeched and glared ferociously at Rose.

'Okay, okay, I don't mean *tame*, exactly,' Rose said, convinced she had gone insane. Perhaps her anxiety medication was too strong? She'd have to check the leaflet when she got home to see if hallucinations were a side effect. 'I meant you're so very clever.'

The rat calmed down. She started to clean her long whiskers.

Rose hadn't seen another vehicle for several miles. The temperature outside was just above zero and only crazy people like her and Malcolm were out on such a bleak night. She was glad she had on her warm puffer jacket, leather gloves and bobble hat. She drove through the hamlet of Lower Piddle, then took a right turn along Mamble Lane, which meandered up a hill and then descended into a valley with dense forest either side of the road. Rose flicked her headlights onto high beam. The deciduous trees' interlocking leafless branches formed a skeletal tunnel, which by day would be beautiful, but at night was deeply disquieting. The branches glittered with frost and the asphalt shone like glass in the car's beams. A fox with glowing eyes skittered across the road and disappeared into a bank of bracken.

Her sat nav announced that she had arrived at her destination. All she could see was the forest. She slowed to a crawl, searching the darkness for a sign or a gate. She rounded a bend in the road and to her relief, a white horse box and Malcolm's car were lit up by her high beams. She dipped the beams and parked facing Malcolm's red Vauxhall. He got out and came over to her window, which was already down. The freezing wind whispered through branches. A fox screamed, the sound uncomfortably like a human's. A creature in the undergrowth rustled near her car. An owl screeched. But no barking.

'Any sign of the dogs?' she asked him.

'It's hard to tell. The forest is pretty dense and it extends for a couple of acres.' Malcolm pointed to a satellite image on his phone. 'There's a driveway through the trees. It leads to the pig sheds and then on to the house where the owner lives. The problem is how we locate and free the dogs without alerting Wiggins. Any ideas?'

'Is he home?'

'No idea.'

'I guess we take a look.'

Malcolm drove a further hundred yards then pulled over. Rose parked behind him and zipped up her coat.

'Do you want to sit in my nice warm pocket?' she asked the rat, thinking, *there you go again, talking to animals.* Rose held open her coat pocket and Hoover dived in, then wriggled around so her head poked out of the top.

'Clever girl.'

Rose opened the car boot and took out the bolt cutters. She already wore her stab jacket under her puffy coat. She felt a pang of guilt because she didn't have a second one for Malcolm. She made sure she had her extendable baton, a torch, a bag of dog treats and Monty's spare lead.

'Great minds think alike,' said Malcolm, holding up a dozen or so leads, no doubt from his vet practice.

Malcolm fitted a head torch on top of his beanie and carried a crowbar. 'It's not a weapon or anything. It's for levering open doors.'

Rose wasn't sure how Malcolm might react to her secret weapon. 'I've got the rat with me. She's wearing Ollie's Rat Cam.' Rose opened her pocket and Hoover's nose twitched, her whiskers glinting in the torchlight.

Malcolm stroked Hoover's head with one finger. 'Intelligent animals. They can navigate their way through mazes. They've even been used to detect landmines. Never seen them carry a camera, though. How much training has she had?'

'I'm not sure. Ollie had a go at instructing her.' She shrugged, 'But hey? What have we got to lose? If we can't rescue the dogs tonight, at least she might be able to get us some proof.'

The rusty gate in front of them was padlocked but there was no fencing either side so it was easy to walk around and follow the rutted driveway through the forest. Underfoot, the frozen mud was rock hard and dangerously slippery. Several times Rose almost ended up on the ground. The stomp of their walking boots sounded loud to her. Too loud. And their torchlight bounced ahead of them along the track and in the denuded branches. Would Wiggins see their lights? Every now and again a twig broke and leaves rustled. Rose's hands ached from gripping her torch too tightly. She was already sweating with anxiety.

'Are you all right?' Malcolm asked. He must have heard her breathing hard.

'Yes.'

Calm down. Slow your breath. You can do this.

She told herself she mustn't let Malcolm down. She mustn't panic.

After what seemed an eternity, the terrain changed. The trees stopped as abruptly as if the forest had been sheared away. A muddy yard confronted them, slashed with tyre tracks. A barn with a roller door that had to be twenty feet high. Two buildings the length of a football field, painted green, with corrugated steel walls and roof. A circular water tank at one end shone silver in the torchlight. Rose heard a pig grunt. There were no vehicles, apart from a tractor. No lights. In the distance, further up the hill, light shone from the windows of house.

'I hope he doesn't have guard dogs,' Rose said, remembering Tank.

Malcolm pulled a plastic spray bottle from his pocket. 'It's like pepper spray for dogs. Stings like hell but won't cause lasting damage.'

They crept forward and Rose pressed her ear to the first shed. All she could hear was pigs grunting. Malcolm pressed his ear to the second and gave her a thumbs-down signal. They looked at the barn. By now Rose was beginning to have serious misgivings about Malcolm's tip-off. She still hadn't heard a single dog, let alone thirty or forty. They headed for the barn, passing the tractor that loomed in the darkness like a metal beast. Malcolm tripped in a deep rut and put an arm out to steady himself. His torch clanked against the tractor's radiator grill. A dog barked. It was the kind of bark Monty made when he'd woken suddenly to warn her of a strange noise. In seconds, other dogs barked too, yelping, howling, yipping, whining.

They both ran at the roller door. A flood of adrenaline coursed through her. Would the farmer hear the noise and investigate? They had to be quick.

She moved her torchlight over the door, trying to find a means to open it.

'Here,' said Malcolm, pressing a button.

With a clank and a whir, the roller door began to rise. They bent low and ducked under it. The stench was bad inside. They shone their torches on the cages. Dogs. Dozens of them. Some were wide-eyed, some snarling, others were terrified and cowered at the back of their metal prison. Others clawed at their confines, biting the wire, making their mouths and paws bleed. Sick dogs, emaciated dogs, some with weeping eyes. Rose's stomach churned, as did her fury. How could anyone be so cruel? She had to film it, to ensure Wiggins was prosecuted.

Rose scooped Hoover from her pocket. The rat struggled and squeaked dementedly, clearly agitated. She was probably terrified by the noise. So many dogs around her. Why hadn't Rose thought of that? Too late now. She raised Hoover so she could talk to the rat's face.

'I need you to film this, okay. The dogs won't hurt you. They're going on leads.'

Rose switched on the Rat Cam and checked it was recording. She then held Hoover so that she and the camera faced the first row of cages. 'There must be at least thirty dogs in this barn on Wiggins Farm. Most are sick and injured. The conditions are abhorrent,' Rose said, hoping her words could be heard above the baying and yowling. Rose then moved the rat and the camera to the other row of cages and put Hoover on the floor. 'Keep filming the dogs and cages, little one.'

'B!' Malcolm called out.

He received a high-pitched yip, yip. A shivering Cavalier King Charles Spaniel puppy wagged the whole back half of her body, not just her tail.

'Thank God you're alive,' Malcolm said, sliding the cage's bolt open and freeing B, who leapt into his arms, licking his cheek.

'Malcolm, give me half the leads. You take that side and I'll take this. We have to hurry.'

Rose took half a dozen leads and drew the bolt of a cage with a filthy, painfully thin Golden Retriever inside it. She had clearly had puppies recently because her mammaries were heavy with milk. The dog cowered at the back of the cage which had no solid floor, just the wire mesh which would have been painful to stand or rest on.

'It's okay,' Rose said, noticing the Retriever had no collar, 'I'm here to free you.' She used her softest voice. She tentatively stretched her arm into the cage, very aware that a terrified dog might attack. Slowly Rose looped the lead around the animal's neck, which tightened as she pulled it. 'Come on girl, I'll look after you.' The Retriever got up on shaky legs and limped forwards. In the semi-darkness, Rose couldn't see much detail, but one of her paws was swollen and smelt bad; it was clearly infected.

Malcolm had B on a lead. 'Hello, Gizmo,' he said to the French Bulldog snarling at him. 'Remember me, it's Malcolm. Come here little girl.'

Gizmo yelped with delight and ran at him. Malcolm looped the lead around her neck. He moved on to the next cage. Rose freed a Chocolate Labrador that almost flew past her. She had to leap onto the dog to stop her running away. 'It's okay, we're going to look after you.'

Footsteps. A thud.

Malcolm cried out, then fell to the concrete floor. Rose swivelled. Gizmo yelped. A wiry man with a steel car jack in one hand and a shotgun in the other loomed over Malcolm's limp body.

Rose instinctively pulled out her baton. Her mouth might be as dry as the Sahara, but she managed to shout a gravelly, 'Police! Step away from him.'

In her torch's spotlight she saw him grin.

B charged at the man's legs, her needle like puppy teeth bared, but his Wellington boots protected him. He kicked her away dismissively. The little dog squealed.

'He warned me you'd come snooping,' said the man she assumed was Wiggins.

He paused. Looked beyond her. Too late she realised that he was looking at someone.

The pain was like a fire in her skull. She stumbled. Her torch and baton fell from her hands and she collapsed to her knees. Her torch rolled on the floor, strobing light across the rows of traumatised dogs jumping and snarling and slamming themselves into the sides of the cages. Her vision blurred into total darkness.

 53

I'm curled up on the floor beneath Ollie's hospital bed. Above me, his breathing is the slow rhythm of deep sleep. The edge of a sheet dangles below the mattress, providing a kind of curtain for me. They have the heating way up and occasionally I pant to lower my body temperature. At least the vinyl floor is cool. Every now and again a noise from the corridor wakes me, and I lift my ears to make sure everything is okay. Visiting hours ended long ago. The noises come from the nurses doing their rounds and their occasional chatter.

Sammy, who told Ollie she was from Thailand, pops in regularly to take his blood pressure and check his pain medications. Earlier, she noticed my paw sticking out from under the bed and bent down to look at me.

'He's a police dog,' Ollie had said. 'He's guarding me.'

'I didn't know, but that's all right. I love dogs. I used to volunteer for a dog rescue centre, the Soi Dog Foundation in Phuket.' She winked at him and smiled at me. 'I won't tell anyone.'

I fell asleep after that.

I have a dream. A nightmare. I'm being chased through a forest of giant ferns that are like octopi. They reach out and try to grab me.

I dodge their grasping tentacles and leap over fallen tree trunks. A hooman chases me. I can't see him but I hear his heavy breathing, mud splashing, twigs snapping. He gains on me. My legs are so, so heavy. I try to speed up but it's as if I'm wading through water. I can sense him about to grab me, almost feel his hand on my collar. He'll kill me if he gets me. I see the glint of a knife.

I wake, paws twitching as if I'm still running. I peer through the darkness at an orange glow. Where am I? I sniff. Ah, the hospital. The orange glow is from a machine connected to Ollie. He shifts in the bed, then is still again. There isn't a sound from the nurses' station. They must be looking in on other patients.

The door to Ollie's room is wider than average. It has a small glass window above the handle through which I see the light in the corridor. And then suddenly it isn't lit up. A hooman peers in, face pressed close to the glass. A man. The door opens slowly. Too slowly. I sniff quietly. He's from the Truscott Estate. He carries its smell on the hoodie pulled down over his face that conceals all but the wispy fringe of hair and the cold dark eyes. He stinks of cigarettes and beer. There is a strong chemical smell coming from his jeans' pocket. It's Nathan Hill. The man who beat Ollie twice already and has come to finish the job.

I prepare to spring from my hiding place and hold back a growl. He takes a step into the room. His gaze is fixed on Ollie and he clearly doesn't know I'm here. The closer he gets, the more scents fill my nostrils. He has handled lots of dogs, more than I can identify, except one: Lady B, who smells of Magic Marker pens. He's definitely handled her, but I know he's not the Bone Ranger. I shudder. This hooman not only threatened to hurt Anna and beat Ollie twice, he also works for the Bone Ranger. My terror threatens to overwhelm me.

Then I think of Rose. She trusted me to keep Ollie safe. That is my duty.

Nathan's black trainers are close to the bed. He trembles and, mingled with all the other smells, I recognise again the pungent whiff of fear. This is bad. Very bad. He's about to do the worst thing a hooman can do – kill another hooman. I creep forwards, then tuck my legs beneath me and prepare to spring. There's a sound of fabric sliding over fabric. In Nathan's hand is a pillow.

Ollie's breathing changes. He exhales. 'Who...?' he begins.

Nathan leans forward and raises the pillow. Ollie starts making choking sounds.

I spring from under the bed and sink my teeth into Nathan's calf. I bite down as hard as I can. He yells. Releases his grip on the pillow and tries to grab my collar, but I shake my head about so he can't get a hold of it. Ollie splutters and gasps for air. Nathan digs his fingers around the scruff of my neck. His grip is painful but instead of letting go, I dig my teeth in deeper. My canines hit bone and the thug howls like a lonely pup.

Ollie shouts for help. He falls to the floor, the tubes attached to him straining. He tries to wrench the tubes out, but he's caught fast like a puppet on strings.

Nathan hits me with his fist, striking my back. My legs slip on the vinyl and my jaw opens, unable to stifle a cry of pain.

'Leave him alone,' Ollie shouts, spread-eagled on the floor, groping his way without his glasses. 'Help!'

Nathan backs away and pulls a flick-knife from his jeans. He opens it, the blade glinting dull orange in the light of the medical monitors. 'I'm going to enjoy this.'

Nathan thrusts the blade at me. Fortunately, I've got pretty good reflexes, and I'm able to dodge the knife. I keep my distance, circling him. I snarl, putting all of my anger and anxiety into it.

'Leave Monty alone!' Ollie shouts.

'She's dead, you stupid mutt. Now it's your turn.'

Nathan jabs the knife at my face. I jump to the side and then leap at the arm clutching the blade before he has time to try again. I only manage to grab a mouthful of hoodie which rips, and I lose my hold.

Ollie lurches at Nathan's ankle. With his free leg Nathan stomps down on Ollie's arm. Ollie howls in pain. I again attack the arm with the knife. This time I get his wrist. I mustn't let go. If I do, he'll kill us both.

The door opens and Sammy screams, 'Oh my God! Help!'

Nathan drops the knife. 'Help me! The dog's killing me!'

Sammy presses a red button on the wall and a ringing sound fills the air, then she grips my collar and tries to drag me off Nathan. 'Stop it, leave the man alone.'

She twists my collar. I'm choking. I have to let go.

Ollie manages to gasp. 'Not the dog. Him! He tried to kill me!'

The nurse drops my collar. But it's too late. I've lost valuable seconds.

Nathan races from the room, leaving a trail of blood from his leg wound. I give chase. He barrels through the ward doors, which swing outwards. I slip on his blood and tumble, ploughing into a wall with an almighty thud.

54

It was as if Rose's brain was wrapped in barbed wire inside her skull. An eye-watering shot of pain zipped up her neck as she tried to lift her face off whatever was digging into her cheek. She felt the sweat, clammy on her forehead in the bitterly cold barn, and panted, clenching her eyes shut. She was on her side, in a foetal position. The ground seemed to sway, as if she were drunk, but it was the pain. She retched and felt the bile spurt from her mouth and down the side of her cheek.

Rose opened her eyes. Bars. More like squares. Rusty and grubby. Across the aisle, she saw dogs in cages. Directly opposite her, another dog paced, then tried to chew at its wire cage. Its muzzle was stained brown with blood.

Rose remembered. She and Malcolm. Wiggins Farm. They'd found the dogs. Wiggins had knocked Malcolm unconscious. Someone then hit her on the back of the head, which explained the thudding pain.

The barn had been pitch black when they broke in, the only light coming from their torches. But a weak glow now filled the barn. Rose dared to turn her head so she could look up. More stabs of pain. The floor seemed to rock again like an angry sea, then it settled. A lone bare bulb hung from a long electrical cord dangling from the barn's high ceiling. Less than two feet above her was wire mesh. *Oh sweet Jesus!* She was in a cage, like the terrified dogs all around her. Beneath her hip, shoulder and ear was wire mesh on concrete, which was what had been digging into her face. Her shoulders were pinned behind her and as she tried to move her arms forward, they burned. Her wrists wouldn't budge. In alarm, Rose realised her wrists were bound and so were her legs. She tested the bindings again, wriggling her wrists up and down. Duct tape held them fast, as did the duct tape around her ankles.

A wave of panic threatened to drown her and she started screaming. But her cries were barely audible amidst all the barking dogs. After a moment, she realised all she would do was alert Wiggins and his mate, whoever he or she was, that she was awake. She clamped her mouth shut to stop herself screaming again.

She tried to tune out the dog noise. She strained to hear voices. From where she lay, she couldn't see if the roller door was up or down.

'Malcolm?' Rose called out. 'Malcolm? Are you all right?'

If Malcolm responded, he was too quiet for her to hear.

A sob escaped her lips. Had they killed him? Were they going to kill her next? She was a police officer. Killing a police officer was a major crime and every cop in Geldeford would hunt the killers down no matter whether they liked her or not. But Rose didn't want to die. The only person who knew what she was doing tonight, other than Malcolm, was her mum, and she doubted Liz would notice her absence until the morning. By then her body might be buried somewhere in the forest, never to be found. She longed for Monty. If he'd been with her, he would have warned her about Wiggins. What a fool she'd been.

Then an idea came to her. Was her mobile still in her coat pocket? With her hands tied, she didn't know. She doubted Wiggins would be dumb enough to leave her with it, but who knew? She had to get up, get out of the cage, and find Malcolm. Call the police.

Fear held her in a vice. She wanted to sit up, but a voice inside her head told her to stay still and pretend she was unconscious. *If you try to escape, Wiggins will shoot you.*

No, no, no. Malcolm might need urgent medical attention. And she was a police officer. *It's your job to preserve life.*

But still she didn't move. Every part of her ached, apart from her hands which had gone numb, her circulation cut off by the bindings.

You can do this. One step at a time. First, sit up.

She shifted into her back, with her knees tucked up to her chest. It was difficult balancing without the use of her arms. A wave of dizziness hit her. She panted like the dogs around her. Then she held her breath and tightened her stomach muscles and attempted to roll forward to get her feet on the floor of the cage. She dropped her chin to her chest and a pain shot down her neck and spine. She gasped. It took several attempts but she managed to sit up, her scalp pressed against the top of her cage, her back against a side panel.

She was soaked in sweat. It trickled down her temple and stung her eyes. It tricked down her spine. She shivered violently. She forced herself to look around. Her eyes filled with tears as she saw chocolate brown fur stuck to the front of her cage. The brown Labrador that she freed must have escaped and she was now in the dog's cage. She found it hard to focus her eyes and the lighting was dim. The roller door was down. The barking quietened. She scanned the cages. Saw Lady B in the cage Malcolm had rescued her from. When they made eye contact B yipped and yipped, wagging her tail.

'It's okay, B. We're getting out of here.' But where was Malcolm? Rose called his name. No answer. Had they taken him away?

Then she saw him at the back of the barn, in a cage large enough to hold an Irish Wolfhound. Hands taped behind his back, ankles taped together, lying on his side. His back was to her and she couldn't see his face, but his black hair was wet and shiny. To her horror, she realised it was blood.

Dear God! Did he have a fractured skull?

She hunched forward and tried to wriggle her wrists free of the tape, but they barely moved. Her chest tightened with panic. Suddenly, she couldn't get enough breath into her lungs.

Not now, I can't have a panic attack now.

There was a tickling sensation against one hand, like a feather brushing her skin. She tried to look over her shoulder but bent over as she was in the cage, she couldn't do it. Unsure if it was a cockroach or maybe a spider she shifted her butt to the right. There was a squeak of protest. Could that possibly be Hoover? A scraping noise was followed by the rat appearing on Rose's right side. To Rose's relief, Hoover was still wearing her webcam equipment and the green LED told her it was recording.

New-found hope gave Rose a burst of energy. Hoover scuttled back to where Rose's hands were bound. Rose pressed them tight against the wire mesh behind her.

'Can you gnaw through the tape?' Rose said.

There was a tickling sensation again. Must be the creature's whiskers. Then Rose felt a slight tug on the tape around her wrist. Rose stayed very still to give the rat every chance. Her lower back ached. Her head pulsed with pain. Time dragged interminably. The dogs had exhausted themselves and most lay, weary and defeated, in their cages. Only one or two still paced up and down.

All of a sudden, there was a sharp prick like a needle and the duct tape came apart. Her hands were free. At first Rose could barely move them because her shoulders had cramped, having been stretched behind her for so long. Gradually, a few centimetres at a time, she brought her arms forward until her hands rested in her lap. The skin on one wrist had a nick in it from where Hoover had mistakenly bitten her. The rat scampered around to where Rose could see her and started cleaning her whiskers. Rose's numb hands were getting blood to them again, and the pins and needles were excruciating. But she fumbled in her coat pockets for her phone, keys, anything that might help get them out of there.

Wiggins must have cleared out her pockets. *Damn!*

Rose stroked Hoover's chest.

'Thank you, little one. I need you to do something for me. I'm going to record a plea for help. I need you to find someone who will look at that video footage. Can you do that for me?'

As Rose spoke, she knew in her heart that she was asking too much of a rat, but what did she have to lose?

The rat squeaked once. Rose ensured the camera pointed at her and spoke.

'My name is Detective Constable Rose Sidebottom. I'm being held against my will in a barn on Wiggins Farm, Lower Piddle. It's 9.55pm, Monday December 13th. My friend, Malcolm Kerr, has a serious head injury inflicted by Harry Wiggins, who attacked us when we discovered his puppy farm. Please call the police and ambulance immediately. Wiggins is armed with a shotgun and is dangerous.' Rose paused. 'Off you go, little one.'

Hoover sat for a moment staring at her, then scurried away.

Now all Rose had to do was find a way out of her cage.

55

'Monty?' Ollie kneels next to me in the hospital corridor.

I slap my tail on the floor in a half wag. My collision with the wall knocked the wind out of me and my lower back throbs where I was punched. But it only takes me a moment to get back on my feet again. Can't keep a good dog down. There's a streak of Nathan's blood on my fur.

Nurses run around like startled ducks. Sammy, at the nurse's station, screams down the phone. 'Stop the guy. In a hoodie. Tattooed hands.'

From the unhealthy state of the security guard I met earlier, I'd say he doesn't stand a chance of catching Nathan, even though the would-be killer is wounded. Another nurse, older and broader, tells Ollie that a doctor is on his way and he should get back into bed.

'I'm fine,' Ollie says. 'I'm more concerned about the dog.' Ollie wraps his arms around my neck and I feel his warm breath on my ear. 'Are you okay, buddy?'

A trickle of blood runs down his hand from where the canula was ripped out. The blood pools on my fur. It's nice to be appreciated, but I have to find Rose. Nathan said she was dead, but I don't believe him. I'd know if she was. I'd feel her loss. Even so, she is in danger and I must find her at once.

'I'm sorry, Monty,' Ollie says. 'This is all my fault. If I'd come clean with Rose, maybe this wouldn't have happened.'

I peer into his eyes. I don't know why Ollie thinks this is his fault but that's not my focus right now. I try to pull away from the boy.

'It's because of the drone,' Ollie continues, holding on to me for dear life. 'Nathan wants the footage.' He sits up. 'You're going to hate me, Monty. I know where the pups were taken. And that's probably what Nat meant. If she's gone to Wiggins Farm, she's in big trouble.'

What! I lift my paws like one of those Spanish dancing horses in my agitation. Then nudge his arm. Repeatedly. *Tell me. Tell me where Rose is.*

Sammy bends over Ollie. 'Police are on their way. Security is looking for him. Let me help you get back to bed.'

With her help, he gets up off the floor. I'm doing loops around him, desperate to know where Rose has gone. I bark to get his attention.

'Shush!' the nurse commands.

But she's not my owner. Rose is. I bark again.

'Where are my glasses and phone?' Ollie asks.

'All your stuff is on a shelf under your bed.'

Ah, yes, the basket hanging just beneath the mattress.

'I have to make a call.'

'Let's get you to bed first.'

'No,' Ollie says, 'I have to go. I need my clothes.'

'You need to see a doctor. You've had a terrible shock. You could be injured.'

'I'm over sixteen. I can discharge myself.'

He heads back to his room. I follow. Sammy does too.

'Ollie, this really isn't a good idea.'

'I've made up my mind.'

'I'll have to call your mum,' Sammy says.

'Whatever.' Ollie pulls the basket on its runners out from under the bed. He paws through his belongings until he finds his glasses. One of the lenses is still cracked. He puts them on, then he wipes away the blood on his hand with a wet paper towel.

I am beside myself. Rose is in danger. I can't wait any longer. I take Ollie's arm in my mouth, very gently, but enough for him to have to stop what he's doing.

'It's okay, Monty, we'll find Rose. We're going there now.'

I release my grip.

Sammy enters with a band aid, which she applies to the back of Ollie's hand. She sighs and leaves the room.

Ollie dresses quickly. He sways dangerously when he leans down to pull on his trainers. He shoves his house keys and mobile phone in a coat pocket. Then he clips my lead onto my collar and walks, a bit unsteadily, past the nurses' station.

'Mrs Fernsby, we can't force him to stay,' says Sammy down the phone. 'Can you get here as soon as…?'

When she sees us leaving, Sammy waves to get Ollie's attention, but the boy doesn't stop. We take the lift to the ground floor. The security guard is nowhere to be seen and the café is shut for the night. We leave. Ollie grips a handrail like it's a life preserver and takes some steps that lead to the car park. He pauses at the top, gasping for breath. I give his hand a reassuring lick. What are we doing here? We don't have a car. Rose drove hers away a long time ago.

I want Ollie to phone Rose. I nudge the pocket that has his phone. He pushes my snout away.

'I don't have treats.'

That's not what I mean. I try to get my nose into the pocket and pull out his phone.

'You want me to call Rose?' He glances behind him. 'Look, Monty, if we don't get out of here, the cops will question me for hours and it could be too late to save Rose. I'll phone her once we got a car, okay?'

I follow him as he inspects the parked vehicles, which have thinned out since earlier in the evening. 'We need an old model.'

Ollie walks past a Ford Fiesta, a Kia four-wheel drive, a Peugeot, a Renault. All look shiny and new. We come to a battered Volvo estate with a dented side door. He peeks inside.

'No good,' says Oli. 'Steering wheel lock.'

Then he spots an old model Vauxhall Astra. 'A manual. Blimey. Suppose I'll work it out.' It's a boxy dark blue car, with an angular front bumper and faded stickers on the back window.

Ollie picks up a loose brick that's part of a flowerbed border. He uses it to smash the driver's side window. I bark my disapproval.

'Shush!' With his sleeve over his hand so he doesn't cut himself, he opens the driver's door. There's an extra cushion for the driver. Ollie uses it to bush away the shattered glass from the seat, gets in, then opens the rear door for me. 'In you get.'

I hop onto the back seat while Ollie fiddles with wires under the dashboard. There's a grinding noise and the engine coughs into life. The car lurches forward. Stalls. I tumble into the footwell and hit my head, but my skull is thick. I climb back onto the rear seat.

'Shit!' Ollie says and starts the car again. 'Bloody manuals!'

He pulls on a seat belt and winces. 'Jeez, that hurts.'

We kangaroo our way out of the car park and follow the signs to the Geldeford bypass. Once we're on the dual carriageway, Ollie doesn't fiddle with the gear stick and his driving is much smoother. He opens the rear windows for me. 'Stick your head out, boy. Lower Piddle's not far.'

Wooferoo! That's where the stolen dogs were taken. That's where Rose must have gone tonight. But why did she go without me? I stick my head through the gap in the window and sniff the air, hoping to pick up the faintest scent of Rose. My ears flap and my jowl wobbles in the wind. I feel more positive already. I bark into the air whooshing by so fast.

'I'm coming for you, Rose,' I howl. 'I'm coming.'

56

The Astra's engine stutters as we approach a roundabout. Fortunately, this late at night there's virtually no-one else on the road, so our leapfrogging goes mostly unnoticed. I've tumbled into the footwell so many times I've decided it's safer to stay there. Ollie peers into the rear-view mirror.

'Watch out for cops, Monty. I get caught wiv a stolen car again and I'm in big shit.'

I jump onto the back seat and watch out for blue flashing lights, although if we passed Big Man Joe I'd want Ollie to stop the car and ask Joe to come with us. We could do with someone big and strong like him.

The world outside the window zooms past. A church clock tolls. I recognise that particular chime. It's from the church in Upper Piddle. We're getting close. I wag my tail. We race through Upper Piddle. People with wobbly walks are tumbling out of the pub. We come to a now familiar T-section and Ollie turns left to Lower Piddle. My paws won't stay still. I'm edgy as a first timer in the main ring at Crufts.

We pass a few slumbering houses then turn up Mamble Lane. It's very dark, but the moonlight reveals a gang of hares in a ploughed field who sit up and watch us go by. The lane dips into a valley full of trees. Inhaling, I smell owl, badger, hedgehog, fox, mole and pig. But all I can see are trees. *Hmm.* Curious.

'It looks so different in the dark,' Ollie says, for the first time sounding unsure. He slows right down. We hop a few more times. 'Where's the bloody entrance?'

I stare at the back of the boy's head. How does he know the way to the Bone Ranger's den? Someone as nice as Ollie couldn't be involved in the puppy farm, could he? I shake my head, trying to throw off my doubts about him.

We round a bend and come upon Rose's Jazz and Malcolm's Crossland X, the latter with a horse box attached. All around us is dense forest. Oddly, the scent of pig is now strong and so is the scent of dogs. I jump up and claw the window, wanting Ollie to stop.

'All right, mate,' Ollie says, seeing my unmistakeable desperation. 'Pullin' over.'

The engine stalls and jerks to a stop. The car's back-end sticks out into the lane. If a car took the bend too fast it would plough into us.

Ollie shrugs. 'That'll do.'

A freezing wind rattles through the frost-covered trees and whispers a warning. My hackles are already up. I have smelt him. The Bone Ranger is near.

'The dogs are in a barn. Not far.' He opens the glove box. 'Shit. Need a bloody torch. It's a long walk through them trees.'

He turns in his seat to look at me. 'I ain't never been here before. It was my drone. I have footage of Wiggins and Nathan unloading the cages of dogs into the barn. That's what Nathan wanted me to give him. He knows it could send them to jail.'

The whole car suddenly jerks sideways. I yelp in shock. I'm thrown against the door with a *thwack*. Metal screeches. The driver's side of the car crumples like tissue paper. Ollie exhales an *Ugh* as his body is shunted sideways. The wheels slide across frozen mud. The windscreen cracks. The car jolts to a halt when it hits a tree trunk. Steam hisses from the bonnet.

The vehicle that slammed into us reverses. The headlights are blinding. I scramble to look out the window. There's a flash of white bodywork.

Ollie's head hangs limply to one side like he's asleep.

I bark like crazy, 'Wake up! We have to get out of here!'

The van's engine ticks over, then revs madly. Is the driver going to ram us again? I poke my head forward between the two front seats and bark right into Ollie's little pink ear. That works. He wakes with a start, blinking.

'Oh my neck hurts.'

Then panic sets in. He scrabbles at the seat belt, stabbing his finger on the release button. Eventually, he frees himself. Ollie then tries to open the driver's door, but it's so bent out of shape it won't budge. He stares at the passenger door, which has a tree-trunk-shaped inward bulge where it is now wrapped around the bole of a large beech.

I bark and claw at the rear door nearest the lane. Ollie understands what I mean and tries to wriggle from his seat so he can climb into the back with me. But the old car's steering wheel has dropped on impact and Ollie is pinned in the driver's seat.

Beyond the van's headlights, a door opens. A figure gets out. Ollie sees him too.

'No!' he cries.

Ollie is rank with terror now. And I don't blame him. The moment the man stepped out of the van I knew it was Nathan. He must have either followed us or come to warn the Bone Ranger. I watch the hooded silhouette saunter towards us. I guess this is round two. Nathan is wounded and I am battered and sore. But I have to stop Nathan fulfilling his plan. How? I can't defend either of us from inside the car. I have to be outside. Darkness is my friend. I can draw him away from Ollie and into the forest. My night vision and my sense of smell will give me an advantage.

I would normally avoid a hooman knowing I can open doors. But this is life and death. I grip the long metal door handle of the rear door between my teeth and pull. It slips from my mouth. I try again. This time there's a clunk. Shoving the door open with my head, I leap out onto the frosty road surface and turn to face my enemy, teeth bared.

'Monty! Don't leave me,' Ollie calls plaintively.

Haloed by white light, Nathan waves a knife at me.

'Here, puppy dog,' he taunts.

I lift my muzzle high and howl, like my wolf forebears. It's a warning. *Stolen puppies. Nathan and Wiggins mean to kill you tonight. Run if you can!*

The response is immediate. Muted dog howls from across the forest. A fox barks.

Nathan stalks closer. I stand between Ollie and Nathan, muscles tensed, head low, ready to pounce. My only hope is to damage his arm so badly that he can't use the knife. Before he gets too close, I run at him. He thinks I'm going to leap at him head on. At the last moment I dart to one side and dive into the thick bracken. Nathan can't see me. The headlights are pointing at Ollie's car, not the forest.

'Fu'ing coward!' Nathan yells at me. I hunker down and crawl beneath the bracken. I know exactly where Nathan stands from his scent. 'Your dog's abandoned you.' I hear Nathan snigger. 'Your turn.'

Ollie pleads, 'Nat, we're mates. You can have the video. I haven't shown anyone, I promise. Don't, please!'

Poking my nose out of the bracken, I can see Nathan's back. He grabs the driver's door handle and tugs on it, determined to get at Ollie. I know it's jammed fast. This is my chance.

I break cover and charge. Nathan starts to turn. Before he can face me I leap and sink my teeth into skin, muscle, and the small bones of the hand clenching the knife. I know he'll hit me with his free fist, so I have to make him drop the knife fast.

He screams in pain and raises a fist, but he doesn't drop the knife.

Just then, the glare of the van's beams is eclipsed by a shape that descends from the sky. Huge black wings. Terrifying eyes. A black beak like the scythe of the Grim Reaper. The magpie's talons dig into Nathan's scalp and the bird pecks viciously, drawing blood.

'Ahh!' Nathan screams.

He tries to hit the bird with his free hand, but he's fighting on two fronts, and my teeth bite down harder. Nathan screams again and drops the knife, his hand dripping blood. I open my jaw and scoop up the knife's handle and run to the edge of the forest. If he comes after me I'll run deep into the trees and drop the knife where he'll never find it. I'm not proud that I bit him. I did it to save a hooman life. I can only hope that Nathan will think twice in future about hurting others.

But Nathan isn't interested in me, or Ollie, or the knife. He's too busy battling an angry bird. Despite Nathan's efforts to swat the magpie away, the enraged bird repeatedly dive-bombs him, stabbing his dagger-sharp beak into the thug's head.

I recognise that plumage. It's Dante.

'You killed my sister!' he squawks furiously.

It all makes sense now. Why he wanted me to steal the photo from Ollie. Ollie's tame magpie, the one Nathan stoned to death. She was Dante's sister.

Dante swoops in again, relentless as a fighter pilot. Nathan runs, hands flailing like he's swatting away wasps. Dante follows like a missile locked on its target. Nathan yanks open the van door and slams it shut behind him. Dante lands on the bonnet and, with his sharp beak jutted forwards, he squawks at Nathan. 'I will hunt you to the end of my days!'

Dante is truly terrifying.

It has the desired effect. Rubber squeals as he accelerates too fast, the tyres skidding on the icy road. Dante scrapes his claws along the metal as the tyres finally grip and the van lurches forwards. The sound is ear-splitting. Nathan shrinks in his seat in fear, then drives away into the night.

Dante gives chase.

 57

Nose to the ground like a Bloodhound, I follow Rose's scent through the forest. My heart lifts because Malcolm's scent is alongside hers. At least she's not facing the Bone Ranger alone. I refuse to believe Nathan. Rose is alive. In trouble, yes, but alive.

Ollie is safe. He's phoned for emergency assistance and from what I could make out, the police, ambulance *and* the fire brigade are on all their way.

'Go!' he said to me. He pointed to a padlocked gate. 'That way!' I barked a thank you and turned to leave. 'Wiggins has a weakness,' Ollie called out. 'Go for his right knee.'

The track is slippery and uneven, the mud frozen hard as granite. I pass puddles of ice that reflect glimpses of the moon between the trees' branches. Forest creatures poke their noses out of hiding places and watch me race by. Some shake their heads. Some cheer me on. A vixen, her eyes golden, peers through tall grass.

'Be careful, young hound. He is cruel and canny. He has poisoned many of my family. My cubs, too.'

The imprisoned dogs still call to me, although their barks grow weaker, their tone more defeated. As their cries die away, a Basset Hound bays mournfully into the night.

'Two hoomans are in cages and they are injured. Hurry!'

I speed up, my paws sliding on the slick surface, but I keep running, my hot breath forming misty clouds. Abruptly, the forest track ends in a wide, muddy yard, bordered by a huge barn and two sheds full of pigs. A tractor in front of the barn gives me a fright, looking as though it is lurking in the darkness. Is the Bone Ranger hiding, waiting to trap me, or worse, shoot me? I lift my head and sniff. No, his scent is weak. He's been here recently but isn't now.

Breaking cover, I creep across the frozen mud, nostrils pulsing, ears on full alert. The closer I get to the barn, the stronger Rose's scent becomes. I gaze up at a metal door the width of the whole of Duckdown Cottage. There's no handle. How does it open?

I don't want to alert the Bone Ranger to my presence but I need to know if Rose is in there. Perhaps she can tell me how to get in? I bark. The barn is almost blown off its foundations by the deafening cacophony of baying that results.

'Save us, Monty!'

'They took my puppies. So young. They need me.'

'The hoomans are in here!' bays the Basset Hound.

Then the yip, yip of Lady B, 'Monty! It's B! Hurry!'

I paw at the door, my nails scraping the metal, but to no avail.

'Monty!' shouts Rose, 'Is that you?'

I want to bark and bark with glee, but I have to control myself. I take a deep breath and bark once. Just the once. A loud and resonating, yes!

'Oh Monty!' Rose calls. 'Malcolm is injured. Run for help. Get the Police. Take something of mine from my car and run to the village!'

I can't abandon them. Rose doesn't seem to know about The Bone Ranger's plans to kill the dogs, and I suspect he isn't going to let Rose and Malcolm live to identify him. By the time the police respond to Ollie's call for help, and Ollie directs them to the barn, it could be too late. I must find a way in. A back door?

Flickering light in the distance distracts me. I see a house up the hill, defined by the lights in the windows. What has me running in tight circles is the vehicle jouncing across a field and heading this way. I correct myself. Four headlights. Two vehicles. One has to be the Bone Ranger. I sprint down one side of the barn, desperate to find an entrance. Nothing but solid steel walls. I reach the back of the barn. No rear exit. I race around the other side. No side door. By the time I have circled the whole barn, a white van, identical to the one Nathan drove earlier, comes to a stop in front of the barn, closely followed by a boxy Land Rover. Their headlights light up the yard.

From cover I watch the hooman I fear most step out of the van – the Bone Ranger. In black from head to toe, including his boots. I stare at his legs. For the first time I notice that he favours his left leg to take the pressure off his right one. Ollie was right – his knee is vulnerable. He carries a shot gun in one hand and a sack of something lumpy and angular in the other. I sniff. Ah, lamb bones. Of course. My mouth is dry, I pant with fear. How can I save them now? I'm no match for a gun.

I almost jump out of my skin when the Land Rover's passenger door creaks open and John Clapper gets out. He's wearing a waxed Barbour coat and the same tweed cloth cap he had on when Rose accosted him for shooting at us, not long after we had viewed Anna's body. He also carries a shot gun. His weapon hangs in the crook of his arms, broken in the middle. A lump forms in my throat that's bigger than the chunk of French bread I once tried to swallow whole.

'You blithering fool,' John says. 'She's a bloody policewoman for Christ's sake!'

'Stop your fussing, John. I'll deal with her. And the guy.'

'The *guy* happens to be my bloody vet!' John throws an arm up. 'The police are bound to think their deaths are linked to me. We've had one too many run-ins.'

'I told you, I'll deal with them,' the Bone Ranger hisses, clearly annoyed. 'Get out of here! Go to the pub. You'll need an alibi.'

'What about the…bodies?' John asks, his voice hoarse.

The Bone Ranger, shorter but stronger than John, stands close to the older man and eyeballs him. 'Leave it to me. The less you know the better.'

'Dead dogs are one thing, Harry, but a police officer? Are you out of your mind?'

'I told you not to press charges. You made yourself a suspect.'

'Shut up, Harry,' said John. 'I need to think.'

I can't let them enter the barn. I might have been able to disarm one of them, but not two. Not with guns. I need a plan.

'There's another way,' The Bone Ranger says. 'Rohypnol.' Looking smug, the Bone Ranger pulls from his jeans a plastic bottle of pills. 'If we give them enough, they won't remember a thing. They'll wake up in his car, clothes dishevelled, and think they've had some hanky-panky in the woods.'

'Good God, man! You deal in drugs too?' John sneers.

'What gives you the right to look at me like that? I hear the cops found that dead girl's key on your land. Now who's the blithering idiot?'

'Shut up!' John snaps. 'Her death had nothing to do with me.'

'Yeah, sure, and I'm the Queen of England.' The Bone Ranger stabs an angry finger into John's chest. 'Me and Nathan had a nice little business going. I bought the stuff into the country – dope, coke, roofies, speed, E, you name it. Hid it in pig crates. Nathan looked after distribution. Now everything's buggered because of you!'

John pushed him aside. 'Will the Rohypnol work?'

'Yes.'

'How do you know?'

'Done it before.'

'Okay, then. Have it your way, but I'm done. We drug them, kill the dogs, then it's over between us,' John says.

'Suits me. I'm skipping out tomorrow anyway. Pigs go to slaughter in the morning, then I'm gone. You should do the same.'

'That's all well and good but I can't just up and leave,' John splutters.

The Bone Ranger shrugs. 'Not my problem.' He stalks towards the barn. 'Let's get on with it.' He slams his palm onto a button to one side of the door. The roller door rises with a metallic screech.

Two hoomans with guns. Rose and Malcolm injured. Dogs trapped in cages. I don't know what to do. I look around, desperate for inspiration. The tractor is just a couple of steps from my hiding spot. It towers above me, the bonnet as tall as the men. If I could climb up the footholds and onto the bonnet, I might be able to leap onto the Bone Ranger, knock him over and steal his gun. But what about Clapper? He has shot at me before and surely won't hesitate to do so again.

Then I think I hear Betty.

'Oh, Mr Monty, there you are! Things have gone 'orribly pear-shaped. Malcolm is asleep and won't wake up. Rose is hiding at the very back, with Malcolm. I'll distract this lot. You get them two out of here.'

In my frantic state of mind, I must be imagining it.

The roller door isn't yet far enough off the ground for The Bone Ranger to duck beneath it. He taps his boot impatiently. I watch the door slowly grind higher. I eye the tractor.

All of a sudden, Betty appears beneath the roller door, lit up like a movie star in a spotlight. She's wearing Ollie's Rat Cam. However did she get hold of that?

She squeaks viciously at the Bone Ranger.

'What the—?!' he says. 'It's wearing a bloody camera.' He tries to stamp on her, but she dodges his boot and scurries out of the barn.

'Kill it!' roars John.

Betty is not as fast as she used to be, which perhaps has something to do with all the pizza she consumes, but it's also because she is carrying a camera on her back that's almost as big as she is. The Bone Ranger tries to stamp on her again and very nearly gets her. Betty scampers behind one of the tractor's massive wheels.

'Leave it to me,' John says, gripping the Bone Ranger's arm. 'You deal with the cop and the vet.'

The Bone Ranger nods and ducks under the roller door. There's a click of a light switch, but it doesn't work. The barn remains pitch black.

'How the hell did that happen?' the Bone Ranger mutters, 'Unless…'

Unless…Rose broke it so they couldn't be seen. Clever Rose.

By now, John is on all fours, peering underneath the tractor. 'Come here you little shit.' John snaps the two parts of his shot gun together and uses the barrel to poke at the space between the tractor tyres. He grips the wooden stock in both hands like it's a club.

I creep from my hiding place, then, before Clapper has time to react, I bite his nearest hand.

He yelps and drops the shotgun. I scoop the wooden stock up between my teeth and run. It bounces across the frozen ground making my teeth judder. I'm into the blackness of the thick undergrowth before John has even managed to stand up.

'It's that bloody dog again!'

I take the killing-machine further into the forest, so Clapper won't find it. Then I run a wide loop through the bracken until I emerge some distance from where I disappeared. Clapper storms across the slippery yard, determined to retrieve his shotgun, and falls over, landing hard on his back. He groans in pain.

Now to deal with the Bone Ranger. I race across the yard, staying at the edge of the headlights so I am nothing but a shadow. Clapper is struggling to get to his feet and doesn't notice me. I steal into the barn.

The Bone Ranger is a dark and menacing presence that seems to float down the central aisle between the rows of cages. His torch beam sweeps across the terrified eyes of imprisoned dogs like a POW camp searchlight. They panic, lunging at their tormentor, yowling and snarling. The cages wobble. He halts at a large cage, the wide door open. On the dusty floor are shiny bits of tape that carry Rose's scent. He flicks his torch at another large cage, also empty. The light glistens on smears of fresh blood on the cage's base.

'No use hiding,' he calls.

My nose tells me that Rose and Malcolm are at the back of the barn. It won't be long before he finds them. I slink along the narrow gap between a row of cages and a wall so the Bone Ranger can't see me, but I keep up with him. The dogs' cries hide any sound I make. I hurry, attempting to beat him to the back of the barn.

At the end of the row I can see Malcolm, eyes closed, lying on his back on the concrete. His hair smells of wet blood. In a far corner, Rose stands in the darkness clutching a pitchfork. I come around the opposite corner. Her eyes must have adjusted to the lack of light because she smiles, looking straight at me.

The Bone Ranger angles his torch down when he comes to the last cage and illuminates Malcolm, pale and still on the dirty concrete.

The Bone Ranger bends at the waist and points his torch at Malcolm's face. Malcolm's eyes don't even twitch. He touches Malcolm's neck. This is my chance. I lower my head and charge, like a battering ram. The top of my head collides with his knee.

Something snaps in his knee. The bone ranger screams so loudly the dogs stop their barking at once. He collapses to his side, narrowly missing Malcolm. When he hits the ground, his leg is at a strange angle. He screams and screams.

I always knew my thick skull would come in handy one day.

He's dropped his gun, but he claws the ground for it.

Out of the darkness, a red Wellington boot stomps down hard on the Bone Ranger's hand, then Rose scoops up the gun and points it at him.

'Enough!' Rose says, 'I'm arresting you for kidnapping and attempted—'

'No, you're not,' says John, a rifle pointing straight at her, nothing like the shotgun I hid in the forest. He must have brought a second weapon with him. 'Put it down, or I'll blow you to Kingdom Come.'

58

Rose slowly places the shotgun on the floor, then stands tall, her hands above her shoulders.

The Bone Ranger screams in agony. 'My knee!'

It distresses me to see a hooman suffering. I instinctively want to help. Then I remember all the dogs the Bone Ranger has stolen, who had miserable lives in cages, and then were shot when they were no longer of use to him, and I feel no regret for causing his pain. What I care about right now is protecting Rose from John Clapper and the rifle he's pointing at her.

I stand in front of her. He'll have to shoot through me to reach her. Rose kneels next to me and hugs me close. 'Good boy, Monty,' she whispers. Then to Clapper she says, 'John, think about what you're doing. Think of your son. Your legacy.'

'Shoot the bloody dog!' the Bone Ranger yells.

'No!' Rose hugs me tighter.

I struggle to put myself in front of her, to protect her.

'Can't. It'll kill her too. And this is a registered rifle. They'll trace it back to me.'

'John, put the gun down,' Rose says. 'Please. You kill a police officer and you'll go to jail for life.'

Clapper laughs. 'I'm not going to prison.'

He slams down the rifle stock onto the Bone Ranger's forehead. Rose yelps in shock. I feel her tremble. The man's head rolls to one side and he's silent. John snatches the Bone Ranger's shotgun from the floor then leans his own rifle against a wall. 'This is how it happens. Harry, here, kills you and Malcolm with this gun.' He's wearing leather gloves, so he won't leave fingerprints. 'Your dog attacks Harry. Harry falls and hits his head. I get the hell out of here. Maybe I get charged with puppy farming. But *not* murder. My life goes on.'

In the distance is the long-drawn-out wail of a fire engine.

'Hear that?' Rose says, 'Police are on their way.' Which is true, even though Rose doesn't know it. It just so happens the fire brigade will get to Ollie first.

'Nice try, but that's a fire engine.'

'Harry needs an ambulance.'

'Don't move,' John orders.

'Enough!' The voice is thin. Weak. It sounds like Malcolm. We all turn. His eyes are half-open. His eyelids flutter. He's awake! 'John. Please. Do the right thing. Call an ambulance.'

Clapper's face is slick with sweat. He blinks as it drips into his eyes. The shotgun trembles in his hands.

'You don't have an alibi,' Rose says. 'Forensics will prove you were here. What will happen to your son then? How can he hold his head high knowing his father's a killer?'

'Shut up!' John screams.

His finger shifts to the trigger. I leap forward but my momentum is stunted by Rose's grip on me. John fires. The roar of the gun is so loud.

I feel a sudden burning pain and my world stops.

59

Rose threw herself to the ground. The gun boomed. Something sharp tore into her upper arm and grazed her ear. It burned like acid on her skin. It took a few seconds for her thoughts to catch up. Clapper had fired at her. He'd tried to kill her!

She couldn't catch her breath. Was she dying? The dogs whimpered but were otherwise quiet, as if in shock. A second siren wailed in the distance. This one sounded like the police, but they would arrive too late.

Monty lay on his side, his tail towards her. He was silent. Too silent.

'No!' she screamed.

She stretched out a hand. She couldn't reach him. She shuffled forward on all fours.

His eyes were shut. His tongue hung limply from his mouth. His fur was bloody in patches. 'Monty?'

She dropped her ear to his ribcage, hot tears blurring her vision. With so much noise, and the ringing in her ears, there was no way she could hear a heartbeat. She pressed her ear closer. She couldn't lose him. He was her best friend. It felt as if she was being ripped in two. She sobbed. 'Don't leave me, Monty. I love you.'

'Why couldn't you leave well alone?' John reloaded the shotgun and tutted. 'Bloody fool. Who only loads the one shell?' He snapped the gun together and raised the barrel.

'You killed my dog,' Rose shrieked at him, tears streaming down her face.

Clapper put his finger on the trigger.

'John, don't,' Malcolm said weakly, before his eyes rolled into the back of his head and he was unconscious again.

Rose buried her face in Monty's warm fur. She closed her eyes and waited for the inevitable.

'Dad?'

Rose opened her eyes and stared at the barn's entrance. In the car headlights stood the tall and lanky figure of Andrew Clapper. Beneath a knee-length, camel-coloured coat his striped pyjama bottoms quivered in the icy breeze.

'Get out of here, son,' John said, keeping the shotgun aimed at Rose.

'Dad?' Andrew crept closer to his father. He glanced at Rose, then at his father. 'I got your message. I'm here to help.'

Surely a partner in a prestigious law firm wasn't going to risk everything to help his father cover up murder. Was he?

John looked askance at his son, taking his eyes off the shotgun's sight for a second. 'It's too late for that. Go home. And remember, whatever happens, I'm proud of you.'

Andrew was next to John. 'You can't do this. *I* can't do this anymore.'

John lowered the shotgun a fraction and gave Andrew a withering look. '*You* can't do it? *You*? Everything I ever did was for you, you selfish little shite.'

As Andrew turned to face his father, the light from the car headlights framed his profile like a solar eclipse. His mouth was an angry line. His nostrils flared. 'You've gambled away my inheritance, Dad. Your debts drove you into puppy farming with that criminal, Harry. I begged you not to.' Andrew flicked an angry look at the body of Harry Higgins, his head in a pool of blood. 'Is he…Jesus, is he dead?'

'Get out of here!' yelled John.

'Don't leave us! He's going to kill us,' Rose cried. 'You can save us. Malcolm needs a hospital. Think of your reputation, Andrew!'

'Is this true?' Andrew asked.

'I have no choice, son.' He relayed his plan to set up the scene so it appeared Harry had shot them and Monty caused Harry to hit his head and die.

Rose expected Andrew to be revolted. To talk sense into his father. She held her breath.

'That could work,' Andrew said. 'Anyone see you coming here?'

'What are you doing?' said Rose.

'Nobody saw me,' said John. 'Stay outside. I've got a change of clothes in the Land Rover. I'll burn the ones I'm wearing when I get home.'

'What a bloody mess! All I wanted was for Anna to go away,' Andrew whined. 'I never asked you to kill her.'

Rose groaned. Was Andrew the mystery boyfriend? It all made sense now. A scandalous relationship that would ruin his career. Did Anna threaten to expose their affair when she discovered she was pregnant?

'Son, if she'd gone to the RSPCA like she said, I'd have lost everything,' John pleaded. '*We'd* have lost everything.'

'I'm not talking about your bloody dogs. She was going to destroy my marriage. My *life*. You said you'd buy her silence. Offer her money to go away. Why didn't you?'

John let the shotgun hang at his side. He passed his free hand over his eyes and looked back at his son with a haunted stare. 'You didn't tell me about the baby. Only the affair. God forgive me for what I did.'

'You killed her, Dad.'

John's head shot up. 'No, son. I didn't. I tried to talk sense into her. She wouldn't take the money. I hit her, yes. But she was alive when I left.'

'You strangled her!' Andrew yelled.

'No, I slapped her. She fell. But she was conscious. I'd withdrawn a couple of thousand in cash. I threw the money at her. Told her to go back to Poland and never return. I walked away, I swear.'

Andrew laughed bitterly. 'Desperate lies from a desperate man. You make me sick.'

'Do I?' said John, fronting up to his son. With each word he stabbed a finger into his son's chest. '*I did not kill her.*'

John stumbled back and leaned against an empty cage. 'There's only one person who knew I was in Hinchley Wood that night. You! You finished her off, didn't you? You used that dog lead you keep in your car to strangle her. Then you made sure Kowalski handled it. Didn't you?' John's eyes were watery. 'That poor girl was carrying my grandchild.'

'Shut up!'

'I won't shut up. I phoned you after I'd left Anna in the woods. And you drove there to finish her off. How could you?'

Andrew wrenched the shotgun from his father's grip and slammed it into the side of John's skull.

60

I open one eye, but the other is squished into the floor. John Clapper lies nearby, his shiny bald pate not far from my nose. Blood trickles down his cheek. He doesn't move. Rose is on her knees, cuddling me. She is alive, that's all that matters.

I attempt to lift my head. My muscles scream. My shoulder burns. A siren, a high-pitched wail, and blue flashing lights strobe the barn's interior. A vehicle skids to a halt, doors are thrown open, and feet pound the hard ground. Big Man Joe and Barika Zaid come to a halt behind Andrew Clapper. They stare at the scene before them. Gripped in Andrew's hand, the bloody barrel pointed to the floor, is the shotgun he must have used to strike his father.

'Police!' says Big Man Joe, aiming a strange weapon. 'Put the gun down, Andrew, nice and slow, or I'll use this Taser.'

Barika has an extended baton.

'I had to,' Andrew says, 'he was going to kill them.' Andrew lowers the shotgun slowly to the floor then raises his arms in surrender. He doesn't take his eyes off his father.

'Andrew murdered Anna!' Rose calls out. 'Arrest him!'

'What utter rubbish!' sneers Andrew.

'He knocked his father unconscious!' Rose says.

Zaid hastily cuffs Andrew.

'You're making a mistake,' Andrew says.

'Call an ambulance!' Rose says. 'Malcolm's badly injured. So are John and Harry Wiggins.'

Despite my pain, I sense Rose's assuredness. She is calm in this crisis. The old Rose has returned.

Joe calls for two ambulances on his radio. He redirects the one that's about to leave Mamble Lane with Ollie inside.

Rose strokes my head. 'Monty's been shot. Barika, I need your mobile.'

With it, she dials Dr Rochester, Malcolm's business partner. Rochester says he'll come immediately. Then she dials Bill Slater from the RSPCA and tells him she's found the pups and to come as soon as he can.

Rose hands the phone back to Barika, then whispers to me, 'Stay with me, Monty. You're my best friend. I love you.'

I love you too!

Rose crawls to where Malcolm lies and takes his hand.

I close my eyes and drift away. I wake again to see Malcolm on an ambulance gurney. The wheels pass close to my face. More sirens blazing. Rose leans over me and kisses my brow. 'Don't die on me Monty.'

Dr Rochester's kindly face peers down at me. I recognise his white hair and pale eyes. 'I'll need to operate immediately,' he says to Rose. He and Joe lift me from the floor, their arms locked beneath me. They are trying to be gentle but even the slightest movement feels like I'm being torn apart.

The RSPCA inspectors are loading the terrified dogs into their vans. The dogs call out to me, wishing me well, thanking me for saving them. We pass a Golden Retriever whose sad eyes, ringed with grime and glazed with pus, follow me. She's in a terrible condition. Her golden coat is matted with so much dirt it hangs in long, grey clumps. She has sores on her skin. Her back legs quiver.

She makes a soft cry, 'Monty? Is that you?'

I manage a soft bark. 'Yes, I'm Monty. Do I know you?'

'I'm Summer. Your mother.'

 61

There's nothing better on a crisp winter's evening than lying under a pub table that's laden with food. Rose looks down and gives me a wink. I look up and give her a wag.

'Don't worry, Monty,' she says, 'I'll keep a bit for 'ron.'

She means "later on". She's keeping aside a tasty morsel for me.

It's Christmas Eve and The Jolly Farmer, a pub that welcomes hoomans as well as dogs, is decorated with colourful lights that hang from the wooden beams of the low ceiling. A potted Norwegian spruce is covered in shiny red and white baubles and boxes wrapped in red and white paper are scattered around its base. When we first arrived, the sight of my shaved fur and scars caused quite a stir. Heads turned. Eyes were pitying. People muttered.

'Poor dog,'

'Oh my God!'

'What happened to him?'

Dr Rochester saved my life, although Malcolm is still my favourite vet of all time, not only because he risked his life to save the puppies, but because Rose smiles a lot when he's around. I'm almost walking normally again, just a slight limp that Malcolm says will go away in time.

The shaved patches make me look like a Poodle with an insane groomer. I have bald spots on my neck, shoulder and rump. The stitches have been removed but the raised scars occasionally sting.

Jenny from Forensics has dubbed me the luckiest dog in the world, and I'm inclined to agree with her – I have Rose. But that's not what Jenny means. She explained that the shotgun was faulty and fired off centre, which is what saved our lives. The pellets didn't hit organs or damage limbs. For a while Rose wore a plaster on her ear, which looked kind of funny, and she has a scar on her arm too.

Strangely, surviving the ordeal at Wiggins' Farm has brought her out of her shell. She believes in herself again. Big Man Joe told Rose how impressed The Leach was by her calm and controlled manner during her witness interview. Her testimony will help send John and Andrew Clapper, and Harry Wiggins, to jail. Andrew is still denying that he murdered Anna Czubinska, but his father has given evidence against him, in exchange for a lesser sentence for himself. Perhaps Anna's parents can now find some peace, knowing that their daughter's killer has been caught.

Until now, Rose and I have been a happy pack of two. But our pack has expanded to include my mother, Summer, who lies next to me under the table, snoozing. Tonight, Malcolm and B have joined our pack, too. Seated opposite Rose, Malcolm tucks into his steak and chips as he tells Rose, in his quiet, stammering way, about treating a hamster with flatulence. Rose bursts out laughing and almost chokes on her deep fried scampi. She has to spit it into her hand to keep from choking. Then she offers the reprobate scampi to me. *Yum!* Summer turns her head. She smells it too. I bite the scampi piece in half and share it with her.

Wedged between Malcolm's shoes with her snout resting on her front paws is Lady B. Her round eyes are droopy, the warmth of the pub making her drowsy. Someone drops a fork on the hard wood floor and B jumps, terrified. These days, she only feels truly safe when she's right next to Malcolm or in his lap. Sadly, she is no longer the dare-devil puppy who guarded the vet practice. But time is a healer.

Malcolm's hand appears beneath the table clutching a tasty treat for B. She sniffs the miniscule bit of beef and takes it delicately, every inch a Lady.

Malcolm had concussion and bruises and spent several days in hospital under observation. Since then, he's been busy helping the RSPCA to find homes for the thirty-seven dogs we rescued. Most of them have been returned to their original owners. For some, the owners could not be found, so they are with foster carers until new homes can be located. Sadly, one of the dogs couldn't be saved.

'Any news on Tank?' Rose asks.

My ears prick up. He's now blind in one eye and his leg is still healing from surgery.

'Doing well. With kindness, patience and training he can learn not to be aggressive. It's not the dog's fault. He was trained to be that way. Did I tell you that Bill's adopting him?'

'That's great news.'

Next to me, Summer sighs contentedly. Her matted, filthy fur was clipped away and her sores and eye infection were treated. She is a beautiful golden colour again and her amber eyes are as clear as I remember them as a pup. I give Summer a lick on the nose. She licks me back.

'How's Ollie doing?' Malcolm asks before taking a swig of his beer.

'Recovered well. He's applying to a college to do his GCSEs. I wrote a letter supporting his application. I hope they accept him.'

'He's a clever lad. I'm still amazed at that Rat Cam of his.'

'I can't wait to see the jury's faces when they are told the video evidence at Andrew's trial was shot by a rat,' Rose laughs.

Betty is now the most pampered rat in the whole county. Ollie comes around often to play with her and Rose keeps her well-fed. She's currently having a quiet night at Duckdown Cottage, happily eating her way through a slab of cheese and some biscuits that Rose left outside her hole in the wall.

'What about Nathan Hill?' Malcolm asks.

'He was tracked down and arrested in the hospital emergency room where he went to have his dog bites seen to. He's standing trial for attempted murder, grievous bodily harm, drug trafficking and several counts of animal cruelty. His aunt, the owner of Pawfect Pets, has also been charged with animal cruelty. Her pet shops have been closed down.'

'I'm glad to hear it. And your mum?' Malcolm asks.

'She's back with Dad. I hope they can save their marriage.' Rose's phone conversations with her mum are less fraught these days.

A young couple with a dog sits at the table next to us. I instantly recognise the lonely Labrador puppy from Pawfect Pets who is in the woman's arms. The pup no longer smells of Anna, or his mother's milk, but I'd know his mewling noises anywhere. I wander over, sit in front of the woman and place my front paw in her lap.

'He's just saying hello,' Rose calls out. 'I hope you don't mind.'

'Not at all,' says the woman. 'Does he like puppies?'

The Labrador pup leans down and yips with excitement. He recognises me. I give him a friendly lick.

'Did you by any chance buy him from Pawfect Pets in Abinger Hammer?' Rose asks, coming over to stroke the little guy.

'Yes, although I never would again. If I'd known he'd come from a puppy farm I'd never have bought him. He's incredibly nervous. Wets his bed constantly. Our vet says it could be because he was born into a world of cruelty.'

I glance behind me at my mother and our eyes meet. *Am I damaged?* my gaze says. *No*, her eyes say in reply. *You're my pride and joy.*

I spot The Leach entering the pub before Rose does. He's in his work suit but he doesn't have his sidekick, Pearl, with him. He makes a beeline for our table, his strides heavy, as if he is punishing the floor.

'Happy Christmas,' The Leach says.

'Sir?'

What Rose means is "what are you doing here?" but she is too polite to ask. I sneak out from under the table and sniff his trouser leg suspiciously. I find no clues as to what he wants.

'And how are you two heroes doing?' Leach says, taking the chair next to Malcolm and sitting down without being invited.

Rose interlaces her hands in her lap. Her knuckles turn white with tension. 'We're fine, thanks.'

'Would you like a drink?' Malcolm offers.

'No thanks. Just want to have a private word with Rose.'

'Anything you have to say to me, you can say in front of Malcolm.'

I stand next to Rose and rest my head on the tabletop so I can eyeball Leach. Leach frowns at me.

'You know, your dog has always given me the evil eye. He's doing it now.'

'Maybe you should try patting him,' Rose suggests. I pick up on the mischievous tone in her voice.

Leach clears his throat. 'Look, I haven't had the chance to thank you for helping us conclude the Anna Czubinska case.'

Conclude the case? Doesn't he mean *solve* the case for them?

'Thank you, sir… I mean, Craig.'

'I'd like you to come back to work.'

Her hands relax. 'Really?'

'You've proved you're ready.'

'In your team, sir?'

'Yes, Rose.'

'And the psychiatrist?'

'I'd like you to continue seeing her.' Rose nods but stays silent. Leach gets up. 'Take Christmas off and we'll see you January 1st.' It's a statement, not a question.

I wag my tail. This is what Rose wanted: she's got her job back. *Wooferoo!* But I'm not sensing the excitement from her I had expected. What's wrong?

Leach turns to leave.

'Can I think about it?'

Leach stares at her. 'Pardon?'

'I need time to think about it.' If dogs could gawp, I'd be gawping. I thought Rose would bite his hand off, so to speak. Malcolm's jaw is hanging open and so is Leach's. 'Can I give you my answer after Christmas?'

'You can.' Leach doesn't budge. 'What has changed?'

'I think maybe *I* have. I have another option I'd like time to explore before I make my decision,' she says with a confidence I have seldom heard.

'Are you going to tell me about this other option?'

'It may be nothing. I'll get back to you after Boxing Day. Happy Christmas, sir.'

The Leach gives Rose a curt nod and leaves.

When the door has closed behind him, Rose picks up her glass of white wine and takes a big sip.

'I'm confused,' Malcolm says.

You and me both, I think.

'I can't believe I just did that,' Rose says. She puts the glass on the table. 'I suddenly realised I don't need his approval to feel good about myself.' She shakes her head. 'No, it's more than that. I mustn't rely on others to bolster my confidence. I have to believe in myself, even when things go wrong.'

'I agree with you, Rose. But why didn't you jump at getting your job back?'

'Because maybe you're right.'

'Me?' Malcolm blanches. 'Right about what?'

'Maybe I'm better off having my own PI business. No more Pearl haranguing me, no more office politics. I just take the investigations I want to do.' She looks down at me. 'Monty and I make a great team. He can be my partner.'

'Look, Rose, it was just an idea. You would make a brilliant PI, just as you are a brilliant police detective. You must do whatever makes you happy.'

Right on, Malcolm. If he were paying me attention, I'd lift my paw and high five him. Instead, I place a paw on Rose's thigh in solidarity.

62

It was ten in the morning on Christmas Day and yesterday's rain had frozen into a white frost. Rose had already exchanged gifts with Monty and Summer. Well, she had bought them each a gift. Monty now wore a new red collar with reflector stripes on it, and Rose wore a new woolly bobble hat that matched the red of her Wellies. Summer had been given her own, extra soft bed.

Rose's plan for the day had been simple: open their presents, go for a walk on Winterfold Heath, then cook Christmas lunch. She had bought the smallest chicken she could find. A turkey was way too big for her to get through. She was going to roast the chicken and have it with all the trimmings. After that, she planned to watch the Queen's speech, the *Doctor Who* Christmas special and maybe a movie.

Then Malcolm had rung unexpectedly.

'There's something you have to see...I don't mean you *have* to, I'm not bossing you around or anything, I'd hate you to think...anyway, will you come and look? Please? Today if you can.'

Intrigued and delighted at the idea of his company, she drove to the vet hospital with Monty, and left Summer behind to snooze in her new bed. Malcolm came out to greet them in the car park with B, sending Monty into a frenzy of excitement and tail-wagging.

'Nice bobble hat,' he said. 'Is it new?'

'Monty gave it to me.'

'He's got good taste.'

Rose held out a small package wrapped in Christmas paper. 'Happy Christmas.' She blushed. 'It's from Monty.'

'For me?' Malcolm stared at it for a moment. 'That's…that's so nice. I…I…wow.'

Rose's cheeks were burning. *Oh no, he thinks I expect a present in return and he hasn't got me one. And it's probably the wrong size.*

Malcolm tore off the wrapping and shoved the remains of it in a pocket. 'A shirt!' He held it up. 'And the right size! However did you know?'

'I guessed. It's the least I could do after your shirt got ruined with blood.'

'Thank you. That's…thank you. I didn't get you one…'

Just as she'd thought. She had embarrassed him. *Damn*! Rose desperately tried to find a way to change the subject.

'Anyway, follow me,' Malcolm said. 'I've got something to show you.'

She and Monty eagerly went with him, past the cattery, to the far end of the car park where there was a shed-like building she'd assumed was a double garage.

'We never use it.' He fumbled with a key. Unlocking the door, he pushed it open, revealing a space as big as her kitchen at home, with a window facing a neighbour's hedge. He flicked a light switch.

The wind blew some brown leaves through the open door into the shed and across the concrete floor. Some chairs and tables were stacked at the back along with what appeared to be an X-ray machine. Otherwise, the space was empty.

'It has two power points and with a heater in here, it could be nice and cosy.'

Monty busily sniffed the floor. Lady B was hot on his heels, following him wherever he went.

'I don't understand,' Rose said.

'It's just an idea. I know it looks a bit of a mess, but I could help you spruce it up.'

'Sorry, still confused.'

'I just thought that if you decide to have your own detective agency, you could set it up here. At no cost.'

Rose blinked rapidly as she tried to catch up. 'Why would you do that?'

'I would be dead if it wasn't for you. And Monty, of course. Because of you, I have my dog back.' He glanced at B, who was chasing a leaf across the floor. 'It's my way of saying thank you.'

It took a while for Rose to find her voice. 'That's amazingly generous. But there's no need to give me anything. And this,' she looked around, 'is way too generous.'

Malcolm shrugged. 'It's here if you want it.'

Monty was busy poking his nose into every nook and cranny. Rose tried to imagine the place with a rug and a heater. A desk and some chairs. She began to wonder what she would call her agency if she went ahead.

'Thank you. Can I think about it?'

Malcolm nodded.

'It's funny how things turn out. There was me convinced I wanted my job back or my life wasn't worth living. But I've realised that sometimes what we *want* and what we *need* are quite different.'

Rose called Monty to her. He sat at her feet, giving her his undivided attention. 'You've got a dirty, nose.' She brushed the dust and a cobweb away.

'You know, if we do have our own agency, I think we'll call it The Nosy Detectives. Named after your very special nose.'

Monty barked once and wagged his tail. He seemed to like the idea.

LOUISA BENNET

Louisa studied Literature at the University of London and went on to learn Canine Linguistics from her Golden Retriever, Pickles, which is how she discovered what dogs really get up to when we're not around.

Truth be told, Pickles came up with the story for the Monty Dog Detective Mysteries, and Louisa just transcribed it. She's faster on the keyboard and less easily distracted by food and passing squirrels.

Louisa worked in magazine publishing before her eyes were opened to the world of woofers. She divides her time between London and Sydney, Australia, and runs courses on crime fiction and creative writing.

Pickles runs courses on wee-mailing, duck toppling and drool management.

To find out more about Monty the sniffer super-sleuth, please go to:

www.lalarkin.com

Louisa Bennet also writes thrillers as L.A. Larkin.

ACKNOWLEDGEMENTS

Thank you to my husband, Michael, and to my good friends David Gaylor and Carolyn Tate, for being my first readers. Your feedback on an early draft was invaluable.

A big thank you to my publisher, Lindy Cameron of Clan Destine Press; my brilliant editor and author, Narrelle Harris; and to Carmel Shute.

My agent, Phil Patterson, has been a real trooper as always. I can't thank him enough.

Selina Power, thank you for combining my L.A. Larkin and Louisa Bennet websites, creating one super snazzy one, and for all your social media advice.

My biggest thanks go to my readers and dog lovers everywhere, and to the wonderful 'hoomans' who rescue dogs and who (spoiler alert!) campaign against puppy farms.

Lastly, I must thank Pickles and Lilly, my Golden Retrievers, who inspired the Monty character and who sit with me while I write.

If you loved *The Bone Ranger*, please write a quick review. It means the world to me to know that you have enjoyed it.

If you'd like to stay in touch with me and my dogs, you can connect with me through my website and social media, as well as GoodReads. Thank you for your company.

Facebook @authorLouisaBennet
Twitter @MontyDogD
Instagram @PicklesandLilly
GoodReads Louisa Bennet
Website: https://lalarkin.com

BOOKS BY LOUISA BENNET

The Monty Dog Detective series:

Monty & Me

The Bone Ranger

The short story 'When the Chips are Down' in **Who Sleuthed It?**

BOOKS AS L.A. LARKIN

The Safe Place

Widow's Island

Prey

Devour

Thirst

The Genesis Flaw

The books of Louisa Bennet & L.A. Larkin
with Clan Destine Press

The CDP version of
Monty & Me
available only
in the USA.

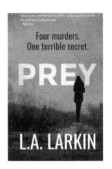